# Air Pollution
# and Lichens

# Air Pollution and Lichens

*Edited by*

B. W. FERRY, M. S. BADDELEY
*and* D. L. HAWKSWORTH

THE ATHLONE PRESS *of the University of London*
1973

*Published by*
THE ATHLONE PRESS
UNIVERSITY OF LONDON
*at 4 Gower Street London* WC 1
*Distributed by Tiptree Book Services Ltd*
*Tiptree, Essex*



---

0 485 11140 3

*Printed in Great Britain by*
WESTERN PRINTING SERVICES LTD
BRISTOL

# Preface

During recent years, there has been a marked upsurge of interest in the problems associated with air pollution, and studies on lichens have played an important part in developments in this field. In 1971, we became convinced of the value of publishing a text covering all aspects of air pollution and lichens, including both ecological and physiological studies, as well as an account of some of the important peripheral topics. Our feelings were confirmed by the considerable enthusiasm shown for this venture by the many workers we contacted at that time. The First International Mycological Congress, held at Exeter, England, in September 1971 subsequently provided an excellent opportunity for finalizing arrangements for the publication of this book. We are very much indebted to Professor C. T. Ingold, his fellow officers and members of the Executive Committee who were responsible for the organization of this congress.

We are extremely grateful to all of the contributors for their considerable efforts in producing what we believe to be a comprehensive and up-to-date survey of the subject. The individual chapters are in most instances review articles, and, in others, either recently published or hitherto unpublished accounts of personal research. Our aims have basically been twofold: firstly, to provide a reference volume covering all aspects of the subject of air pollution and lichens, and secondly, to encourage current and prospective investigators to relate their work to a broad basis of knowledge.

In addition, we would especially like to thank Mrs C. R. Hodgson for providing an excellent first translation of Dr Margot's paper, and Dr D. C. Smith for his helpful and encouraging comment and criticism, made at various times, concerning the problems of investigating lichen physiology. Our thanks are also due to Miss B. Wager who, as well as being involved in some of the research reported on in Chapter 14, read and commented on all of the papers at the manuscript stage. Finally, we would like to express our thanks to the staff of the Athlone Press for their patience and enthusiasm during the preparation of this volume.

September 1972

B.W.F.
M.S.B.
D.L.H.

# Contents

# List of Contributors

M. S. BADDELEY *formerly Botany Department, Bedford College, Regent's Park, London*

B. J. COPPINS *Department of Geography, c/o King's College Field Centre, Rogate, Petersfield, Hampshire*

J. F. FARRAR *Department of Agricultural Science, Oxford University*

B. W. FERRY *Botany Department, Bedford College, Regent's Park. London*

E. J. FINEGAN *present address Department of Biology, Laurentian University, Sudbury, Ontario, Canada*

O. L. GILBERT *Department of Landscape Architecture, University of Sheffield, Sheffield*

D. L. HAWKSWORTH *Commonwealth Mycological Institute, Ferry Lane, Kew, Surrey*

F. N. HAYNES *Department of Biological Sciences, Portsmouth Polytechnic, Portsmouth, Hampshire*

P. W. JAMES *Department of Botany, British Museum (Natural History), Cromwell Road, London*

J. R. LAUNDON *Department of Botany, British Museum (Natural History), Cromwell Road, London*

J. MARGOT *Laboratoire d'Écologie Végétale, Université Catholique de Louvain, Héverlé, Belgium*

D. I. MORGAN-HUWS *Department of Biological Sciences, Portsmouth Polytechnic, Portsmouth*

T. H. NASH III — *Department of Botany and Microbiology, Arizona State University, Tempe, Arizona, USA*

L. C. PEARSON — *Division of Life Sciences, Ricks College, Rexburgh, Idaho, USA*

K. J. PUCKETT — *Department of Biology, Laurentian University, Sudbury, Ontario, Canada*

D. H. S. RICHARDSON — *Department of Biology, Laurentian University, Sudbury, Ontario, Canada*

F. ROSE — *Department of Geography, King's College, Strand, London*

P. J. W. SAUNDERS — *Pollution Research Unit, University of Manchester, Manchester*

C. M. WOOD — *Pollution Research Unit, University of Manchester, Manchester*

# 1 : Introduction

P. W. JAMES

> Everyone wishes to abolish the damage which may be caused to man and to wild life by pollution from every source. As, however, we are not always agreed as to when damage is being caused, or how exactly some obvious damage arose, an easy solution will not be found. Man has always polluted his environment; he has always suffered from pests, but because of the 'population explosion', these problems have become more serious in recent years. The need for more research in these subjects is obvious, if irreparable damage to wild life, and to man, is to be avoided. Equally important, we must make sure that the results of such research are quickly and efficiently applied.
>
> Mellanby (1967, p. 30)

Although the sensitivity of lichens to air pollution has been acknowledged since the observations of Grindon in south Lancashire in 1859 (Grindon, 1859), the lack of recording gauges effectively delayed all critical study in this field prior to 1958. However, since then, detailed research and surveys, carried out independently by scientists in the British Isles, Canada, Czechoslovakia, Germany, Scandinavia, USA and the USSR, have convincingly demonstrated that it is now possible to correlate the distribution of lichens around air pollution sources with mean levels of air pollutants and, in some cases, to utilize their behaviour as a means of monitoring the distribution and severity of the pollutant emissions. Sulphur dioxide has been proved to be the most important major pollutant adversely affecting lichen vegetation over wide areas of the northern hemisphere. Over two hundred papers dealing with lichen vegetation of areas affected by air pollution have now appeared in the scientific press (ch 3), and recent laboratory (ch 13 and 14) and transplant studies (ch 3) have corroborated the data obtained from field observations.

The compilation of the present book, the first on this aspect to have appeared, received its main stimulus as a result of the symposium devoted to *Lichens and Air Pollution* organized as part of the *First International Mycological Congress*, held in Exeter, England, in September 1971. At this meeting it was confirmed that there was a very substantial output of published but dispersed information, as well as important unpublished data on this aspect, a concise summation of which, it was felt, would considerably benefit future studies and research in the field of air pollution as well as advising on its recognition and control. Pertinent reviews of the behaviour of sulphur dioxide in the air (ch 2), the effects of air pollutants on plants other than lichens (ch 10) and the effects of other pollutants on lichens (ch 8 and 9) are included. The volume is not only designed for the specialist studying the effects of air pollutants on lichens, but also for those interested in the broader spectra of pollution studies. Several volumes on the latter topic, concerned at least in part with matters of air (atmospheric) pollution, have appeared in recent years. The recent publication of Bach (1972) is to be particularly recommended. The aims of the present book are to introduce and aid in an understanding of the wealth of data currently available on lichens and air pollution, and above all to stimulate the reader and suggest to him new and rewarding avenues of further research (ch 17).

There has been a general lack of the appreciation of the effects of long-term low levels of sulphur dioxide and fluoride on vascular plants, such as conifers, the corrosion rates for metals, the decay of stonework, and considerable concern is still being expressed on its effects on human health (Anon., 1970). Lichens are among the most sensitive organisms to sulphur dioxide pollution known and because different species are affected by different concentrations of this pollutant, it has been possible to construct scales for the estimation of the mean sulphur dioxide levels in an area, solely from the lichen vegetation present (*see* ch 3). The lichen scales are of particular value in areas with mean sulphur dioxide levels in the range 30–170 $\mu g/m^3$, and most sensitive in the range 30–70 $\mu g/m^3$. Representative scales have been compiled with the non-specialist in mind; these are quick and cheap to apply, and clearly not only of academic interest as they now cover a range of this pollutant at which, for example, coniferous trees are affected.

Nearly all lichens are composite plants, each basically comprising a fungal component, the mycobiont, and an alga, the phycobiont. The mycobionts are usually of Ascomycete affinity and are very rarely encountered in a non-lichenized state; the phycobionts are either green (Chlorophyceae) or blue-green (Cyanophyceae) and although many can thrive in a free-living condition, a few, such as *Trebouxia*, are rarely found to do so. Most of the pertinent literature on the group, including references to introductory texts, may be traced through Ainsworth (1971). The two bionts live in a symbiotic relationship forming a thallus whose morphology, anatomy and physiology are quite distinct from that of either of the two symbionts when separated and grown in axenic cultures. Lichens are extremely slow-growing plants, capable of living to a great age (up to 4500 years). They colonize natural substrata such as bark, lignum, rock, as well as man-made materials such as mortar, asbestos and glass on which they cause little harm. As a group, their extreme resistance to exposure, variation in temperature and degree of environmental desiccation are well known; their capabilities for enhanced uptake of radioactive and heavy metal fallout are less well studied. In recent years research into the physiology of the intact thallus and the interrelationships between the bionts, especially with regard to the transfer of carbohydrates, has proved to be important in the understanding of other symbiotic systems (ch 12).

That the lichen vegetation in areas which have become subjected to air pollution has become considerably depleted is seen from comparisons between the past and present floras of particular sites and changes in distribution of different species (*see* ch 16). Unfortunately, this decline is still continuing in many countries, the result of the increase in sources and consequently in the spread of sulphur dioxide emissions, existing to such an extent that in some cases certain species are in danger of extinction. This is a matter of considerable, urgent concern to those interested in conservation, and particularly to lichenologists. However, lichens are also important from other standpoints: they form, like most other organisms, an important integral part of the ecosystem, and any disruption in their communities affects other organisms dependent on them as food material or as protection in micro-habitats. Kuenan (1971) has stressed the need for detailed quantitative studies of the fauna of trees from which lichens are disappearing due to air pollution, and Schofield and Hamilton (1970) comment that damage by sulphur dioxide to the extensive lichen vegetation of the tundra would certainly lead to famine in areas of economically important reindeer and caribou husbandry which are particularly dependent on lichens for winter fodder.

Lichens produce an impressive array of secondary metabolic products (Culberson, 1969) many of which are unknown in other plant groups. Some of these have acclaimed antibiotic qualities and for this reason are commercially used in the pharmaceutical trade.

On environmental grounds, lichens add much to the aesthetic beauty of the landscape. Over most of western Europe much of the original lichen vegetation, composed of brightly coloured, grey or yellowish-green, large pendant bearded or leaf-like species, has now been replaced by a monotonous grey-green crust consisting of a single, particularly tolerant species (*Lecanora conizaeoides*). Whilst visitors to parts of southern and western Britain still frequently remark on the richness of the lichen vegetation there, it is salutary to reflect that early in the last century similar communities were present in the London area (ch 6, 16).

The prospect of reducing sulphur dioxide levels to those at which lichens are completely unaffected is clearly unrealistic besides being prohibitive in cost; in any case their importance cannot justify such drastic action even on a European scale. It is, however, important that at least some areas are left unaffected for the reasons outlined above and all attempts should be made to limit the current trend of increasing sulphur dioxide emissions in Europe, especially along the Atlantic seaboard. The Swedish Royal Ministry for Foreign Affairs and the Royal Ministry for Agriculture (1971) recommend that mean sulphur dioxide levels of only 56 $\mu g/m^3$ should be permitted in order to prevent damage to coniferous trees. If this standard were adopted, considerable improvements can be expected in the lichen vegetation in many areas of Europe.

## References

Ainsworth, G. C. (1971). *Ainsworth & Bisby's Dictionary of the Fungi.* Ed. 6. Kew: Commonwealth Mycological Institute.

Anon. (1970). Back to smoke pollution. *Br. med. J.* **4,** 256.

Bach, W. (1972). *Atmospheric pollution.* New York: McGraw-Hill.

Culberson, C. F. (1969). *Chemical and botanical guide to lichen products.* Chapel Hill: University of North Carolina Press.

Grindon, L. H. (1859). *The Manchester flora.* London: W. White.

Kuenen, D. J. (1971). Integratie van kennis. *Entomol. Ber., Amst.* **31,** 84–92.

Mellanby, K. (1967). *Pesticides and Pollution.* London: Collins.

Schofield, E. and Hamilton, W. L. (1970). Probable damage to tundra biota through sulphur dioxide destruction of lichens. *Biological Conservation* **2,** 278–80.

Swedish Royal Ministry for Foreign Affairs and Royal Ministry of Agriculture (1971). *Air pollution across national boundaries, Sweden's case study for the United Nations conference on the human environment.* Stockholm: Swedish Preparatory Committee for the United Nations Conference on the Human Environment.

# 2: Sulphur Dioxide in the Environment: Its Production, Dispersal and Fate

P. J. W. SAUNDERS and C. M. WOOD

Sulphur dioxide is a reactive, colourless gas which is heavier than air and has an odour detection limit of between 500 and 3000 μg/m³. At above 8500 μg/m³ it has a very pungent, irritating odour. In the atmosphere, sulphur dioxide is partly converted to sulphur trioxide and sulphuric acid and its salts by photochemical and catalytic oxidation processes. The degree of oxidation is dependent upon a number of factors including the residence time of the gas, the intensity and duration of sunlight, and the atmospheric concentrations of moisture, catalysts and alkaline materials.

A great deal of work has been done to identify the damage caused to plants, animals, humans and materials by sulphur dioxide and its derivatives. High concentrations of sulphur dioxide with particulates, including sulphuric acid, have been associated with injury of the respiratory system and premature death due to a variety of causes. Sulphur dioxide is known to corrode metals, stonework, textiles, leather and paints. At concentrations above 500 μg/m³ it can induce chlorosis and necrosis in some species of plants. Coniferous trees may be adversely affected at mean annual levels of only about 56 μg/m³ (*see* ch 10). Particulates generated by sulphur dioxide in the atmosphere contribute significantly to reductions in visibility.

Lichens, bryophytes and fungi have proved to be some of the most sensitive receptors of atmospheric pollution, some species reacting to sulphur dioxide concentrations of much less than 100 μg/m³ (*see* ch 3, 4, 5 and 10). For this reason, lichens have been frequently adopted as biological indicators of pollution by sulphur dioxide (*see* ch 3). This paper discusses the production, dispersal and fate of sulphur dioxide in the atmosphere with special reference to its fate on surfaces that may serve as substrates for lichens. The possible mode of toxic action of sulphur dioxide as a gas and in solution in surface moisture is reviewed.

## Production of sulphur dioxide

The relationship between sulphur dioxide and the other sulphur compounds present in the atmosphere is first described. The natural and anthropogenic sources of sulphur dioxide are then listed and the UK, USA and global emissions from these sources are estimated. Finally trends in sulphur dioxide emissions together with some tentative forecasts are discussed.

### *Sulphur in the atmosphere*

Sulphur dioxide is only one of several sulphur compounds present in the atmosphere, the other important ones being hydrogen sulphide and sulphates (including sulphuric acid). Because of the close relationships between the various sulphur compounds, it is necessary to discuss them generally before considering sulphur dioxide in more detail. 'Primary' sulphur dioxide is emitted almost entirely from pollution sources (Robinson and Robbins, 1970) and is generally accompanied by small amounts of sulphur trioxide which are converted to sulphuric acid in the presence of moisture (National Air Pollution Control Administration, 1969*a*). The sulphur dioxide molecule has an average lifetime in the atmosphere of only a few days (Meetham, 1950).

Hydrogen sulphide, in contrast, is derived mainly from natural sources such as the decay of organic material on land, in swamps (Junge, 1963) and in intertidal flats (Eriksson, 1959) and volcanic activity. Measured as sulphur, total global emissions of hydrogen sulphide (including a small proportion from industrial sources) are about 30 per cent greater than those of sulphur dioxide. Hydrogen sulphide is rapidly oxidized to 'secondary' sulphur dioxide by ozone in a heterogeneous reaction on surfaces, for example those of aerosols, and its lifetime in the air ranges from about two hours in urban areas to about two days in remote rural areas (Robinson and Robbins, 1970).

Sulphate particles are produced by certain human activities, by the oxidation of sulphur dioxide, by volcanoes and by the sea, the spray of which generates about 60 per cent as much atmospheric sulphur as sulphur dioxide emissions (Robinson and Robbins, 1970). About half the mass is made up of particles smaller than 0.15 μm and sulphates make up about one-quarter of the total global aerosol loading by weight (Barrett, 1970). Loss from the air occurs by gravitational settling and removal by precipitation, the average lifetime of particulate sulphates being about 20–30 days (Junge, 1963).

Robinson and Robbins (1970) estimate the average global concentrations of sulphur dioxide, hydrogen sulphide and sulphate measured as sulphur to be 0.25, 0.14 and 0.7 $\mu g/m^3$ respectively. The contribution of sulphur dioxide to the background sulphur concentration thus appears to be only 23 per cent, whereas hydrogen sulphide accounts for 13 per cent and sulphate (some of which is derived from hydrogen sulphide and sulphur dioxide) the remainder. Measurements of sulphur dioxide (Junge, 1956; Egnér and Eriksson, 1955), particulate/sulphur dioxide (Georgii, 1960) and sulphur dioxide/hydrogen sulphide (Junge, 1960) ratios, although obviously demonstrating considerable local variation, are in approximate agreement with these estimates.

### *Sources of sulphur dioxide*

Secondary sulphur dioxide is formed by the oxidation of hydrogen sulphide derived mainly from natural processes, but the only natural sources of primary sulphur dioxide appear to be volcanic eruptions and forest fires. Most primary sulphur dioxide is, in fact, emitted from two anthropogenic sources: the combustion of fossil fuels containing sulphur and certain industrial processes involving sulphur compounds or impurities.

Coal and oil, the principal fossil fuel sources of sulphur dioxide, are used to heat domestic, industrial and commercial premises and to generate electricity. Coal is also employed in gas works and in the manufacture of coke, a by-product of which, coke oven gas, is the main gaseous source of sulphur dioxide. Natural gas contains very little sulphur. Some sulphur is retained in the coke which is used as a source of heat and in blast furnaces. Sulphur dioxide is produced during the refining of oil, the lighter fractions of which are extensively utilized as a source of power for transportation. The most important fuel-burning sources of sulphur dioxide are power stations, private dwellings and industrial premises (Warren Spring Laboratory, 1967; National Society for Clean Air, 1971*a*).

Industrial processing is a considerably less important source of sulphur dioxide than the combustion of fossil fuels. The main industrial processes emitting sulphur dioxide are the sintering of iron ore, sulphuric acid manufacture, the smelting of metal ores (especially those of copper), the processing of wood pulp and brick making (Massachusetts Institute of Technology, 1970). In addition, coke ovens, blast furnaces and petroleum refineries are sometimes considered as industrial processes rather than as fuel combustion sources (National Air Pollution Control Administration, 1970).

### *Emissions of sulphur dioxide*

No estimates of natural sulphur dioxide emissions have been made, largely because of the unpredictable nature of volcanic activity. However the amounts of sulphur dioxide emitted from various human activities have been calculated. Several different estimates of UK sulphur dioxide emissions have been prepared (Warren Spring Laboratory, 1968; National Society for Clean Air, 1971*a*), but the most authoritative is probably that by National Society for Clean Air (1971*b*). Table 1 summarizes the 1969 position, the figures being arranged by type of fuel and height of emission. The significance of emission height will be examined later but it is necessary to state that low level refers to heights of up to a few metres, whereas high level signifies chimney heights of 100 m or greater, with medium level intermediate between the two. High-level emissions are considerably greater than those at medium level which in turn are greater than low-level emissions. Sulphur dioxide emissions from industrial processes (iron ore sintering, sulphuric acid manufacture and brick making) are only a small proportion of the total, being estimated at between 0.10 and 0.15 million tonnes (National Society for Clean Air, 1971*b*).

The 1968 US emissions are summarized in Table 2. The combustion of coal is again the most important source of sulphur dioxide and power stations emit just over half the total amount. Industrial processes contribute rather more than 20 per cent of total emissions (National Air Pollution Control Administration, 1970).

*Table 1 Estimated UK sulphur dioxide emissions from fuel burning, 1969 (million tonnes)*

| Source | Fuel Type | | | |
|---|---|---|---|---|
| | Solid | Liquid | Gaseous | Total |
| Domestic | 0.54 | 0.02 | 0.01 | 0.57 |
| Agriculture | 0.01 | 0.03 | — | 0.04 |
| Commercial and Public Services | 0.15 | 0.25 | — | 0.40 |
| Rail Transport | — | 0.02 | — | 0.02 |
| Road Transport | — | 0.04 | — | 0.04 |
| Water Transport | — | 0.03 | — | 0.03 |
| Total low level Emissions | 0.71 | 0.39 | 0.01 | 1.10 |
| Collieries | 0.06 | — | — | 0.06 |
| Iron and Steel | 0.03 | 0.29 | 0.07 | 0.39 |
| Coke Ovens | — | — | 0.09 | 0.09 |
| Gas Works | 0.01 | 0.01 | — | 0.02 |
| General Industry | 0.58 | 0.80 | 0.01 | 1.39 |
| Total medium level Emissions | 0.68 | 1.10 | 0.16 | 1.94 |
| Refineries | — | 0.21 | — | 0.21 |
| Power Stations | 2.05 | 0.39 | — | 2.44 |
| Total high level Emissions | 2.05 | 0.60 | — | 2.64 |
| *Grand Total* | 3.44 | 2.08 | 0.17 | 5.69 |

*Source:* adapted from NSCA (1971*b*)
N.B. Figures may not necessarily be consistent, due to rounding off

Robinson and Robbins (1970) have estimated total global sulphur dioxide emissions in 1965 at 132 million tonnes, over 70 per cent of which are thought to derive from the combustion of coal. Although the Massachusetts Institute of Technology (1970) concluded that it is not possible to calculate global coal and oil emissions from the fuel statistics available because of

*Table 2 Estimated US sulphur dioxide emissions, 1968 (million tonnes)*

| Source | Emission | | Source | Emission | | |
|---|---|---|---|---|---|---|
| Fuel combustion: stationary sources | 22.1 | | Transportation: | 0.7 | | |
| Coal | | 18.2 | Motor vehicles | | 0.3 | |
| Oil | | 3.9 | petrol | | | 0.2 |
| Industrial processes | 6.6 | | diesel | | | 0.1 |
| Smelting | | 3.6 | Railways | | 0.1 | |
| Petroleum refining | | 1.9 | Water transport | | 0.3 | |
| Sulphuric acid manufacture | | 0.6 | Solid waste disposal | 0.1 | | |
| Coking | | 0.5 | Coal spoil combustion | 0.6 | | |
| | | *Total* 30.1 | | | | |

*Source:* adapted from NAPCA (1970)

the number of undetermined parameters, they did estimate emissions from major industrial sources in 1968 at 27 million tonnes, the smelting of copper, lead and zinc accounting for a large proportion of the total. The 1965 and 1968 estimates are presented in Table 3.

*Table 3 Estimated global sulphur dioxide emissions 1965 and 1968 (million tonnes)*

| Source | 1965 | | 1968 | |
|---|---|---|---|---|
| Coal burning | 92 | | — | |
| Oil combustion | 21.2 | | — | |
| Industrial processes | 18.8 | | 27.3 | |
| Smelting | | 14.2 | | 16.2 |
| Petroleum refining | | 4.6 | | 6.4 |
| Sulphuric acid manufacture | | — | | 1.7 |
| Coking | | — | | 2.8 |
| Wood pulp processing | | — | | 0.2 |
| *Total* | 132 | | — | |

*Sources:* 1965 data adapted from Robinson and Robbins (1970), 1968 data: MIT (1970)

### *Sulphur dioxide emission trends*

Total UK sulphur dioxide emissions appear to be increasing, and the proportional contribution of the various sources to the total is changing. Low-level sulphur dioxide emissions remained fairly constant between 1950 and 1960, but have fallen by about 30 per cent since then. The main reason for this drop appears to be a reduction in the use of coal for heating by domestic and commercial users and its replacement by fuels which either emit virtually no sulphur dioxide (gas), less sulphur dioxide (light fuel oil) or which transfer emissions to a higher level (electricity). Medium-level emissions have remained roughly constant during the last 20 years, but oil has replaced coal as the major source of sulphur dioxide pollution. Emissions from high-level sources have nearly trebled since 1950, those from coal doubling, and those from oil increasing nearly eightfold. Had the sulphur content of heavy residual fuel oil remained at its former level (4 per cent) instead of falling to the present 2.5 per cent, high-level sulphur dioxide emissions from oil would be much greater (National Society for Clean Air, 1971*b*).

The most likely forecast is that total sulphur dioxide emissions will continue to increase, but not at a rapid rate. Oil will probably continue to replace coal in many sectors of the economy and on balance this should reduce emissions slightly. Low- and medium-level emissions may be expected to fall marginally during the next decade. High-level emissions, on the other hand, will probably continue to increase, though at a slower rate than during the last 20 years. By 1980 they may well constitute two-thirds of all sulphur dioxide emissions (National Society for Clean Air, 1971*b*). In the longer term emissions will depend on total energy demand, and how much is met by natural gas and nuclear power. Unless control measures are implemented, energy forecasts indicate that total UK sulphur dioxide emissions are unlikely to alter greatly by the year 2000.

Total US emissions are increasing, with sulphur dioxide from power stations accounting for most of the rise. Because the US have always used a much higher proportion of oil and natural gas than the UK, no significant change in fuel usage is taking place (National Air Pollution Control Administration, 1970). By 1980 power stations are expected to contribute 70 per cent of the total sulphur dioxide emission of 53 million tonnes. This proportion may well increase to 80 per cent by 2000 when emissions from electricity generation will be more than treble current levels (National Air Pollution Control Administration, 1969*b*). A number of startling projections to the year 2020 have been made, based on assumptions about the type of nuclear power and the level of control to be employed (Joint Committee on Atomic Energy, 1969). The alternative generating the greatest quantities of sulphur dioxide indicates that power station emissions might be 170 million tonnes by 2020.

Global emissions have doubled during the last 30 years. Total emissions in 1937 have been estimated at 62 million tonnes, made up by emissions from the combustion of coal (42 million tonnes) and oil (7 million tonnes) and from smelting (13 million tonnes) (Katz, 1958). By 1965 world-wide emissions from coal had doubled, whereas those from oil had trebled. Global sulphur dioxide emissions seem certain to continue to increase. Forecasts of energy consumption (Massachusetts Institute of Technology, 1970) show that solid fuel usage may increase by 60 per cent between 1967 and 1980, and that oil consumption may double.It appears safe to assume that if pollution controls are not implemented, sulphur dioxide emissions in 1980 will be almost double those in 1965.

### Dispersal of sulphur dioxide

After some introductory comments on dispersal and the measurement of sulphur dioxide, this section describes the parameters which determine the process of dispersion. It then reviews sulphur dioxide concentrations in the urban and rural areas of the UK and concludes by discussing long-distance dispersal of sulphur dioxide together with its possible effects upon climate.

Dispersal refers to the way in which sulphur dioxide emitted from anthropogenic sources mixes with the surrounding air, and is diluted by it. The sulphur dioxide contained in an emission from a given height diffuses through a large volume of air and eventually returns to earth, either in gaseous form or as a derivative. It is the ground-level concentration (the quantity of pollutant per unit volume of air) which determines whether or not damage is caused, and with which the last section of the chapter is concerned. The measurement of concentrations is clearly of great importance.

The colorimetric West-Gaeke method (Hochheiser, 1964) is

generally used in the USA. In the UK, however, the hydrogen peroxide method (Craxford, Slimming and Wilkins, 1960) is employed to give 24 hr average sulphur dioxide concentrations in $\mu g/m^3$. Total acidity is measured and therefore acidic gases other than sulphur dioxide yield high values, whereas ammonia, derived from such sources as sewage disposal plants, lowers results. Accuracy is extremely limited at low concentrations ($\leqslant 20\ \mu g/m^3$). The lead peroxide method (Department of Scientific and Industrial Research, 1957), which measures the degree of sulphation over a period of one month, is also used in this country. Because hydrogen sulphide, sulphuric acid and particulate sulphates also react to give lead sulphate, this method supplies only a rough indication of sulphur dioxide concentrations. Both UK methods thus have serious shortcomings (Katz, 1969). The results obtained from one type of instrument cannot readily be compared with those from the other (Eaves and Macaulay, 1957).

*Dispersion*

The magnitude of ground-level sulphur dioxide concentrations resulting from an emission from a single chimney depends upon a number of factors which determine the extent of mixing and dilution with surrounding air (National Air Pollution Control Administration, 1969*c*). The rate of emission and the height of the chimney are important parameters relating to the emission. In addition, the temperature and efflux velocity of the emission determine the buoyancy of the gases and thus the effective height of a plume may be several times the chimney height.

There are also a large number of parameters associated with the environment into which the plume is released. Two of these are the topography of the region surrounding the chimney and the juxtaposition of the chimney and the building upon or near which it is located. When air flows over a building or hill, the flow on the lee side is very disturbed. Unless a chimney is sufficiently high, pollutants may be carried to the ground rapidly and in high concentrations by the disturbance (Wanta, 1968).

The temperature and stability structure of the atmosphere and their variations in time and space are also important. Normally air temperature decreases with height and gases are able to rise freely. However, if the temperature increases with height (inversion condition) diffusion rates are reduced by the lack of buoyancy. On clear nights with light winds, inversions frequently form above cities (particularly those sited in valleys or bowls), often breaking up in the morning. Pollutants emitted below the inversion layer will cause high ground-level concentrations, whereas those emitted above it will disperse freely and have no effect on these concentrations (Robinson, 1971).

Wind speed and direction also affect dispersion, since strong winds will produce more dilution and the variation of wind speed with height will determine the extent of mixing. The intensity and distribution of atmospheric turbulence are also important. Turbulence causes random eddies to mix pollutants with air in cross-wind and vertical directions (Pasquill, 1962).

There have been a large number of attempts to model mathematically the diffusion process (Pasquill, 1962; Central Electricity Research Laboratories, 1967; Warren Spring Laboratory, 1967; Strom, 1968). However, no generally applicable formula for the prediction of ground-level sulphur dioxide concentrations in all conditions has been unearthed, though acceptable answers are obtainable in some cases. Scorer (1970) has suggested that the complex formulae incorporated in most models are of questionable value.

This discussion of emissions from a single chimney is really only relevant to power stations and other high-level sources. The wind and temperature structure of the atmosphere becomes increasingly complex close to the ground in cities, due to the building pattern and the heat generated from fuel combustion (Chandler, 1971; Peterson, 1969). Strong winds are decelerated and light ones accelerated as they cross cities, turbulence and temperatures being increased. These parameters have a marked effect on sulphur dioxide emitted at low level, and to a lesser extent, at medium height. Emissions from a single source interact with those from others to form a diverse pattern of ground level concentrations.

Mathematical models of the urban sulphur dioxide situation have been constructed (Stern, 1970; Organization for Economic Co-operation and Development, 1971). These models normally employ emission data for a parcel of land, and are generally reasonably successful in predicting concentrations over a long time period for a large area. More detailed forecasts are not feasible at present.

Sulphur dioxide measurements are thus employed to provide knowledge of concentration patterns in urban areas. Twenty-four hour measurements are normally made (Warren Spring Laboratory, 1958–71) but it is clear that sulphur dioxide concentrations at a given point will vary almost second by second. Daily, monthly, seasonal and annual averages will provide little indication of peak concentrations. As a rough guide 3 minute maxima may be up to 150 times the annual mean, with hourly maxima 10–30 times this mean, and 24 hour maxima ranging from 4 to 7 times the annual mean (National Air Pollution Control Administration, 1969*a*). Maximum monthly and winter means also exceed the yearly average.

### *Sulphur dioxide in urban areas*

Sulphur dioxide concentrations in polluted areas vary between about 50 and 3000 $\mu g/m^3$ in the UK (Robinson, 1971). American figures are similar (National Air Pollution Control Administration, 1969*a*). The large number of sulphur dioxide readings obtained in urban areas have been averaged, over the whole of the UK for the year 1970–1, to give a concentration of just over 100 $\mu g/m^3$ (Craxford, Weatherley and Gooriah, 1970). Concentrations have fallen markedly over the last decade as shown in Fig. 1. The downward trend contains fluctuations due largely to changes in weather conditions, which affect the quantity of sulphur dioxide emitted and the degree of atmospheric dispersion. The decline in concentrations is closely correlated with the fall in low level emissions, but bears no relationship to trends in medium and high level emissions. This correlation indicates that the domestic home is the principal determinant of urban ground level sulphur dioxide concentrations.

The UK regional pattern, however, shows considerable variation in concentrations. Table 4 demonstrates that the industrial north and Greater London have the highest sulphur dioxide concentrations (Craxford, Weatherley and Gooriah, 1971). Again concentrations have been falling in almost every region over the last few years (Craxford, Weatherley and Gooriah, 1970). The trend for the North West is shown in Fig. 1. Despite differences in geography, climate and industrial activity, concentrations in towns and cities in different parts of the country appear to be

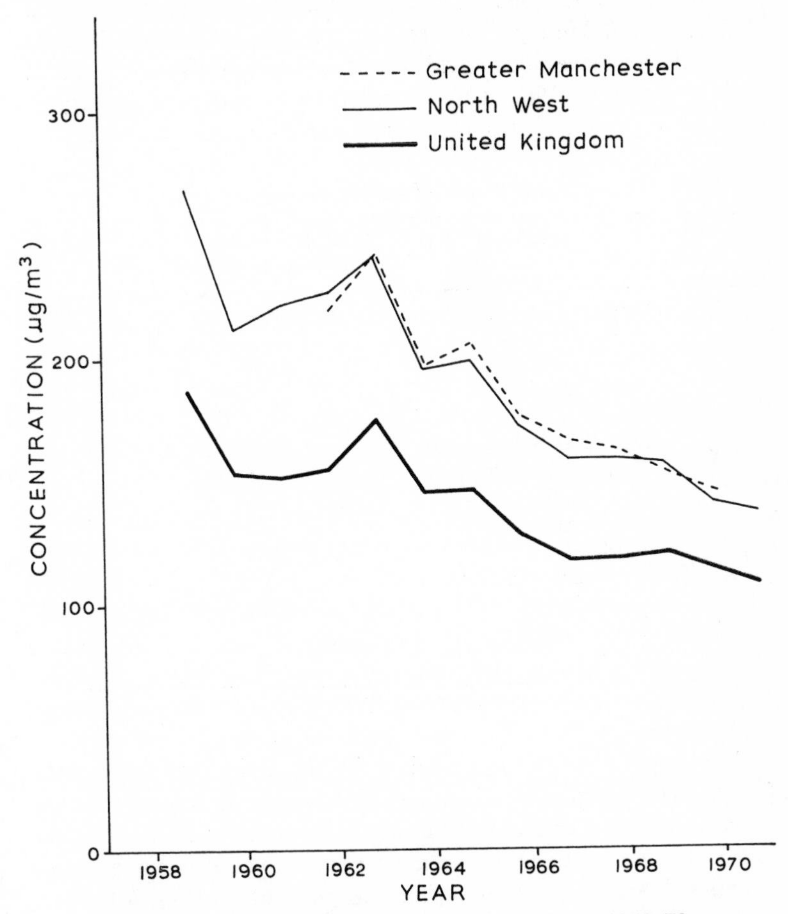


Fig. 1 Urban sulphur dioxide concentrations, 1958–70

approaching the same level, again pointing to the domestic home as the major source of sulphur dioxide pollution (National Society for Clean Air, 1971*b*).

Within a region, some towns have much greater concentrations than the average, whereas others have smaller ones. Fig. 1 shows the sulphur dioxide trend for Greater Manchester, though the averaging process disguises the fact that many individual local authorities have concentrations higher and lower than the mean. Twenty-four hour peak concentrations, as well as the annual means, have fallen in urban areas during the last few years. Only 15 readings above 500 μg/m³ were recorded in 1968, compared with over 400 in 1962. Concentrations in excess of 1000 μg/m³ are now very rare (National Society for Clean Air, 1971*b*).

*Table 4 Regional distribution of sulphur dioxide 1969–70*

| Region | Sulphur dioxide concentration (μg/m³) |
|---|---|
| Greater London | 143 |
| Yorkshire and Humberside | 140 |
| North Western | 130 |
| West Midlands | 113 |
| East Midlands | 99 |
| Northern Ireland | 86 |
| East Anglia | 86 |
| Northern | 85 |
| Scotland | 85 |
| South Eastern, excl. London | 79 |
| South Western | 66 |
| Wales | 56 |

*Source:* Craxford, Weatherley and Gooriah (1971)

A measuring instrument tends to be affected only by pollution from sources within a kilometre of it. For this reason average sulphur dioxide concentrations for a town may hide not only considerable variations between districts but variations over time. Garnett (1967) has shown that the sulphur dioxide situation within a city may be very complex, with considerable changes between one hour and the next. The central core of a town may typically have pollution levels twice those in the residential suburbs, which may again be twice those in nearby rural areas (National Society for Clean Air, 1971*b*). Sulphur dioxide concentrations appear to be much more closely related to population density than to the physical size of an urban area or to pollution from other towns (Craxford, Weatherley and Gooriah, 1971). Concentrations at measuring sites in urban areas are expected to continue to decline with the introduction of smoke control, changes to more convenient fuels and the redevelopment of older areas.

*Sulphur dioxide in rural areas*

The tendency for concentrations in rural areas to be about half those in suburban areas has been mentioned above. The limited information available from instruments in rural areas suggests that, although there are yearly fluctuations, there are no marked trends in sulphur dioxide concentrations (*see* ch 3). Isolated high readings of sulphur dioxide at rural sites often correspond with wind directions promoting drift from cities as distant as 50 km (Gooriah, 1968). On these occasions the higher concentrations tend to be associated with low wind speeds (less turbulence and mixing).

The National Society for Clean Air (1971*b*) has used the available data to draw a map showing the approximate annual mean sulphur dioxide concentrations expected in rural areas away from sources of pollution. Fig. 2 shows that there is sufficient drift in the long term to create slightly higher background sulphur dioxide concentrations around the major urban areas and to the east of the country, towards which the prevailing winds blow.

From measurements made at directional background stations in the UK, it would appear that drift is limited to a few hundred km (Robinson, 1971). In remote rural regions apparently anomalous results, such as higher sulphur dioxide readings in summer than in winter and higher readings at completely rural sites than in neighbouring small towns, are often recorded. These suggest that at concentrations of about 10–20 $\mu g/m^3$ the effect of sulphur dioxide of natural origin is beginning to predominate over that of man-made sulphur dioxide (National Society for Clean Air, 1971*b*; Hawksworth and Rose, 1970).

This hypothesis is supported by precipitation analyses which indicate that sulphur in rural areas is of different origin from that in industrial areas (Junge, 1963). In urban areas, the highest sulphur values occur in winter due to increased fuel consumption, whereas in remote rural areas, the highest values occur in

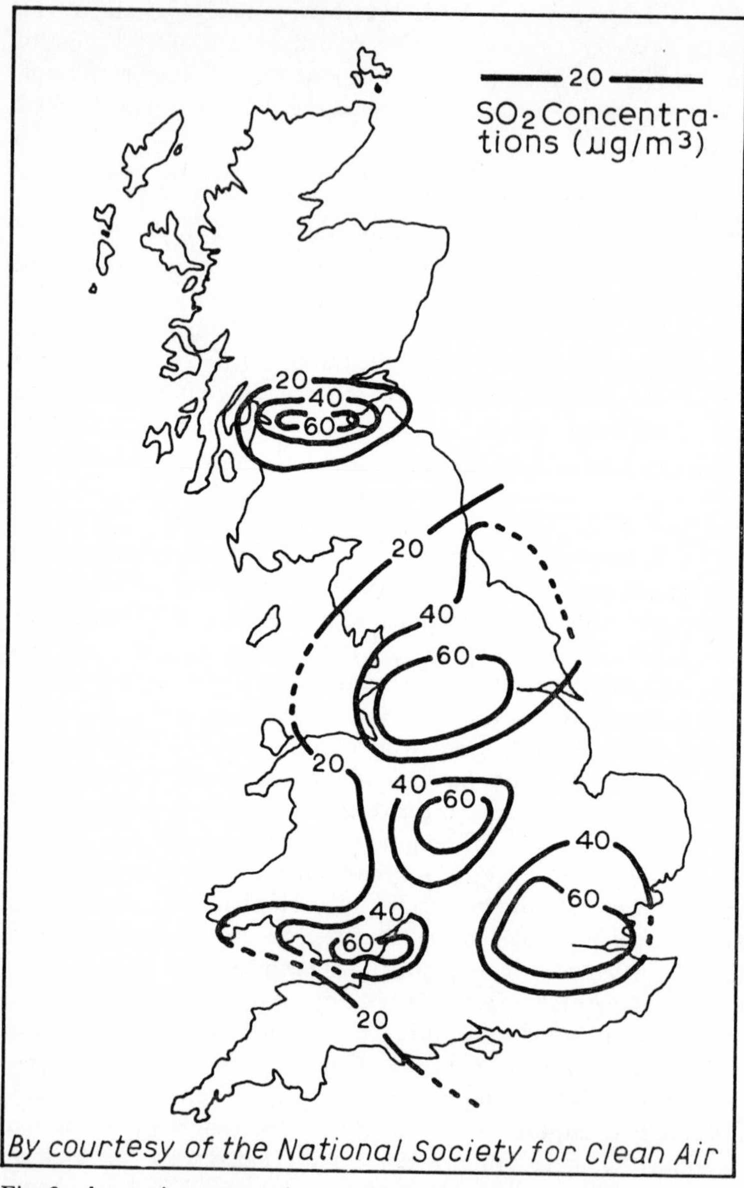


Fig. 2 Approximate annual mean sulphur dioxide concentration at sites remote from local pollution

summer possibly due, at least in part, to increased escape of hydrogen sulphide from the soil. It is also probable that the increased air temperature, lower humidity and reduced rainfall in the summer months, favour plume rise from high level emission sources, and so lead to longer-range dispersal than that of the winter months. This would further increase summer values in rural areas.

Rainfall acidity in the UK has been measured for a number of years, but there has been no discernible trend in readings, either upwards or downwards, during the past decade (National Society for Clean Air, 1971*b*). The lack of any trend in acidity is important, since it throws considerable doubt on the suggestion that sulphur dioxide emissions in the UK have contributed to increased acidity of rain falling on Scandinavia. On the other hand, comparatively little work has been done to analyse trends in sulphate concentrations in rainfall. Such analysis would not be simple since, near the coastline at least, the amount of sulphate from sea spray may well be greater than that of anthropogenic origin.

*Sulphur dioxide in remote areas*

The half-life of industrial sulphur dioxide is about four days (Robinson and Robbins, 1970), the gas being removed by a variety of methods described in the next section before it reaches the very remote areas of the world. Sulphur dioxide in these areas would appear to be entirely of natural origin (Junge, 1956). Insufficient data exist to make any estimate of whether there has been an increase in world atmospheric sulphur concentrations during the last hundred years, as has occurred in the case of carbon dioxide. Measurements of sulphur in Greenland ice (Junge, 1960) showed no increase in concentration since 1915, despite much higher world-wide emissions. However, this is hardly surprising since, if the half-life of anthropogenic sulphur dioxide is only a few days, very little sulphur dioxide pollution would reach Greenland. In general, gaseous sulphur dioxide appears not to have any global significance (Massachusetts Institute of Technology, 1970), at least at the present time.

Particulate matter derived from sulphur dioxide has a longer half-life than the gas. Mixing of particulates in the troposphere (lower atmosphere) appears to be complete in a matter of weeks within one hemisphere, whereas mixing between the troposphere and the stratosphere (upper atmosphere) is much more difficult (Barrett, 1970). The possibility that sulphates derived from sulphur dioxide emissions affect the tropospheric climate can therefore not be ruled out. They may have an effect on cloud cover by acting as condensation nuclei, and may affect temperature and visibility by scattering radiation (Junge, 1963). On the other hand, measurements of sulphate (mostly of volcanic origin) in the stratosphere give no indication of pollution by particulate derivatives of man-made sulphur dioxide (Massachusetts Institute of Technology, 1970).

## Fate of sulphur dioxide

Atmospheric sulphur dioxide plays an important part in the global cycling of sulphur. This process is briefly described before the removal of sulphur dioxide from the atmosphere and its fate upon surfaces are discussed in more detail.

### *Cycling of sulphur in the environment*

Fig. 3 is a representation of the cycling of sulphur in the global environment with percentage loadings along each pathway (derived from Junge, 1963; Robinson and Robbins, 1970). In addition to the processes of production and dispersal discussed in previous sections, there is a substantial output of gases and particulates from the atmosphere over land to that over the sea. This is not compensated by the minor reciprocal movement of sea spray. Atmospheric sulphur as sulphur dioxide, sulphates, hydrogen sulphide and other compounds is returned to the land by dry and wet deposition, terrestrial vegetation being a substantial scavenger of sulphur dioxide. At ground level, additions to the environmental sulphur cycle occur by the application of fertilizers and by natural erosion of rocks. Approximately 50 per cent of the sulphur on and in the land is discharged to the sea in run-off and drainage waters, the rest being returned to the atmosphere by biological decay and perhaps by the production of natural aerosols. Sea spray and biological decay return approximately 40–5 per cent of total oceanic sulphur to the atmosphere with a net accumulation of sulphur (*c* $86 \times 10^6$

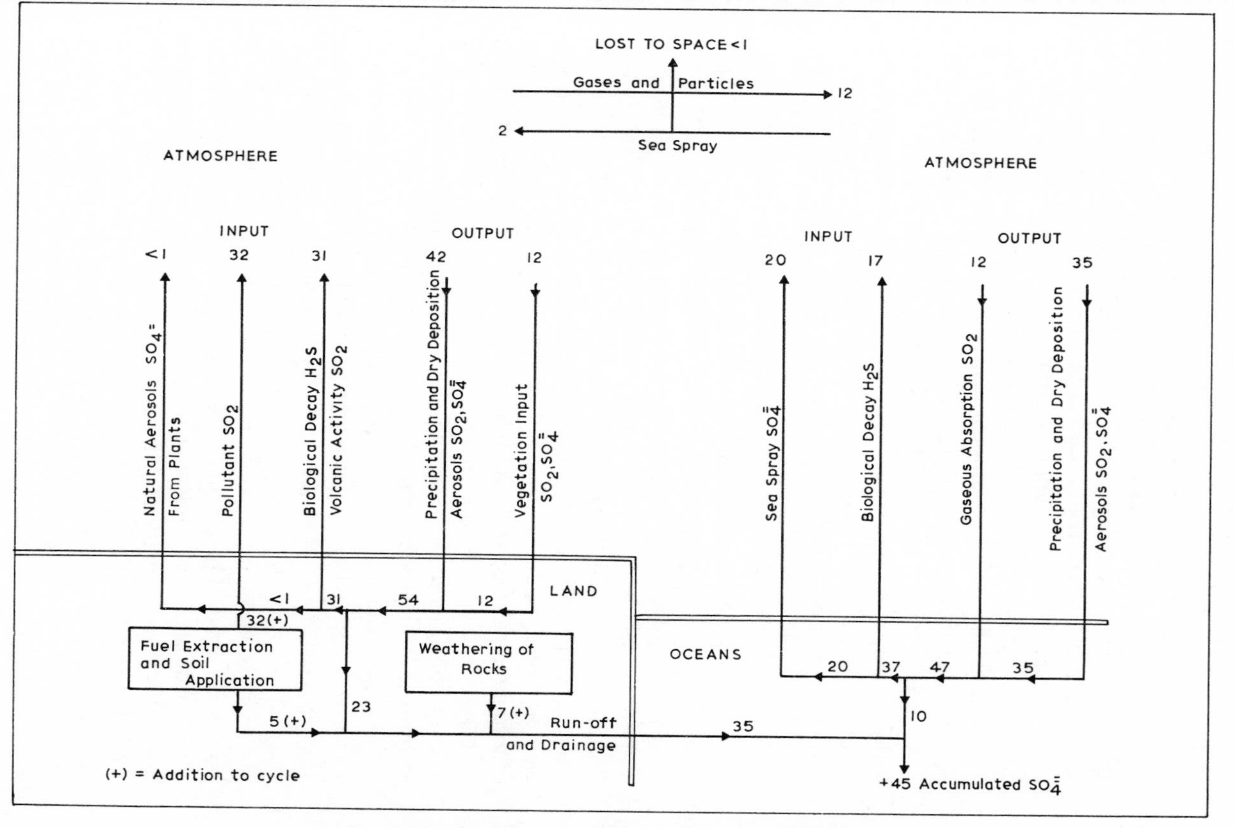


Fig. 3 Schematic representation of the sulphur cycle

tonnes/yr), mainly as sulphate, within the oceans. The rate of accumulation is slow and almost undetectable at current dilutions. It must be emphasized that the processes of the sulphur cycle and the amounts transferred by each process are not fully known, many estimates being based on very limited experimental and observational data. Inevitably, there are discrepancies between various estimates. For instance, Junge (1963) attributes a substantially greater proportion of the removal of sulphur to scavenging by vegetation than do Robinson and Robbins (1970). Fig. 3 also makes no allowance for the contribution of atmospheric sulphur to aerosols that may be accumulating in the atmosphere with long-term effects on climate (Massachusetts Institute of Technology, 1970).

*Removal of sulphur dioxide from the atmosphere*

On emission to the atmosphere, sulphur dioxide is exposed to a complex situation that can alter its physical and chemical form in a variety of different ways. Any schematic representation (e.g. Saunders, 1970) cannot comprehensively illustrate the various reactions. The likelihood of conversion of sulphur dioxide increases with distance from the source of pollution since the half-life of a molecule of sulphur dioxide is only a few days. Photochemical oxidation of sulphur dioxide to sulphur trioxide in the atmosphere occurs only slowly and on a very limited scale. Direct combination of any sulphur trioxide with water to form sulphuric acid predominates.

The oxidation of sulphur dioxide occurs both in the formation of aerosols and when sulphur dioxide dissolves in water. Irradiation and oxidation of gaseous sulphur dioxide in bright sunlight may involve oxygen and ozone. In the presence of water the reaction is accelerated to form small hygroscopic particles of sulphuric acid. Oxidation is relatively slow, however, in the absence of a catalyst such as manganese chloride. Smoke can also transport small quantities of sulphur dioxide adsorbed to each carbon particle both reversibly and irreversibly. Some conversion to sulphate may occur here. The conversion process is pH (alkaline)-dependent and can be accelerated by alkaline metals such as calcium. Ammonia is particularly effective and will produce ammonium sulphate until most of the ammonia is consumed. These oxidation processes are, in many cases, dependent upon each other and all can proceed at the same time.

Physical changes of sulphur dioxide involve the transformation of the gas to aerosols by oxidation forming hygroscopic nuclei of sulphuric acid, which probably act as condensation nuclei. The sulphate will remain as sulphuric acid unless cations and ammonia are present. As indicated previously, hydrogen sulphide is also rapidly oxidized to sulphur dioxide by ozone at the surface of aerosols. The sulphate particles formed by these processes have a longer half-life than sulphur dioxide and may well be better indicators of total pollution by sulphur dioxide than the gaseous form. Additional contributions to the aerosol population occur by the photo-oxidation of unburnt fuels and by emissions of smoke. However, it should be remembered that aerosols originating from human activities supplement those from natural sources such as sea spray, dust storms and photochemical reactions between ozone and natural trace gases, including hydrocarbons, sulphur dioxide and hydrogen sulphide. Most atmospheric sulphur ultimately arrives at ground level by wet and dry deposition of aerosols and gaseous sulphur dioxide.

*Wet deposition*

The most important method of aerosol deposition is by precipitation involving two processes—rainout within clouds and washout below clouds. Aerosol particles enter cloud droplets primarily by the consumption of condensation nuclei but attachment to water vapour gradients is of some importance. Rain droplets leave clouds to collect large aerosol particles (washout) and start to evaporate as they fall thus increasing the concentration of absorbed sulphur (primarily as sulphate).

Gaseous sulphur dioxide is also removed by passing into solution in cloud water and undergoing oxidation by the processes described earlier. This absorption of gaseous sulphur dioxide also increases the sulphur content of clouds and of aerosols during rainout. If the gaseous sulphur dioxide below the clouds is more concentrated than the sulphur dioxide within them, or if the conversion of hydrogen sulphide and sulphur dioxide to sulphate within raindrops is incomplete (i.e. an excess of cations), then further concentration of sulphur will occur by washout from the atmosphere. Washout of sulphur dioxide appears to be an exponential or logarithmic function of frequency of rain periods. Certainly frequency is a more efficient scavenging factor than heaviness of rain. In theory heavy rain also has a relatively smaller area for absorption of sulphur dioxide than fine rain but the difference is by no means consistent. With increasing frequency and duration of rainfall, therefore, a decrease in the average concentrations of sulphur dioxide in the atmosphere, and of sulphur in rainwater can be expected. Certainly the average annual atmospheric concentration of sulphur dioxide is typically about twice the average level during rainfall periods. About 17 per cent of atmospheric sulphur dioxide over Britain is removed by precipitation (Meetham, 1950; Chamberlain, 1960; Spedding, 1969*a*). This is somewhat similar to the percentage of total atmospheric sulphur (10–20 per cent) found as sulphate in aerosols over terrestrial areas (Junge, 1963). These facts suggest that dry deposition accounts for the majority of sulphur dioxide removed from the atmosphere.

*Dry deposition*

This process may account for about 80 per cent of atmospheric sulphur dioxide which arrives at ground level on waters, soils, structures and vegetation (Meetham, 1950; Chamberlain, 1960; Junge, 1963; Spedding, 1969*a*). Vegetation covers most of the surface of Great Britain and probably accounts for most of the sulphur dioxide absorbed. This seems to be borne out by the estimated deposition velocities for sulphur dioxide onto vegetation (Spedding, 1969*a*). The various sub-processes of dry deposition are far less well understood than those of wet deposition. Certainly the sedimentation of aerosols can be estimated if their size distribution is known. In most situations ground turbulence induces an almost constant concentration of aerosols with height above the ground. This provides reasonably stable conditions for sedimentation and, in the absence of eddy diffusion, the residence time ($t$) is equivalent to:

$$t = H/V_g$$

where ($V_g$) is the velocity of deposition and ($H$) is the specified height of a homogeneous layer of aerosol particles. The value ($t$)

decreases with increased particle size. Thus particles of $\leqslant 2\mu m$ diameter are removed more quickly by wet deposition than by sedimentation but the latter process becomes much more appreciable where diameters are $\geqslant 10\mu m$ (Junge, 1963). Impaction of aerosols, especially under conditions of high wind speed, may well be important particularly in coastal areas with effective scavengers such as pine trees (Madgwick and Ovington, 1959; Georgii, 1960).

Dry deposition of gases is even more complex and less well understood. Much of the information is based on radiation studies and the behaviour of gaseous radioactive iodine ($^{131}I$) during fallout. Sedimentation appears to be of limited importance but, as an approximation, it has proved useful to calculate a theoretical velocity of gaseous deposition to the ground surface. $^{131}I$ has a velocity of approximately 1 cm/sec in the laboratory (Chamberlain, 1960) and this is increased to 2 cm/sec over pastures (Chamberlain and Chadwick, 1953). Velocities for sulphur dioxide over soils and plants are about the same but one order of magnitude smaller (0.1 cm/sec) for ionic sulphate in precipitation. Assuming that particulate-type sedimentation of gases occurs, wind and eddy diffusion may introduce impaction as a secondary process and molecular adhesion may also occur. The mode of deposition onto surfaces, however, is somewhat speculative. Dry deposition seems to occur by absorption and/or chemical reaction at the surface of soils, plants and materials. The concentration at the boundary layer near a surface is lower than that above (*see* also Gilbert, 1967) thus promoting a diffusion flux towards the surface. The flux is influenced by the rates of physical and chemical absorption at the surface and/or by eddy diffusion in free air. Soils with low sulphur content may therefore absorb sulphur dioxide and soils with a high content of sulphur may even show a net output of sulphur as hydrogen sulphide (Johansson, 1959). The situation at surfaces of vegetation is complicated by the boundary layer being composed of laminar sub-layers over individual plants and leaves across which molecular diffusion transports sulphur dioxide to the plant surface.

The approximate amount of atmospheric sulphur arriving as sulphur dioxide at plant surfaces is about 12 per cent, equivalent to about 35 per cent of sulphur dioxide emitted in the UK

Other surfaces may account for smaller quantities of emitted sulphur dioxide (e.g. soils at 5–10 per cent and structures at 1–5 per cent). Given that precipitation accounts for a further 17 per cent of emitted sulphur dioxide the rest (35–40 per cent) must be distributed between deposition on seas and possibly other countries, dry deposition of aerosols (about 5 per cent), output to space and retention (mainly as aerosols) in the stratosphere. These figures have little meaning, however, in individual situations particularly where sulphur dioxide emissions and atmospheric concentrations are high enough to be phytotoxic to susceptible lichens, bryophytes and fungi. The most important aspect of pollution by sulphur dioxide in relation to the ecology of lichens is the fate and activity of sulphur dioxide when it has been deposited on the surfaces of lichens and their substrates.

### *Fate of sulphur dioxide upon surfaces*

The behaviour of sulphur dioxide upon surfaces, especially of plants, has been little studied although many of the reactions are identical to those occurring in the atmosphere especially during aerosol formation. The pattern and rate of absorption of sulphur dioxide and the oxidation of sulphur dioxide upon surfaces are governed by many factors including the physico-chemical structure of the surface, its metabolic activity, its sulphur content, its inherent resistance to mass transfer, the presence of surface contaminants and microclimatic conditions of temperature, surface moisture and relative humidity, exposure and sunlight.

Absorption onto metals and particulates (e.g. oxides, carbon, aerosols) is a mixture of physical and chemical bonding, the latter usually being irreversible and forming sulphates. Chemisorption tends to increase with temperature and humidity and is particularly important in the corrosion of metals (Uhlig, 1948; Goss, 1967). Sorption by exposed wood surfaces occurs in three forms—reversibly sorbed sulphur dioxide gas, conversion to sulphate by oxidation of sulphur dioxide gas, and formation of sulphonic acids by chemical combination with lignins in the wood (Spedding, 1970). The penetration of sorbed sulphur dioxide is limited largely to the outer 50 μm of exposed timber. Similar phenomena in bark have not been effectively examined but the same reactions probably occur with extensive modifications by the surface configuration, chemical structure, and contamination of the bark. High relative humidity will accelerate conversion to sulphuric acid, and particulate contaminants, especially alkaline earth metals, will accelerate conversion to sulphate by providing cations and maintaining high pH levels. Alkaline contaminants augment the inherent buffering capacity of bark that assists in maintaining the rate of conversion to sulphate and the subsequent survival of lichens using bark as a substrate (Coker, 1967; Skye, 1968).

Stone and concrete also act as substrates for microplants. Concrete absorbs sulphur dioxide (Spedding, 1969*b*), probably with substantial conversions to sulphate in view of its alkaline nature. Walls, buildings and exposed rocks of limestone are very susceptible to corrosion by sulphur dioxide (Henley, 1967; Goss, 1967; Spedding, 1969*b*). Uptake increases greatly with increasing humidity, saturation of the surface occurring in soft limestone matrices in 10 min at high relative humidities. The rate of absorption and erosion is highest in the softest and most loose-textured materials. In all cases the basic product is a porous, crystalline crust of gypsum ($CaSO_4 . 2H_2O$). It may also contain black carbonaceous deposits and other particles, possibly of iron oxide. The crust tends to expand with the crystallization of calcium products and to flake away rapidly thus exposing fresh limestone below. The process of sorption, erosion and exposure is thus virtually continuous. Asbestos does not suffer the same degree of erosion. However, it is porous and highly alkaline, thus producing copious quantities of sulphate (often gypsum) but it retains a high buffering capacity.

The apparent survival of lichens and bryophytes in damp sites within polluted areas has been interpreted as indicating the ability of the substrate to retain water and the importance of desiccation in urban areas as a major determinant of lichen survival (Rydzak, 1958; Brightman, 1959). Examinations of available data (e.g. Gilbert, 1969) do not readily substantiate these beliefs (*see* ch 7). Obviously increased wetness of substrate will assist in survival and development but it also has great significance for the fate of deposited sulphur dioxide. The basic reactions of sulphur dioxide under conditions of high humidity or surface moisture are accelerated producing less toxic sulphates and indirectly raising the pH. The capacity of each substrate to absorb water and gaseous sulphur dioxide, its level of contamination, especially with catalytic and alkaline metals, and its overall buffering capacity probably control this process more effectively than the ability to retain moisture. In fact, moisture retention could be distinctly disadvantageous where cations are exhausted and the buffering capacity overcome because, with decreasing pH, sulphur dioxide could be increasingly accumulated in solution.

Wetness is related frequently to microclimatic shelter. Lichens survive within some highly polluted areas, particularly in dense woodland, long grassland, deep valleys, crevices in bark and stonework and the roof edges over gutters. Overhanging structures such as tree canopies screen out pollutants by creating protective shelter and laminar boundaries (Gilbert, 1968). This principle has been applied on a larger scale in the construction of tree screens or shelter belts around polluting industries (e.g. Bernatzky, 1969).

The role of sulphur content of the receptor in controlling sorption and diffusion of sulphur dioxide has already been mentioned in respect of soils. Its role in sorption by wood and other inanimate surfaces is probably similar. Little is known about the role of sulphur content in influencing sorption by plants although it may contribute to the internal resistance of an organism. Spedding (1969*a*) expressed the velocity of deposition ($V_g$) as the reciprocal of total resistance of a plant/plant part ($r$) to mass transfer of sulphur dioxide by:

$$r = r_a + r_i = 1/2\ V_g$$

Where external resistance ($r_a$) is determined by the aerodynamics of flow over a leaf and internal resistance ($r_i$) is determined by stomatal resistance ($r_s$) and internal resistance of tissues ($r_{mes}$). Although sulphur dioxide has considerable influence on the degree of opening of stomata (Mansfield and Majernick, 1970), species vary in their response. Maximum opening of stomata ensures maximum absorption of sulphur dioxide. Increasing humidity not only increases the degree of stomatal opening, and therefore total sorption of sulphur dioxide, but it also increases sorption through the cuticle when stomata are closed (Spedding,

1969*a*). The $V_g$ value for barley leaves with closed stomata is about one-sixth of that when stomata are open at the same relative humidity. These features are underlined by the increase in non-stomatal absorption that may occur if the cuticle is damaged and by the increased resistance of wilting plants to damage by sulphur dioxide. The latter phenomenon appears to suggest that desiccation might also protect lichens from the effects of sulphur dioxide pollution to some degree.

Direct penetration of the thallus of lichens by gaseous sulphur dioxide is not improbable in view of the findings with higher plants. Lichens could absorb sulphur dioxide and its derivatives directly through their surfaces in gaseous and liquid form and indirectly via their substrates. However, the differential survival of individual species on various substrates in polluted areas *suggests* that one of the main routes of access of atmospheric sulphur to the thallus is in solution via the substrate. It seems reasonable to suppose that even if gaseous sulphur dioxide can penetrate plants, it is absorbed into the water film between individual cells and on cell walls prior to any metabolic disturbance or physical damage. Sorption of atmospheric sulphur dioxide into the water on the external surfaces of substrates may be a similar prerequisite for toxic activity. Some circumstantial support for this hypothesis can be found in the increasing inhibition of germination of certain fungal spores by sulphur dioxide with increasing relative humidity, maximum inhibition occurring in the presence of surface moisture (Couey and Uota, 1961; Couey, 1965). The activity of sulphur dioxide in solution is particularly important in the failure of some lichens, fungi and bryophytes to establish themselves in polluted areas (Gilbert, 1968, 1970; Saunders, 1966, 1970, 1971). In many cases the adult form is more resistant to sulphur dioxide than its spores as demonstrated by the survival of old lichen colonies in polluted areas (Laundon, 1967; Saunders, 1970; ch 3, 6, 16).

The behaviour of sulphur dioxide in solution on substrate surfaces is exceedingly complex (Saunders, 1966, 1970, 1971; Gilbert, 1968, 1970; Hill, 1971). There are three possible modes of toxicity, (*a*) accumulation of sulphate, (*b*) decrease in pH, and (*c*) accumulation of sulphur dioxide and/or sulphates. All three processes can occur on the same surface. Sulphate is generated by the oxidation processes mentioned earlier. Temperature and pH can greatly influence the rate of oxidation, which is also affected by the state of equilibrium between sulphur dioxide in the atmosphere and in solution. Absorption ceases when the two media are in equilibrium. The diffusion gradient is reversed when the atmospheric concentration declines still further, sulphur dioxide being released by volatilization which in turn decreases the rate of conversion to sulphate in solution. Since exposures to sulphur dioxide are constantly varying in the environment the equilibria of such reactions are continually in flux. The equilibrium concentrations are not known but it has been tentatively suggested that 100 $\mu g\ SO_2/m^3$ (3.5 pphm) in air is roughly equivalent to 35 ppm in solution (Saunders, 1966). In general, conversion to sulphate is continuous and quite rapid particularly in substrates with a high buffering capacity. There is ample evidence, however, to show that sulphates and sulphuric acid are less toxic to microplants than sulphur dioxide in solution.

Undoubtedly sulphur dioxide and its derivatives can and do reduce the pH of surface waters. Tests exposing spores, thalli and mycelia to different levels of pH using various combinations of buffered and unbuffered solutions, both free of sulphur compounds and containing sulphite or sulphur dioxide, have demonstrated that the pH of the solution alone is not the major toxic factor (Saunders, 1966; Gilbert, 1968; Hill, 1971). However, the form in which sulphur dioxide is distributed is determined by the pH of the solution. According to the Michaelis equation (Vas and Ingram, 1949; Joslyn and Braverman, 1954) sulphur dioxide in solution occurs as sulphite ($SO_3^{2-}$), bisulphite ($HSO_3^-$) and undissociated sulphurous acid ($H_2SO_3$) the components reaching maximum proportions at pH 8, 3.5 and 0 respectively (Table 5). Two additional complications arise from the unknown rates of oxidation to sulphate for each component and the impossibility of distinguishing between sulphur dioxide in solution and undissociated sulphurous acid at very low pH values (Heslop and Robinson, 1963). Solutions of sulphur dioxide are most toxic to many fungi, lichens and bryophytes at $\leq$pH 4 when the largest component is bisulphite and undissociated sulphurous acid increasingly occurs. The toxicity of these components to some micro-organisms has been demonstrated by food chemists (Rahn and Cohn, 1944; Vas and Ingram, 1949).

*Table 5 Distribution of the derivatives of sulphur dioxide in solution with pH*

| pH | % total sulphur | | |
|---|---|---|---|
| | Sulphite ($SO_3^{2-}$) | Bisulphite ($HSO_3^-$) | Sulphurous acid ($H_2SO_3$) |
| 8 | 100 | 0.01 | 0 |
| 7 | 96 | 4 | 0 |
| 6 | 85 | 15 | 0 |
| 5 | 37.5 | 62.5 | 0 |
| 4 | 7 | 92 | 1 |
| 3 | 1 | 90 | 9 |
| 2 | 0.01? | 65 | 35 |
| 1 | 0 | 15 | 85 |
| 0 | 0 | 4 | 96 |

*Source:* adapted from Vas and Ingram (1949)

It seems, therefore, that the deposition of atmospheric sulphur dioxide and its absorption into surface moisture on substrates may form the main route of sulphur dioxide to sites of toxic activity. Once in solution, a great deal depends on the buffering capacity of the substrate and the efficiency of the oxidation of sulphur dioxide to sulphate. If the pH falls conversion to sulphate also decreases and the sulphur dioxide in solution becomes increasingly distributed into the highly toxic bisulphite and undissociated sulphurous acid forms. These reactions on surfaces merely reflect the great complexity of the dispersal and fate of atmospheric sulphur dioxide emitted primarily by human activities.

## References

Barrett, C. F. (1970). Air pollution. *R. Inst. Chem. Rev.* **3,** 119–34.

Bernatzky, A. (1969). Die Bedeutung von Schutzpflanzungen gegen Luftverunreinigungen. In: *Air Pollution, Proceedings of the first European Congress on the influence of air pollution on plants and animals, Wageningen 1968*, 383–95. Wageningen: Centre for Agricultural Publishing and Documentation.

Brightman, F. H. (1959). Some factors influencing lichen growth in towns. *Lichenologist* **1,** 104–8.

Central Electricity Research Laboratories (1967). Symposium on chimney plume rise and dispersion, 7 October 1966. *Atmos. Environ.* **1,** 351–440.

Chamberlain, A. C. (1960). Aspects of the deposition of radioactive and other gases and particles. *Int. J. Air Pollut.* **3,** 63–88.

Chamberlain, A. C. and Chadwick, R. C. (1953). Deposition of airborne radioactivity as an atmospheric tracer. *Nucleonics* **11,** 22–5.

Chandler, T. J. (1971). Air pollution and urban climates. In: *Proceedings of the Clean Air Conference, Folkestone 1971*. Brighton: National Society for Clean Air.

Coker, P. D. (1967). The effects of sulphur dioxide pollution on bark epiphytes. *Trans. Br. bryol. Soc.* **5,** 341–8.

Couey, H. M. (1968). Inhibition of germination of *Alternaria* spores by sulphur dioxide under various moisture conditions. *Phytopathology* **55,** 525–7.

Couey, H. M. and Uota, M. (1961). Effect of concentration, exposure time, temperature, and relative humidity on the toxicity of sulphur dioxide to the spores of *Botrytis cinerea*. *Phytopathology* **51,** 815–19.

Craxford, S. R., Slimming, D. W. and Wilkins, E. T. (1960). Measurement of air pollution. In: *Proceedings of the Clean Air Conference, Harrogate 1960*. Brighton: National Society for Clean Air.

Craxford, S. R., Weatherley, M.-L., P. M. and Gooriah, B. D. (1970). Air pollution in urban areas in the U.K. *Proceedings of the 2nd International Clean Air Conference, Washington, 1970*. [Preprint.]

Craxford, S. R., Weatherley, M.-L., P. M. and Gooriah, B. D. (1971). The National Survey of Smoke and Sulphur Dioxide: the first ten years. *Proceedings of the Clean Air Conference, Folkestone 1971*. Brighton: National Society for Clean Air.

Department of Scientific and Industrial Research (1958). *Measurement of air pollution*. London: H.M.S.O.

Eaves, A. and Macaulay, R. C. (1964). Sulphur dioxide pollution: statistical analysis of results from adjacent lead dioxide and hydrogen peroxide instruments. *Int. J. Air Wat. Pollut.* **8,** 645–55.

Egnér, H. and Eriksson, E. (1955). Current data on the chemical composition of air and precipitation. *Tellus* **7,** 134–9.

Eriksson, E. (1959). The yearly circulation of chloride and sulphur in nature; meteorological, geochemical and pedological implications. Part I, II. *Tellus* **11,** 375–403, **12,** 63–109.

Garnett, A. (1967). Some climatological problems in urban geography with reference to air pollution. *Publs Inst. Br. Geogr.* **42,** 21–43.

Georgii, H. W. (1960). Untersuchungen uber atmospherische Spurenstoffe und ihre Bedeutung fur die Chemie der Niederschlage. *Geofis. pura appl.* **47,** 155–71.

Gilbert, O. L. (1968). Bryophytes as indicators of air pollution in the Tyne Valley. *New Phytol.* **67,** 15–30.

Gilbert, O. L. (1969). The effect of $SO_2$ on lichens and bryophytes around Newcastle upon Tyne. In: *Air Pollution, Proceedings of the first European Congress on the influence of air pollution on plants and animals, Wageningen 1968*, 223–35. Wageningen: Centre for Agricultural Publishing and Documentation.

Gilbert, O. L. (1970). Further studies on the effect of sulphur dioxide on lichens and bryophytes. *New Phytol.* **69,** 605–27.

Gooriah, B. D. (1968). *Distribution of pollution at some country sites.* Stevenage, Herts: Warren Spring Laboratory.

Goss, J. R. (1967). *Corrosion by air pollution: a review.* Stevenage, Herts.: Warren Spring Laboratory.

Hawksworth, D. L. and Rose, F. (1970). Qualitative scale for estimating sulphur dioxide air pollution in England and Wales using epiphytic lichens. *Nature, Lond.* **227,** 145–8.

Henley, K. J. (1967). Some minerological aspects of air pollution damage to limestone. In: *Proceedings of the Clean Air Conference, Blackpool 1967.* London: National Society for Clean Air.

Heslop, R. B. and Robinson, P. L. (1963). *Inorganic Chemistry.* London: Elsevier.

Hill, D. J. (1971). Experimental study of the effect of sulphite on lichens with reference to atmospheric pollution. *New Phytol.* **70,** 831–6.

Hochheiser, S. (1964). Methods of measuring and monitoring sulphur dioxide. *National Air Pollution Control Administration Publ.* **999-AP-6.** Washington: U.S. Government Publishing Office.

Johansson, O. (1959). On the sulphur problem in Swedish agriculture. *K. Lantbrtlögsk. Annlr* **25,** 57–169.

Joint Committee on Atomic Energy (1969). *Environmental effects of producing electric power,* **1.** Washington: U.S. Congress.

Joslyn, M. A. and Braverman, J. B. S. (1954). The chemistry and technology of the pre-treatment and preservation of fruit and vegetable produce with sulphur dioxide and sulphites. *Adv. Fd Res.* **5,** 97–114.

Junge, C. E. (1956). Recent investigations in air chemistry. *Tellus* **8,** 127–39.

Junge, C. E. (1960). Sulphur in the atmosphere. *J. geophys. Res.* **65,** 227–37.

Junge, C. E. (1963). *Air Chemistry and Radioactivity.* London and New York: Academic Press.

Katz, M. (1958). In: Magill, P. L., Holden, F. R. and Ackley, C. (ed.) *Air Pollution Handbook.* New York: McGraw-Hill.

Katz, M. (1969). *Measurement of air pollutants.* Geneva: World Health Organization.

Laundon, J. R. (1967). A study of the lichen flora of London. *Lichenologist* **3,** 277–327.

Madgwick, H. A. I. and Ovington, J. D. (1959). The chemical composition of precipitation in adjacent forest and open plots. *Forestry* **32,** 14–22.

Mansfield, T. A. and Majernik, O. (1970). Can stomata play a part in protecting plants against air pollutants? *Enrivon. Pollut.* **1,** 149–54.

Massachusetts Institute of Technology 1970). *Man's Impact on the Global Environment.* Massachusetts: Massachusetts Institute of Technology Press.

Meetham, A. R. (1950). Natural removal of pollution from the atmosphere. *J. R. meteorol. Soc.* **76,** 359–71.

National Air Pollution Control Administration (1969*a*). Air quality criteria for sulphur oxides. *National Air Pollution Control Administration Publ.* **AP-50.** Washington: U.S. Government Printing Office.

National Air Pollution Control Administration (1969*b*). *Estimates of future air pollutant emissions.* Raleigh, N.C.: National Air Pollution Control Administration.

National Air Pollution Control Administration (1969*c*). Tall stacks, various atmospheric phenomena, and related aspects. *National Air Pollution Control Administration Publ.* **APTD 69-12.** Washington: U.S. Government Printing Office.

National Air Pollution Control Administration (1970). Nationwide inventory of air pollutant emissions, 1968. *National Air Pollution Control Administration Publ.* **AP-73.** Washington: U.S. Government Printing Office.

National Society for Clean Air (1971*a*). *Clean Air Yearbook, 1970–1971.* Brighton: National Society for Clean Air.

National Society for Clean Air. (1971*b*). *Sulphur dioxide.* Brighton: National Society for Clean Air.

Organization for Economic Co-operation and Development (1971). *Models for the prediction of air pollution.* Paris: Organization for Economic Co-operation and Development.

Pasquill, F. (1962). *Atmospheric Diffusion.* London: Van Nostrand.

Peterson, J. T. (1969). The climate of cities: A survey of recent literature. *National Air Pollution Control Administration. Publ.* **AP-59.** Washington; U.S. Government Printing Office.

Rahn, O. and Cohn, J. E. (1964). Effect of increase in acidity on antiseptic efficiency. *Ind. Engng Chem. int. Edn* **36,** 185.

Robinson, A. J. (1971). Air pollution. *Jl R. Soc. Arts* **119,** 505–19.

Robinson, E. and Robbins, R. C. (1970). Gaseous sulphur pollutants from urban and natural sources. *J. Air Pollut. Control Ass.* **20,** 233–5.

Rydzak, J. (1959). Influence of small towns on the lichen vegetation. Part VII Discussion and general conclusions. *Annls Univ. Mariae Curie-Skłowdowska,* C, **13,** 275–323.

Saunders, P. J. W. (1966). The toxicity of sulphur dioxide to *Diplocarpon rosae* Wolf causing blackspot of roses. *Ann. appl. Biol.* **58,** 103–14.

Saunders, P. J. W. (1970). Air pollution in relation to lichens and fungi. *Lichenologist* **4,** 337–49.

Saunders, P. J. W. (1971). Modification of the leaf surface and its environment by pollution. In: Preece. T. F. and Dickinson, C. H. (ed.)

*Ecology of leaf surface microorganisms*, 81–9. London and New York: Academic Press.

Scorer, R. S. (1970). Air pollution: its implication for industrial planning. *Long Range Planning* **3,** 46–53.

Skye, E. (1968). Lichens and air pollution. *Acta phytogeogr. suec.* **52,** 1–123.

Spedding, D. J. (1969*a*). Uptake of sulphur dioxide by barley leaves at low sulphur dioxide concentrations. *Nature, Lond.* **224,** 1229–31.

Spedding, D. J. (1969*b*). The fate of sulphur-35/sulphur dioxide released in a laboratory. *Atmos. Environ.* **3,** 341–6.

Spedding, D. J. (1969*c*). Sulphur dioxide uptake by limestone. *Atmos. Environ.* **3,** 683.

Spedding, D. J. (1970). Sorption of sulphur dioxide by indoor surfaces. II. Wood. *J. appl. Chem., Lond.* **20,** 226–8.

Stern, A. C. (ed.) (1970). Proceedings of the Symposium on multiple-source urban diffusion models. *Air Pollution Control Office Publ.* **AP-86.** Washington: U.S. Government Printing Office.

Strom, G. H. (1968). Atmospheric dispersion of stack effluents. In: Stern, A. C. (ed.) *Air Pollution* **1,** *227–74.* Ed. 2. New York: Academic Press.

Swedish Royal Ministry for Foreign Affairs and Swedish Royal Ministry of Agriculture (1971). *Air pollution across national boundaries. The impact on the environment of sulfur in air and precipitation, Sweden's case study for the United Nations conference on the human environment.* Stockholm: Swedish Preparatory Committee for the United Nations Conference on the Human Environment.

Uhlig, H. H. (1948). *Corrosion Handbook.* New York: Wiley & Sons.

Vas, K. and Ingram, M. (1949). Preservation of fruit juices with less $SO_2$. *Fd. Mf.* **24,** 414–16.

Wanta, R. C. (1968). Meteorology and air pollution. In: Stern, A. C. (ed.) *Air Pollution* **1,** 187–226. Ed. 2. New York: Academic Press.

Warren Spring Laboratory (1958–71). *The investigation of air pollution, National Survey, smoke and sulphur dioxide.* Stevenage, Herts.: Department of Trade and Industry.

Warren Spring Laboratory (1967). *The investigation of atmospheric pollution, 1958–1966.* London: H.M.S.O.

# 3: Mapping Studies

D. L. HAWKSWORTH

A knowledge of the distribution and frequency of lichen species in relation to the degree of air pollution is fundamental both to discussions of the sensitivity of individual species and their use as practical indicators. The earliest investigations on the lichen vegetation in polluted areas were often limited in extent, included relatively little descriptive data, and were based on rather casual observations. More detailed and comprehensive studies carried out by many different investigators during the last fifteen years have, however, substantiated the view of Nylander (1866) that lichens can provide a reliable indication of the degree of air pollution (Hawksworth, 1971*a*).

Different techniques have been employed to study the lichen flora and vegetation in affected areas, in producing cartographic representations of the field data obtained, correlating this information with the concentrations of air pollutants, and in using these data to assess the concentrations of the same air pollutants in adjacent areas. This chapter discusses these various methods.

## Methods

### *Species distribution*

Detailed plotting of the distribution of selected species on maps may be considered as the 'classical approach' to studies of the effects of air pollutants on lichens. The earliest workers in this field, however, did not publish many maps but often provided such detailed locality lists that later workers have been able to construct maps from their information.

The first series of species distribution maps for an area affected by air pollution was that of Haugsjå (1930) who mapped the distribution of twenty species in Oslo. By the end of February 1972 studies of this type including maps, or information from which maps could be constructed, had been published for about eighty areas affected by air pollution. Maps of this type merely indicate the presence and absence of particular species, and most investigators have dealt principally or only with corticolous and lignicolous taxa. Examples of this type of detailed map are given in chapter 4, Figs. 1–5.

Some authors (e.g. Skye, 1958; Gilbert, 1965; Lundström, 1968; Moberg, 1968) have employed base maps with all stations examined indicated on them and used an additional symbol (e.g. blacking in an open circle) to show in which the species occurred (Fig. 1). This approach is clearly more satisfactory than dot maps alone as it is readily apparent from them which sites have been studied. A site examined and the species not found is obviously of greater significance than a site not investigated.

Authors of comprehensive studies of this type have often presented detailed information on the sites examined, frequently of individual trees (e.g. Haugsjå, 1930; Rydzak, 1954, 1956–9, 1969, etc.: Lundström, 1968; Skye, 1968). Data on the species, bark pH, diameter, aspect and inclination of the host tree, the percentage cover of each lichen species, and sometimes also notes as to the luxuriance and fertility of specimens, are examples of the types of information which may be included. These data will be of particular value to future workers in the same area as they will enable particular trees to be identified and their past and present lichen vegetation to be compared extremely accurately. The cost of publication of so much information may sometimes prove prohibitive but it is recommended that where such data have been obtained they are deposited in a local library so that they may be referred to by future workers.

A further approach to mapping is to indicate the inner limits of particular species on particular substrates. This method was first used by Haugsjå (1930) but more recent examples are the maps of Gilbert (1970*a*) and Rose (1970, ch 4, Fig. 6).

Detailed mapping of individual species is, however, very time-consuming and, as DeSloover and LeBlanc (1968, p. 46) point out, has an important disadvantage in not taking into account the lichen vegetation as a whole. A single spot may indicate either a tree with 60 per cent cover of luxuriant specimens of the species or a single fragment of it a few millimetres tall in a bark fissure near its base. This problem may be partly overcome by the use

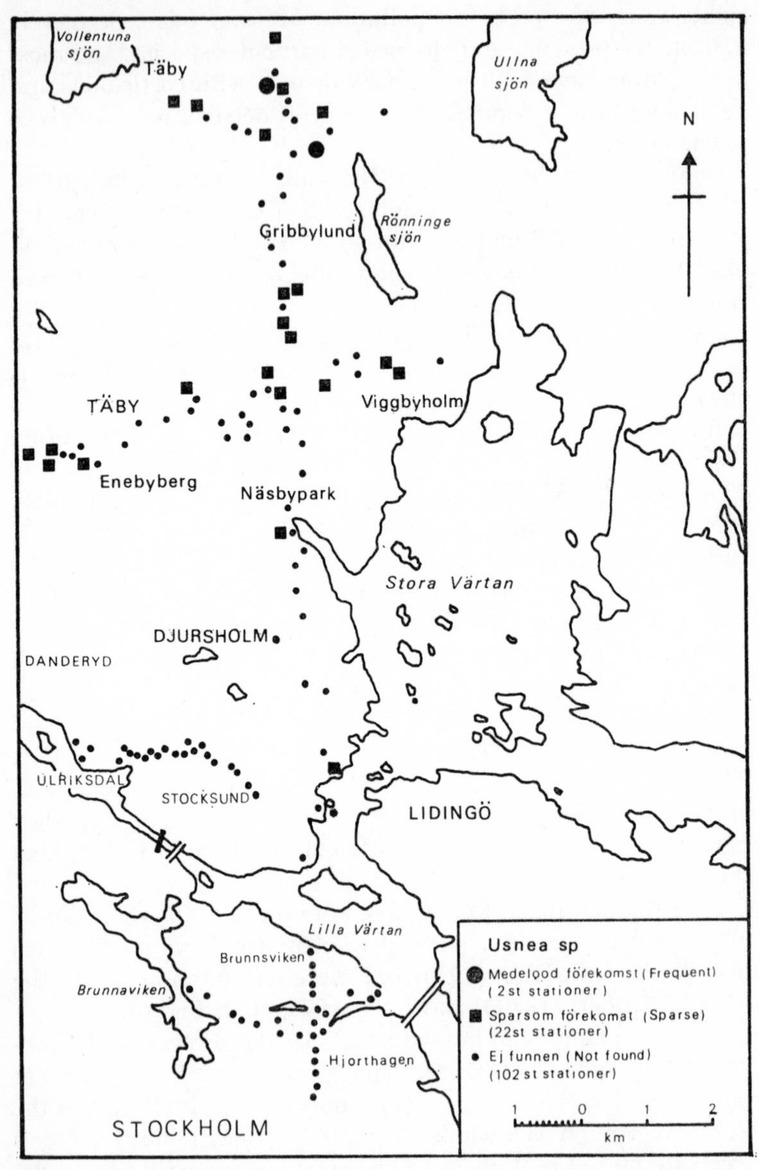


Fig. 1 Distribution of *Usnea* species on coniferous trees in the area north of Stockholm (after Lundström, 1968, p. 34)

of spots of different sizes as the maps of Lundström (1968, Fig. 1), Moberg (1968) and Skye (1968) indicate, but practical cartographic problems increase rapidly with each successive level of information content attempted. If a map based on the lichen vegetation is to be used by non-specialists as a guide to air pollution levels in an area it must be as simple as is consistent with accuracy.

Detailed mapping of individual species is, however, a prerequisite for studies of other types using more sophisticated techniques considering the frequency and abundance of particular species and communities as a whole. It is only through such studies that a clear understanding of the tolerance of particular species can be obtained and those most suitable for use as indicators selected. For the purposes of investigations incorporating 'tolerance' but not based solely on this it is often adequate to carry out detailed mapping of particular species in a broad transect out from the pollution source to ascertain their relative sensitivity. In an area of fairly uniform topography and climate, conclusions from such a pilot study can be extrapolated into adjacent parts of the region.

### *Species numbers*

The number of species present at comparable sites (e.g. trees of the same age and species in similar situations) also reflects the degree of air pollution. Many early workers were clearly aware of this but only rarely have such data been expressed either graphically or cartographically. Jones (1952) prepared graphs from Haugsjå's (1930) data for Oslo which showed that the number of corticolous species declined along transects into the centre of that city. Jones constructed similar graphs for some cities and towns in England which revealed identical trends. Gilbert (1965, p. 37) showed that the number of species on all substrates declined from 56 to 5 along a 10-mile transect from the centre of Newcastle upon Tyne, and Griffith (1966, p. 29) obtained similar results along a transect westwards from the Consett iron and steel works in Co. Durham. A modification of this approach has been used by Pyatt (1969, 1970, p. 51) who constructed graphs based on the number of species in each one kilometre square along four 9-mile transects in the Port Talbot area, South Wales.

As part of his detailed investigation of the Midden-Limburg area of Belgium, Barkman (1963) produced a zone-map based on the number of epiphytic species present at each station. A map indicating the number of corticolous species per one kilometre square in ancient parkland and open-woodland sites in England and Wales is presented in chapter 16, Fig. 1.

In the future the use of computer methods to prepare contour maps from the number of species in sites standardized in particular ways may prove an important approach to the study of lichens in polluted areas (*cf* p. 50).

*Percentage cover and frequency*

Changes in the percentage cover of particular species as the centres of areas affected by air pollution are approached were first demonstrated by Jones (1952). When the total lichen vegetation rather than individual species is considered, however, the situation is complex. In western Europe *Lecanora conizaeoides* is the least sensitive epiphytic species to sulphur dioxide and this is a crustose species whose thallus is able to cover all available bark surfaces so that a tree in an area affected by this pollutant at mean levels of *c* 80–130 $\mu g/m^3$ may have an 80–95 per cent cover of this single species. In areas affected by lower mean levels of this pollutant (e.g. $<60$ $\mu g/m^3$), as noted by Gilbert (1969, p. 225), similar trees have floras including foliose and fruticose species in a dynamic state with individual thalli dying and leaving bare spaces so that the cover of the total lichen vegetation may amount to only 60–80 per cent. The use of percentage cover alone is, as Mellanby (1967, p. 39) points out, consequently of little practical value as an indication of the degree of air pollution when all species are considered. In contrast, where single species are studied percentage cover assumes considerable significance and can be incorporated together with other data to produce maps and scales.

Percentage cover graphs have also been prepared for particular life-forms (e.g. Fenton, 1960; Griffith, 1966). Epiphytic foliose and fruticose species generally constitute the major part of the total on well-lit trees (but not shaded ones) in relatively unpolluted areas whilst crustose species (often only *Lecanora conizaeoides*) may account for the whole total in more severely affected sites. This is not to say, however, that all crustose species are more tolerant than all foliose and fruticose ones. To the contrary, some crustose species are much more sensitive than many foliose and fruticose taxa (*cf* Barkman, 1958, 1961, 1969; Hawksworth and Rose, 1970; Hawksworth, 1971*a*).

The only recent paper to emphasize percentage cover alone as an indication of the degree of air pollution is that of Domrös (1966) who studied the central Rhine-Westphalian industrial complex. It is evident that this approach may have further applications in areas where *Lecanora conizaeoides* is the only epiphytic species present as its abundance is related to the degree of sulphur dioxide pollution of the air (Gilbert, 1969; Hawksworth and Rose, 1970).

Brodo (1966) employed percentage frequency in part of his study on Long Island, New York, constructing graphs based on the percentage occurrence of particular species on trees in samples of fifty trees per locality.

### *Zone-maps*

From detailed studies of the distribution and frequency of individual species many investigators since Sernander (1912, 1926) have worked out generalized zone systems based on the distribution and frequency of various numbers of different species. Zone-maps have been constructed for individual industrial plants, towns, cities, provinces and even whole countries (Haugsjå, 1930; Vaarna, 1934; Vareschi, 1936, 1953; Felföldy, 1942; Krusenstjerna, 1945; Zurzycki, 1949; Sauberer, 1951; Barbalić, 1953; Steiner and Schulze-Horn, 1953; Schmid, 1956; Schinzel, 1957; Barkman, 1958, 1961, 1963, 1969; Beschel, 1958; LeBlanc, 1960, 1961; Mägdefrau, 1960; Villwock, 1962; Pišút, 1962; Bortenschlager and Schmidt, 1963; Natho, 1964*a*; Gilbert, 1965, 1968*c*, 1971*b*; Domrös, 1966; Rao and LeBlanc, 1967; Moberg, 1968; Skye, 1968; Pyatt, 1969, 1970; Hawksworth and Rose, 1970; Spenling, 1971). A detailed comparison of the various zones used and the criteria adopted in defining them is outside the scope of this chapter but the main points are summarized by Hawksworth (1971*a*).

Three or four zones have most frequently been distinguished: (1) an inner 'lichen desert' with no corticolous lichens at all, or at least no foliose and fruticose species; (2) an 'inner transitional (struggle) zone' with foliose but lacking fruticose species; (3) an 'outer transitional (struggle) zone' in which fruticose species appear (often united with the 'inner transitional zone'); and (4) a 'normal (unaffected) zone'. Five-zone systems have been employed by Sauberer (1951), Beschel (1958), Bortenschlager and Schmidt (1963), Rao and LeBlanc (1967) and Skye (1968). Barkman (1963) used phytosociological units, and Hawksworth and Rose (1970) proposed a 0–10 zone scheme for England and Wales.

The adoption of phrases such as 'lichen desert', 'struggle zone' and 'normal zone' is not satisfactory and should be avoided by future workers as these terms have been used in very different senses and now constitute a source of confusion. The definition of 'normal' is particularly difficult, for what may be considered 'normal' in a local survey may not be so when the whole region is considered (compare Figs. 1 and 3 in Hawksworth and Rose, 1970).

All maps so far produced employing zones, except that of Barkman (1963), have characterized zones by the frequency and occurrence of various species and life-forms. This map of Barkman's is unique in that it is based primarily on phytosociological associations, but, as DeSloover and LeBlanc (1968, p. 47) state, 'Barkman's beautiful mosaic colour map . . . is so sophisticated and the various contour patterns so complicated to follow, that we doubt the usefulness of such maps to express in an easily readable form the long-range effects of air pollution in a particular region.'

The most satisfactory zone-maps for practical use will be ones based on easily recognized species which become abundant or appear at different levels of air pollution. The 0–10 zone system of Hawksworth and Rose (1970) employs such species (Table 1) and takes into account the height to which they ascend the trunks of trees, and some geographical variations which occur in the region they studied. Several workers since Sernander (1912) and Nienburg (1919) have noted the differences which occur on eutrophiated and non-eutrophiated barked trees and Hawksworth and Rose proposed separate but parallel scales for these types of bark. Hawksworth and Rose's (1970) zone-map for England and Wales is reproduced here as Fig. 2; these authors also used their scales to prepare maps for south-east England and the city of Leicester.

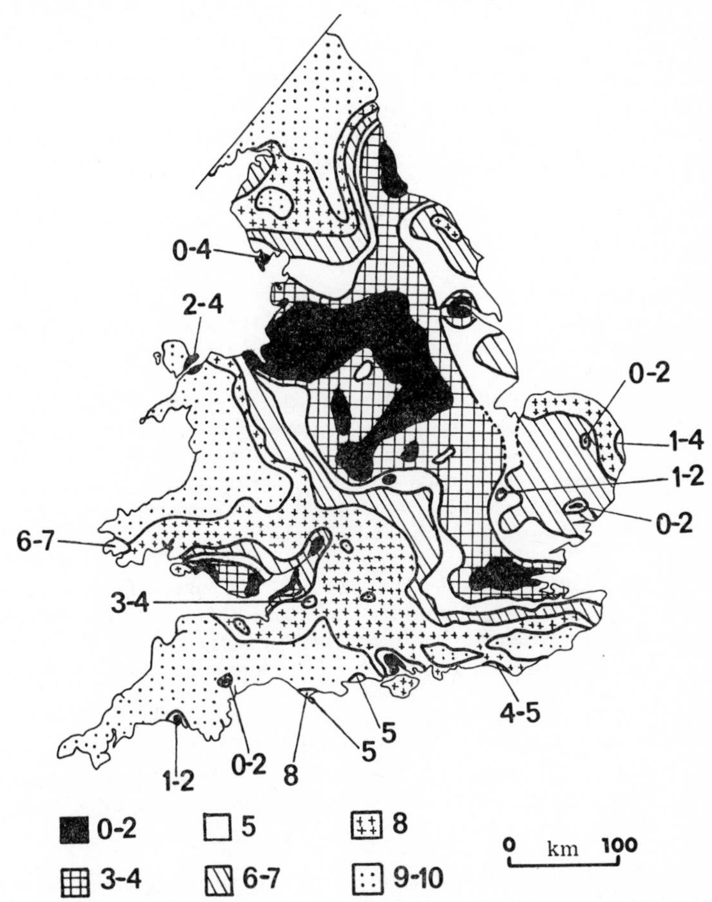


Fig. 2 Preliminary zone-map showing the extent of $SO_2$ air pollution in England and Wales based on the scales in Table 1 (after Hawksworth and Rose, 1970, p. 146)

*IAP maps*

The 'Index of Atmospheric Purity' (IAP) proposed by DeSloover

*Table 1 Qualitative scale for the estimation of mean winter $SO_2$ air pollution in England and Wales using epiphytic lichens (after Hawksworth and Rose, 1970)*

| Zone | Non-eutrophiated bark |
|---|---|
| 0 | Epiphytes absent |
| 1 | *Pleurococcus viridis* s.l. present but confined to the base |
| 2 | *Pleurococcus viridis* s.l. extends up the trunk; *Lecanora conizaeoides* present but confined to the bases |
| 3 | *Lecanora conizaeoides* extends up the trunk; *Lepraria incana* becomes frequent on the bases |
| 4 | *Hypogymnia physodes* and/or *Parmelia saxatilis*, or *P. sulcata* appear on the bases but do not extend up the trunks. *Lecidea scalaris*, *Lecanora expallens* and *Chaenotheca ferruginea* often present |
| 5 | *Hypogymnia physodes* or *P. saxatalis* extends up the trunk to 2.5 m or more; *P. glabratula*, *P. subrudecta*, *Parmeliopsis ambigua* and *Lecanora chlarotera* appear; *Calicium viride*, *Lepraria candelaris*, *Pertusaria amara* may occur; *Ramalina farinacea* and *Evernia prunastri* if present largely confined to the bases; *Platismatia glauca* may be present on horizontal branches |
| 6 | *P. caperata* present at least on the base; rich in species of *Pertusaria* (e.g. *P. albescens*, *P. hymenea*) and *Parmelia* (e.g. *P. revoluta* (except in NE), *P. tiliacea*, *P. exasperatula* (in N)); *Graphis elegans* appearing; *Pseudevernia furfuracea* and *Alectoria fuscescens* present in upland areas |
| 7 | *Parmelia caperata*, *P. revoluta* (except in NE), *P. tiliacea*, *P. exasperatula* (in N) extend up the trunk; *Usnea subfloridana*, *Pertusaria hemisphaerica*, *Rinodina roboris* (in S) and *Arthonia impolita* (in E) appear |
| 8 | *Usnea ceratina*, *Parmelia perlata* or *P. reticulata* (S and W) appear; *Rinodina roboris* extends up the trunk (in S); *Normandina pulchella* and *U. rubiginea* (in S) usually present |
| 9 | *Lobaria pulmonaria*, *L. amplissima*, *Pachyphiale cornea*, *Dimerella lutea*, or *Usnea florida* present; if these absent crustose flora well developed with often more than 25 species on larger well-lit trees |
| 10 | *L. amplissima*, *L. scrobiculata*, *Sticta limbata*, *Pannaria* spp., *Usnea articulata*, *U. filipendula* or *Teloschistes flavicans* present to locally abundant |

| Eutrophiated bark | $SO_2$ (μg/$m^3$) |
|---|---|
| Epiphytes absent | ? |
| *Pleurococcus viridis* s.l. extends up the trunk | >170 |
| *Lecanora conizaeoides* abundant; *L. expallens* occurs ocasionally on the bases | About 150 |
| *Lecanora expallens* and *Buellia punctata* abundant; *B. canescens* appears | About 125 |
| *Buellia canescens* common; *Physcia ascendens* and *Xanthoria parietina* appear on the bases; *Physcia tribacia* appears in S | About 70 |
| *Physconia grisea, P. farrea, Buellia alboatra, Physcia orbicularis, P. tenella, Ramalina farinacea, Haematomma ochroleucum* var. *porphyrium, Schismatomma decolorans, Xanthoria candelaria, Opegrapha varia* and *O. vulgata* appear; *Buellia canescens* and *X. parietina* common; *Parmelia acetabulum* appears in E | About 60 |
| *Pertusaria albescens, Physconia pulverulenta, Physciopsis adglutinata, Arthopyrenia gemmata, Caloplaca luteoalba, Xanthoria polycarpa,* and *Lecania cyrtella* appear; *Physconia grisea, Physcia orbicularis, Opegrapha varia* and *O. vulgata* become abundant | About 50 |
| *Physcia aipolia, Anaptychia ciliaris* (in E), *Bacidia rubella, Ramalina fastigiata, Candelaria concolor* and *Arthopyrenia biformis* appear | About 40 |
| *Physcia aipolia* abundant; *Anaptychia ciliaris* occurs in fruit; *Parmelia perlata, P. reticulata* (in S and W), *Gyalecta flotowii, Ramalina obtusata, R. pollinaria,* and *Desmazieria evernioides* appear | About 35 |
| *Ramalina calicaris, R. fraxinea, R. subfarinacea, Physcia leptalea, Caloplaca aurantiaca,* and *C. cerina* appear | Under 30 |
| As 9 | 'Pure' |

(1964, p. 556) provides a numerical assessment of the degree of air pollution based on the number, frequency, and tolerance of the lichen (and bryophyte) species present on trees at each site. The IAP is defined by the formula:

$$\mathrm{IAP} = \frac{n}{100}\left(\sum_{n}^{1} Q \times f\right)$$

where $n$ = the number of species at the station, $f$ = the frequency of each species, and $Q$ = the index of toxiphoby (or CMS, see below) of each species. A slightly modified formula was proposed by LeBlanc and DeSloover (1970, p. 1488) which has also been used by LeBlanc, Rao and Comeau (1972*a*):

$$\mathrm{IAP} = \sum_{n}^{1} (Q \times f)/10$$

When the numerical value for each station has been calculated the IAP values are plotted cartographically and (or) zones based on ranges of IAP values constructed.

Maps using the IAP method have been prepared for the Gand-Terneuzen (Iserentant and Margot, 1964; DeSloover, 1964; Fig. 3), Dendre (DeSloover and LeBlanc, 1968), and Ottignies, Louvain (Margot, unpublished) areas of Belgium; and the Montreal (LeBlanc and DeSloover, 1970, 1972), Sudbury (LeBlanc, Rao and Comeau, 1972*a*), and Arvida, Quebec (LeBlanc, Rao and Comeau, 1972*b*) areas of Canada. DeSloover and LeBlanc (1968) also prepared an IAP map for the Kvarntorp oil-shale works in Sweden from the data of Skye (1958).

The earlier Belgian studies employed Barkman's (1958, pp. 119–20) twelve-point 'Index of Poleophoby' worked out for the Netherlands for their values of $Q$. This is necessarily somewhat subjective and so DeSloover (1969) proposed the use of the 'cortège moyen specifique' (CMS), the mean number of other lichens (and bryophytes) growing with the particular species in the area surveyed. CMS values have been used for $Q$ in the studies of LeBlanc and DeSloover (1970) and LeBlanc, Rao and Comeau (1972*a*). In his study of the Ottignies, Louvain, area Margot (unpublished) used both Barkman's 'Index of Poleophoby' and CMS values together to provide three classes of tolerance.

Trass (1968*a–c*, 1971) has worked out his own ten-degree scale of poleotolerance for lichen species in Estonia and proposed a value 'P' (the 'poleotolerance of lichen synusiae') to provide an

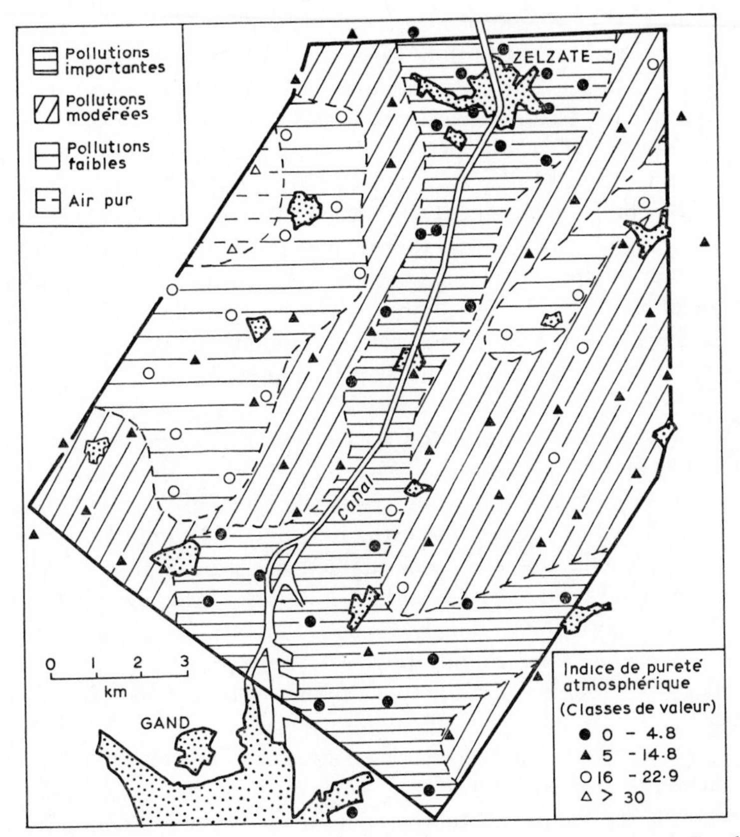


Fig. 3 Map of air pollution zones based on the IAP method for the Gand-Terneuzen, Belgium, prepared by Iserentant and Margot (after DeSloover, 1964, p. 557)

indication of the degree of sulphur dioxide pollution of the air (*see* p. 63). This value P is defined by the formula:

$$P = \sum_{i=1}^{n} \frac{a_i \times c_i}{C_i}$$

where $C_i$=the total lichen cover, $n$=the number of species, $a_i$=the poleotolerance of each species, and $c_i$=the percentage cover of each species.

Numerical methods of the IAP and P types are, however, necessarily more time-consuming to employ as compared with either species distribution maps or zone-maps produced by direct methods. For the extra work involved to be justified it is essential that the numerical values provide a better indication of air pollution levels than the alternative techniques. For this reason Granger (1970, 1972) has carried out a SYMAP computer analysis of LeBlanc and DeSloover's (1970) data for Montreal. Granger's studies showed that when the IAP map and the total number of species at all stations were compared an $R^2$ (the indicator of the degree of information retained expressed as a percentage) value of 97 per cent was obtained. When the IAP data were compared with the distribution of four selected species $R^2$ values of 91.4 per cent and 95.7 per cent were produced for urban and rural parts of the area respectively; the addition of fertility factors added little.

Granger's studies are discussed further by LeBlanc (1971) and support the view of Hawksworth (1971*a*, p. 289) that only results similar in reliability to those obtained by less complex methods are obtained by using numerical techniques of these types. Also, the IAP method is unlikely to be within the capabilities of a non-specialist who might, however, be expected to learn to recognize the few indicator species employed in other zone-map systems.

The SYMAP method enables contours to be computed from figures at different sites and consequently has considerable potential for the production of contour maps from data obtained by methods other than the IAP (*see* p. 42).

### *Transplants*

Since Arnold carried out transplants in Munich towards the end of the last century (Barkman, 1958, p. 116) this approach received little attention until Brodo (1961*a*) developed a bark-disc technique and applied it in a study on Long Island, New York (Brodo, 1967). Discs bearing the lichen are cut from the same tree or group of trees with the aid of a specially constructed large diameter circular hollow punch with a sharp cutting edge and secured in holes of the same diameter cut in the bark of similar trees in the affected area and control trees in an unaffected site. The discs are then photographed at intervals using standard (flash) lighting and compared with controls. Brodo showed that the death of transplants of *Parmelia caperata* were related to their distance from the centre of Brooklyn. This same technique was used in the Sudbury area of Canada by LeBlanc and Rao (1966) who employed sixteen lichen species and obtained results comparable to those of Brodo, clearly demonstrating that individual species differed in their tolerance to sulphur dioxide.

The scarcity of suitable trees in severely polluted and built-up areas may restrict the use of transplants onto trees. Schönbeck (1969) overcame this difficulty by attaching ten discs of *Hypogymnia physodes* to wooden boards secured to posts 1.5 m above the ground and facing an air pollution source in the Ruhr. The percentage death of the transplants was recorded on colour-sensitive film and found to provide a reliable method of indicating differences in air pollution levels when compared with control boards. Schönbeck's method has also been used by LeBlanc, Comeau and Rao (1971), and LeBlanc and Rao (1972). Hoffman (1972) has constructed a bark sampler similar to that of Brodo (1961*a*) but with a saw-edge so that by rotating it a disc can easily be cut out.

Other transplant experiments in connection with air pollution studies have been carried out by Gilbert (1968*a*,*c*, 1969, 1970*b*), Pyatt (1969), Hawksworth (1969, 1971*b*, unpublished), Coppins (unpublished) and Rose (unpublished) in the British Isles, and Nash (1971*a*) in the USA. Following Richardson (1967), Rose has confirmed that non-volatile epoxy-resins such as 'Araldite' may be used for attaching transplants free from bark directly onto other trees with no apparent adverse effects, and considers that the cutting of bark plugs involves unnecessary extra time and damage to the trees used.

All the experiments referred to above have been concerned with epiphytic species but in connection with investigations on respiration rates in polluted areas Schubert and Fritsche (1965) carried out some transplants with terricolous species.

While transplant experiments are necessary to prove the

sensitivity of particular species which it is proposed to use as indicators in mapping studies they are too time consuming to employ for practical assessments of air pollution levels over large areas. Although in severely affected sites significant damage can occur in a few days (Schönbeck, *in* Barkman, Rose and Westhoff, 1969, p. 238), in less affected ones death may take 1–2 years (Brodo, 1966; LeBlanc and Rao, 1966; Hawksworth, 1969, 1971*b*).

*Total sulphur content*

Gilbert (1965, p. 43; 1969, p. 230) found that the sulphur content of *Parmelia saxatilis* thalli was related to that of the air, and Griffith (1966) also showed this to be true for *Hypogymnia physodes*. The absorption of sulphur into live material of *Usnea filipendula* was found by Gilbert (1968, 1969) to be six times greater than that in dead material of the same species.

The determination of the concentration of metal elements in lichen thalli has been used as an indication of heavy metal contamination (ch 8) but because of technical difficulties in the determination of total sulphur in lichen thalli, this characteristic has not yet been widely used as an indicator of sulphur dioxide levels in the air. The recently developed technique of Bowen (1970*b*) involving the replacement of sulphur by radioactive Iodine-131, may, however, partly overcome this problem. Bowen was able to demonstrate that the sulphur content of thalli of *Usnea subfloridana* was much higher in material of this species from sites affected by sulphur dioxide pollution of the air than in material from relatively unaffected areas. A study based on the estimation of the sulphur content of lichen thalli is currently in progress in Norway (Nordforsk, 1971).

A modification of this approach is the estimation of the total sulphur in transplanted specimens as has been carried out by LeBlanc and Rao (1972) in Canada and by Dr H. Krog (unpublished) in Norway. This method has the advantage that all the material used would have approximately the same sulphur content at the start of the experiment and that all specimens can be analysed after exposure for known limited periods of time.

**Indicator species**

The value of species distribution or zone-maps using a limited number of species as practical indicators of air pollution levels is dependent on the careful selection of the species employed. In determining the most suitable species to use as indicators the following points require consideration.

(1) The species must always be ones which, from a detailed knowledge of their ecology and distribution in the area under investigation, would be expected to occur in the affected region on phytogeographical grounds. The most reliable evidence to support this requirement is proof that the species were widespread in the area before it became affected by air pollution. In many western European countries this information may be ascertained from herbarium and literature sources. Maps which show changes in distribution patterns with species disappearing from affected areas such as those produced for the Netherlands (Barkman, 1958, pp. 287–96) and the British Isles (ch 16) constitute the ideal basis on which to make decisions of this type. Where large geographical regions are being considered, a species may only meet this requirement in part of the region. In England, for example, *Anaptychia ciliaris* is an excellent indicator in the south-east, but not in the south-west (*see* ch 16, Fig. 4) because of what appears to be a climatic restriction of range. This same species, however, is a satisfactory indicator throughout the more 'continental' Netherlands (*see* Barkman, 1958, p. 286).

(2) The species selected must be ones which occur on substrates which still persist, in as far as can be ascertained an unaltered state, in the area. A species confined to well-lit deciduous trees, for example, will not be a satisfactory indicator in an area where all well-lit deciduous trees have been felled, or where all the deciduous trees are shaded or affected by agricultural sprays (*see* ch 8). This enables factors other than air pollutants to be eliminated as far as possible.

(3) Sufficient healthy material of the same species must be present either on different substrates in the polluted area or on the same substrate under consideration in adjacent unaffected areas. Where a species has been eliminated so completely from a region that its diaspores are unlikely to be dispersed into at least

the margins of the affected area a decrease in the level of air pollution is not likely to result in its immediate return. In the British Isles *Evernia prunastri*, *Parmelia caperata* and *Usnea subfloridana*, for example, clearly meet this requirement occurring on the same substrates in adjacent unaffected areas (ch 16, Figs. 2, 6 and 9). In the Midland and northern counties of England *Parmelia saxatilis* and *Pseudevernia furfuracea* extend further into polluted areas on siliceous wall-tops and tombstones than they do on trees and so the potential for them to spread onto adjacent trees is present. *Buellia canescens*, *Caloplaca citrina*, *Candelariella vitellina*, *Lepraria incana* (*cf* Bailey, 1971, p. 985) and *Physcia ascendens* behave in a parallel way on calcareous substrates in England and Wales.

(4) The species must be proved to be sensitive to sulphur dioxide. This may be ascertained by transplanting material into areas affected by this pollutant and observing the death of the plants.

(5) Because of discussions that have emphasized the possible significance of drying and wetting regimes, drought, and temperature differences in urban areas (*see* ch 7, 12) it is preferable to select xerophytic species, in as far as this is compatible with the other requirements enumerated here, and to pay particular attention to their behaviour in the most humid parts of the region being investigated (*cf* Barkman, 1958, p. 127). Species which, for example, are widespread inland in the Mediterranean region are unlikely to be affected by any small changes in these factors in English towns (e.g. *Anaptychia ciliaris*, *Buellia canescens*, *Hypogymnia physodes*, *Parmelia caperata*, *Xanthoria parietina*).

(6) Skye (1958) recommended species which were neither too sensitive nor too insensitive as the most satisfactory indicators. Subsequent work, however, has clearly demonstrated that the most reliable results are obtained by using several species ranging from the most tolerant to the most sensitive.

(7) Finally, if the scales are to have a practical value, non-specialists must be able to recognize the indicator species readily in the field. Species distinguished by gross morphological characters and which are not likely to be confused with any others of a superficially similar appearance will consequently be the most satisfactory.

**Standardization**

In order that factors other than air pollutants can, as far as possible, be eliminated from consideration, the stations from which data are obtained must be standardized. Most studies (*see* pp. 38–53) have been concerned primarily or solely with corticolous and lignicolous species, because trees of the same species and approximate age (as deduced from their diameter at a particular height above ground level) growing in similar situations provide a standard habitat from which to record. If a single tree species is not available in sufficient numbers throughout the area under consideration other tree species may be employed if they have similar types of bark (i.e. pH range, texture, friability) and bear similar lichen floras in adjacent areas unaffected by the pollutant under consideration.

Because of variation in the chemical composition and consequently the buffering capacity of rocks and walls, which affects the lichen vegetation they support in areas affected by sulphur dioxide (*cf* Hawksworth, 1971*a*, ch 2), saxicolous habitats are more difficult to standardize accurately. Gilbert (1968*b*, 1970*c*), however, was able to include saxicolous data in his scale for the estimation of mean annual sulphur dioxide levels, and has provided separate scales for acid stonework and old asbestos roofs or calcareous stonework (Gilbert, 1970*b*).

Towards their inner limits species are sometimes able to persist on older tombstones (Laundon, 1967, 1970) and particularly ancient trees (ch 16, p. 359), although they are unable to spread onto adjacent more recently erected tombstones and younger trees. This reduction in the ability to colonize new substrates is an important consideration in mapping studies, and data obtained from ancient substrates with lichen vegetation atypical for the site consequently require careful interpretation.

Many of the lichens which have been found to be the most suitable indicators of air pollution are photophilous. For this reason only free-standing unshaded trees should be considered. Close-canopy woodlands and trees in narrow ravines are also frequently not representative because of (*a*) the effects these features have on air-flow patterns and consequently the levels of air pollutants, and (*b*) the different lichen communities including photophobous species which characterize such habitats in relatively unaffected areas. Gilbert (1968*a*, p. 23) has shown that the sulphur dioxide levels in a wooded narrow valley in Newcastle upon Tyne are reduced as compared with the surrounding plateau, and this finding is in agreement with field observations (*see* Hawksworth, 1971*a*). Nevertheless, the lichen flora of such sites, and of ancient substrates, can be compared in different areas and may provide valuable information on air pollution levels over the region as a whole.

Trees lining main roads often also support communities which are atypical as compared with those of similar trees some distance away from them (*see* Barkman, 1958, p. 23; Rydzak, 1970). Lichens characteristic of eutrophiated habitats are frequently abundant on roadside trees affected by manure and dust, but in some areas may be exceptionally poor especially if the trees are along a road enclosed by hedges or walls. This paucity does not appear to be due to automobile exhaust gases (although the role of lead merits further study; *see* ch 8) as trees by roads carrying heavy traffic sometimes have luxuriant lichen floras (*see* Rose, Hawksworth and Coppins, 1970). In the British Isles, field observations suggest that this phenomenon is most probably due to salt scattered on the roads during the winter months which is splashed onto adjacent trees by the passing traffic, although no experimental work on this problem has been carried out. Because of these considerations little significance can be attached to the absence of species on roadside trees at least when they are present on nearby trees of the same age and species away from the roadside.

Some agricultural sprays also affect the lichen vegetation on trees in pastures (*see* ch 8) and so data from trees subjected to such sprays is also likely to be unrepresentative.

Because of variations which occur between individual trees it is preferable to treat a group of similar trees as a single station (*cf* Skye, 1958). Hawksworth and Rose (1970) recommend that the average point on a scale to which the group of trees belongs should be employed; alternatively, a fixed number of trees may be used for each station. A mapping study employing this approach is described in chapter 5.

The published data indicate that some species may be affected by slightly different mean sulphur dioxide concentrations in different parts of their geographical ranges (Barkman, 1958; Hawksworth, 1971*a*). This might either be due to the presence of ecotypes (Gilbert, 1971*a*; Baddeley, Ferry and Finegan, 1971) or to differences in the periods of time when relative humidity levels permit the species to be physiologically active and take in air pollutants in solution (*cf* Lange, Schultze and Koch, 1970; *see* ch 12). Field evidence indicates that the tolerance of some lichen species to sulphur dioxide is higher in drier more continental climates than in more oceanic ones (*cf* Hawksworth, 1971*a*). It is also possible that the existence of ecotypes characterized by physiological parameters other than their response to air pollutants may also be important in explaining this observation (*see* Harris, 1971; Kershaw and Harris, 1971). Because of these considerations, it is clear that scales and tolerance limits cannot be reliably employed in geographical areas other than those for which they were originally worked out.

## Correlation with sulphur dioxide levels

All the available evidence from laboratory and field studies demonstrates that sulphur dioxide is the principal factor in air pollution which affects lichens over large areas. No correlations with smoke levels appear to occur, at least in the British Isles (*see* ch 8, Table 4); fluorides have severe effects but act only over relatively short distances (ch 9); and temperature and humidity differences which might occur in urban areas cannot explain the field observations (ch 7). Nitrogenous gases may have some significance locally (Rydzak and Stasiak, 1971). One factor which may merit further consideration, at least in the United States, is ozone, although at moderate concentrations (*see* ch 10) this has been shown to have a stimulating effect on the regeneration of leaves of the moss *Funaria hygrometrica* at least over short periods of time (Comeau and LeBlanc, 1971). No account of the effects of ozone on lichens appears to have been published (ch 8).

Several early papers indicated that sulphurous effluents might be responsible because the lichen vegetation was found to be particularly poor in industrial parts of towns (Britzelmayer, 1875; Haugsjå, 1930; Krusenstjerna, 1945; Sauberer, 1951; Vareschi, 1953; Barkman, 1958) but no physical measurements of sulphur dioxide levels were available to these workers who were consequently unable to prove that any relationship existed.

The first evidence of a correlation between field observations and sulphur dioxide levels was produced by Mrose (1941) who discovered that the sulphate content of hoar-frost and snow was significantly (100–200 times) higher in forests near Jena, from which *Usnea* species had disappeared over the preceding fifty years, than in forests in which species of this genus still grew. Skye's (1958) detailed study of the rurally-situated Kvarntorp oil-shale works in Närke, Sweden, showed a clear correlation between the distribution of several lichen species and the sulphur content of tree leaves, a measure of the mean sulphur dioxide levels in the air (*see* Lihnell, 1969, p. 350; Fig. 4). Pišút (1962) came to similar conclusions as a result of studies in an industrial area of Czechoslovakia.

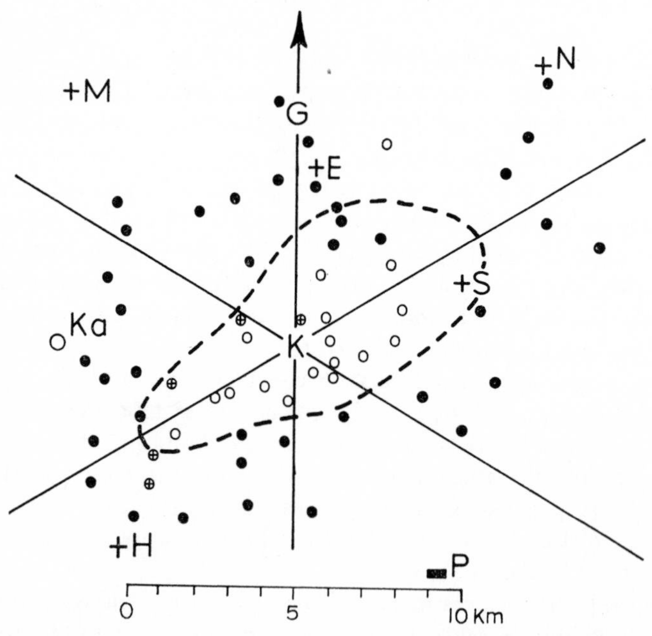


Fig. 4 Correlation between the distribution of *Xanthoria parietina* and the 50 isarithim for the sulphate content of *Betula* leaves for 1953 (broken line) around the oil-shale works at Kvarntorp, Sweden; ○ : lichen absent; ⊕ : damaged thalli; ● : lichen present (after Lihnell, 1969, p. 350)

The lack of sufficient sulphur dioxide recording gauges has been a limiting factor in establishing correlations in many areas. Skye (1964), for example, was able to demonstrate an approximate correlation between the total number of species and mean annual sulphur dioxide levels in the Stockholm area but unable to take his observations further because of this lack of equipment. Independently Fenton (1964) was able to suggest some sulphur dioxide levels at which particular species seemed to be affected in the Belfast area of Northern Ireland but was unable to separate his data from smoke values. Tallis (1964) considered that in south Lancashire *Hypogymnia physodes* and *Parmelia saxatilis* were limited by critical levels of atmospheric sulphur dioxide of between 0.05 (140 $\mu g/m^3$) and 0.08 ppm (220 $\mu g/m^3$).

Rao and LeBlanc (1967), in their study of the effects of an iron sintering plant at Wawa, Ontario, found a correlation between the lichen vegetation and the sulphate content of the surface soil (a reflection of the sulphur dioxide content of the air). LeBlanc, Rao and Comeau (1972*a*) compared IAP zones in the Sudbury area with zones based on mean sulphur dioxide concentrations in the air and were able to conclude that the IAP method provided a valid and rapid method for assessing the effects of air pollution in the area.

Laundon (1967, p. 282; 1970, p. 26) mapped the distribution of nine species in the London area on base maps indicating the mean annual sulphur dioxide levels and found that good correlations existed (Fig. 5).

As a result of their investigations, both Jones (1952) and Fenton (1960) were convinced that it would eventually be possible to draw up tables which would enable air pollution levels in an area to be assessed from the lichen vegetation alone. More volumetric recording gauges are probably present in the British Isles than any other area of a similar size; about 1300 were operating in 1968 (Clifton, 1969, p. 307) although many of these are sited in urban areas. This wealth of information has enabled British workers to produce scales for the practical estimation of mean sulphur dioxide levels calibrated by comparing the readings from volumetric gauges with the immediately adjacent lichen vegetation. Gilbert (1968*b*, 1970*b*,*c*) proposed a six-zone scale based on mean annual sulphur dioxide levels for use in lowland areas of Britain based primarily upon the communities occurring near gauges in the Newcastle upon Tyne area.

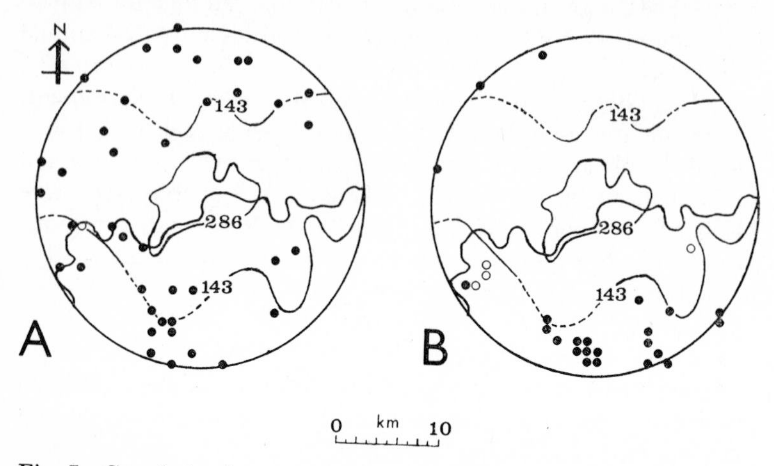


Fig. 5 Correlation between mean annual $SO_2$ levels (in $\mu g/m^3$) and the distribution of (A) *Calopalca heppiana*, and (B) *Xanthoria parietina* aggr. in the London area; ○: pre-1950 records; ● post-1950 records (after Laundon, 1970, p. 26)

As a result of extensive field-work in England and Wales and a comparison of the field data with sulphur dioxide readings from volumetric gauges, Hawksworth and Rose (1970) were able to elaborate upon Gilbert's scale for epiphytic species and proposed a 0–10 zone scale (Table 1) for use in England and Wales employing readily recognized species whose distributions are known to have changed in areas affected by this pollutant (*see* ch 16). Gilbert (1968*a*, p. 29) had previously indicated a correlation between mean winter sulphur dioxide values and two species of lichens, and Hawksworth and Rose found that a better correlation existed between mean winter sulphur dioxide values than mean annual values (although no statistical comparison between these values has been made). Villwock (1962) had previously indicated that air pollution was probably the most important factor during the winter months in Hamburg, and it seems probable that the higher relative humidity values characteristic of the winter months in England and Wales are responsible for this.

In this period the lichens would be most active physiologically (ch 12) and species are known from laboratory experiments to be more sensitive to sulphur dioxide at higher humidities (Hawksworth, 1971*a*; *see* ch 7, 13).

As noted by LeBlanc (1971, p. 117) scales of this type are of considerable practical value as they enable a value for the degree of sulphur dioxide pollution of the air to be obtained rapidly and without recourse to elaborate instrumentation. They are, however, of little value in areas where the mean winter sulphur dioxide levels exceed about 170 $\mu g/m^3$ because almost all epiphytic lichens in western Europe have been lost before this value is reached. Some coniferous trees are, as noted by Gilbert (1970*b*; ch 10), affected at values considerably below this and consequently the scales are of economic and not only scientific importance.

In Table 2 mean winter sulphur dioxide values obtained from volumetric recording gauges in England and Wales are compared with the scale of Hawksworth and Rose (1970). The thirty sites listed in this table have been selected only to indicate lichen zones 0–10 of this scale and the type of correspondence obtained between the two methods. If the values for the zones given in Table 1 are compared with those in Table 2 it will be seen that no significant differences occur. Where slight deviations are noted (e.g. Didcot 9, Camborne 1), these are usually less than 10 $\mu g/m^3$ and almost certainly due to the trees studied being some distance away from the air intake to the volumetric gauges. A study of all readings from gauges in England and Wales has not revealed any differences which cannot be attributed to local factors. If the smoke values at these same thirty stations are compared with the lichen zones no such correlation is found (*see* ch 8, Table 4) and there is no evidence to indicate that sulphur dioxide toxicity is increased by the presence of smoke.

The only other country for which a method for the estimation of sulphur dioxide levels based on the lichen vegetation has so far been devised is Estonia. In this country Trass (1968*a*, 1971) has been able to correlate mean annual sulphur dioxide values with his index 'P' (*see* p. 49; Table 3) to cover levels in the range <10–300 $\mu g/m^3$. As more data become available from volumetric recording gauges in other countries it is evident that

*Table 2 Comparison between mean winter sulphur dioxide readings of volumetric gauges and the adjacent lichen vegetation in sites in England and Wales according to the scale of Hawksworth and Rose (1970)*

| Site | C | Nat. grid ref. | *Sulphur (dioxide µg/m³)*[1] 1967 –8 | 1968 –9 | 1969 –70 | Mean | Lichen zone |
|---|---|---|---|---|---|---|---|
| Leicester 3 | D1/E | 43/586044 | N | 226 | N | 226 | 0 |
| Leicester 14 | D1/E | 43/590045 | N | 180 | 170 | 175 | 0–1 |
| Leicester 13 | A1 | 43/599049 | 182 | 182 | 163 | 169 | 2 |
| Belper 1 | D2 | 43/349479 | 178 | 155 | 151 | 161 | 2 |
| Kew 1 | B2 | 51/172757 | 150 | 170 | 131 | 150 | 2–3 |
| Buxton 2 | B3 | 43/068738 | 186 | 66 | N | 126 | 3 |
| Farnsfield 1 | R | 43/647566 | 104 | N | N | 104 | 3 |
| Leicester 10 | B1 | 43/583002 | 91 | 90 | 89 | 90 | 3 |
| Sheffield 60 | O1 | 43/268856 | 87 | 101 | 76 | 88 | 3 |
| Dursley 5 | O1 | 31/761988 | N | 92 | 73 | 87 | 3–4 |
| Hayfield 2 | O2 | 43/053881 | 84 | N | N | 84 | 3–4 |
| Aspley Heath 1 | R | 42/923345 | 88 | 69 | 93 | 83 | 3 |
| Plymouth 13 | A1 | 20/483550 | 77 | 87 | 82 | 82 | 3–4 |
| Kingsnorth 5 | O1 | 51/871646 | 76 | N | 69 | 72 | 4 |
| Abbots Ripton 1 | O1 | 52/202798 | 58 | 63 | 64 | 61 | 5 |
| Prestwood 1 | R | 42/872012 | 49 | 72 | N | 60 | 6 |
| Didcot 9 | O1 | 42/562010 | 50 | 56 | 48 | 51 | 6 |
| Didcot 4 | O2 | 41/462927 | 48 | 58 | 42 | 49 | 6 |
| Didcot 14 | O2 | 41/583848 | 37 | 56 | 40 | 44 | 6–7 |
| Plymouth 12 | B3 | 20/478598 | 36 | 55 | 43 | 44 | 7 |
| Balcombe 2 | O1 | 51/284310 | N | N | 43 | 43 | 7 |
| Didcot 1 | O2 | 41/493808 | 41 | 48 | 36 | 41 | 7 |
| Sparsholt | O2 | 41/341847 | 41 | N | N | 41 | 7 |
| Didcot 6 | O1 | 41/423995 | 40 | 44 | 35 | 39 | 7 |
| Rogate 1 | O2 | 41/794241 | N | N | 34 | 34 | 8 |
| Torquay 3 | B1 | 20/922657 | 32 | 33 | N | 32 | 8 |
| Camborne 1 | O1 | 10/628407 | 26 | 40 | 14 | 27 | 8 |
| Llanberis 1 | R | 23/577601 | 24 | 28 | 28 | 27 | 9 |
| Weymouth 1 | O1 | 30/703820 | 24 | 29 | 14 | 22 | 9 |
| Pembroke 13 | O1 | 11/955990 | N | 8 | N | 8 | 9–10 |

C: site classification of Warren Spring Laboratory; A–E: urban and industrial; O: open country; R: rural community; 1–3: sub-classifications
N: no data available
[1] mean winter sulphur dioxide values abstracted from Warren Spring Laboratory (1969–71)

it will also be possible to construct and calibrate similar scales for other climatically more or less uniform areas in them.

Rydzak (1969) and Rydzak and Piórecki (1971) have attempted to correlate the lichen vegetation with maximum values of sulphur dioxide recorded rather than with mean values. Short-term values fluctuate so markedly, however (*see* ch 2), that it is not surprising that no correlations with maxima have so far been demonstrated. Rydzak and Piórecki (1971, p. 345), for example, found ranges of the order 2–658 $\mu g/m^3$ at a single recording station. Furthermore, Gilbert (1970*b*) transplanted material of *Hypogymnia*

*Table 3 Correlation of the 'Poleotolerance of lichen communities (synusiae)', P, with mean sulphur dioxide levels in Estonia (after Trass, 1968)*

| P | 1–2 | 2–5 | 5–7 | 7–10 | 10 |
|---|---|---|---|---|---|
| Sulphur dioxide ($\mu g/m^3$) | 'pure' | 10–30 | 30–80 | 80–100 | 100–300 |

*physodes* into areas of Newcastle upon Tyne affected by high levels of sulphur dioxide for short periods and then returned them to relatively unaffected areas. Gilbert's material remained in a healthy condition indicating that short-term high concentrations of this pollutant are not lethal to this species. It appears as if many species are able to convert toxic forms of sulphur dioxide in their thalli to less toxic forms (*see* ch 14) when exposed to short-term levels of this pollutant which considerably exceed the mean values with which their distribution is correlated. This aspect does, however, require further investigation before it can be assumed that this is true for all species sensitive to sulphur dioxide.

## Conclusions

Webster (Agricultural Research Council, 1967, p. 43) indicated that more direct methods than employing lichen vegetation were preferable in assessing air pollution levels, but subsequent studies carried out in many countries by different investigators using a variety of techniques have, particularly in the last four years, established that they can provide a reliable method for assessing mean sulphur dioxide levels. Where sufficient data from volumetric recording gauges are available, scales can be constructed and calibrated which provide a rapid and accurate estimate of mean annual or mean winter sulphur dioxide levels based solely on the lichen vegetation.

The scales so far proposed are of particular value in areas with mean sulphur dioxide levels in the range <30–170 $\mu g/m^3$, and are most sensitive in the range <30–70 $\mu g/m^3$. In England and Wales values of these orders predominate in small towns and rural areas where volumetric gauges are rarely established and are often difficult to maintain. As some economically important coniferous trees are affected at values within these ranges (*see* ch 10) the scales based on the lichen vegetation assume considerable practical importance.

Epiphytic lichens have been found to be the most suitable indicators. Scales and zone-maps based upon a number of carefully selected species which are readily recognizable by non-specialists in the field, and which also take into account the frequency of these species, prove to be the most satisfactory.

At a conference on health aspects of air pollution held in Milan in 1957 Schinzel (1957, p. 99) concluded that 'This method presents a sensitive indicator for detection of air pollution and its exact degree.' The First European Congress on the Influence of Air Pollution on Plants and Animals, held in Wageningen in April 1968, passed the resolution '. . . that cryptogamic epiphytes should be strongly recommended for general use as biological pollution indicators, because (1) they are so easy to handle, (2) they show a vast range of specific sensitivity to air pollutants greatly exceeding that of most higher plants' (Barkman, Rose and Westhoff, 1969, p. 241). A detailed consideration of the mapping studies carried out together with the correlations which have been established between field observations and mean levels of air pollutants entirely endorses these views.

**Acknowledgements**

I am very grateful to Dr F. Rose for his valuable comments on a first draft of this chapter; to Mr B. J. Coppins and Dr H. J. M. Bowen for providing some data used in Table 2; to Professor F. LeBlanc, Dr J.-M. Granger and Dr J. Margot for making copies of some papers unpublished when this chapter was written available to me; to Dr T. Ahti for information on three papers I had not seen; to Miss S. Daniels for her assistance in tracing a number of references; and to the following for permission to reproduce the figures used in this chapter: Royal College of Forestry, Stockholm (Fig. 1), Macmillan Journals Ltd, London (Fig. 2), Dr J. DeSloover and Dr J. Margot (Fig. 3), Centre for Agricultural Publishing and Documentation, Wageningen (Fig. 4), and Mr J. R. Laundon and the London Naturalists Society (Fig. 5).

## References*

Agricultural Research Council (1967). *The effects of air pollution on plants and soil.* London: Agricultural Research Council.

*Ahti, T. (1965). Notes on the distribution of *Lecanora conizaeoides*. *Lichenologist* **3,** 91–2.

*Ahti, T. (1968). Puiden jäkälät ilam saastumisen ilmaisijoina. In: Kivi, E. and Lokki, J. (ed.) *Luonnon puolesta,* 17–22. Porvo and Helsinki: Werner Söderström Oy. [Not seen; reference supplied by Dr Ahti.]

*Almborn, O. (1943). Lavfloran i botaniska trädgården i Lund. *Bot. Notiser* **96,** 167–77.

*Andrews, F. M. (1928). A study of lichens. *Proc. Indiana Acad. Sci.* **37,** 329–30.

*Arnold, F. [G. C.] (1891–1901). Zur Lichenflora von München. *Ber. Bayer. bot. Ges.* **1–2, 5–8.** [As supplements.]

Baddeley, M. S., Ferry, B. W. and Finegan, E. J. (1971). A new method of measuring lichen respiration: Response of selected species to temperature, pH and sulphur dioxide. *Lichenologist* **5,** 18–25.

*Baddeley, M. S., Ferry, B. W. and Finegan, E. J. (1972). The effects of sulphur dioxide on lichen respiration. *Lichenologist* **5,** 283–91.

*Bailey, R. H. (1968). *Lecanora conizaeoides* in Iceland. *Lichenologist* **4,** 73.

Bailey, R. H. (1971). Some lichens from northern Spain. *Revue bryol. lichén.* **37,** 983–6.

Barbalić, L. J. (1953). Raspored epifitskih lišaja u Zagrebu. *Glasn. biol. Sekc. hrv. prirodsl. Društ.*, IIB, **7,** 99–100.

Barkman, J. J. (1958). *Phytosociology and ecology of cryptogamic epiphytes.* Assen, Netherlands: Van Gorcum.

Barkman, J. J. (1961). De verarming van de cryptogamen-flora in ons land gedurende de laaste honderd jaar. *Natura, Amst.* **58,** 141–51.

* In addition to including references cited in the text of this chapter all papers relevant to the study of the distribution of lichens in polluted areas known to me on 1 May 1972 are listed here. Papers which are not cited in the text are prefixed by an asterisk (*); further information on the content of many of these may be obtained through the reviews of Barkman (1958), DeSloover (1964), Hawksworth (1971*a*) and Skye (1968, 1969). See also p. 378.

*Barkman, J. J. (1962). Bibliographia phytosociologica cryptogamica, pars I: Epiphyta. *Excerpta Bot.*, B, **4,** 59–86.

Barkman, J. J. (1963). De epifyten-flora en -vegetatie van Midden-Limburg (België). *Ver. K. ned. Akad. Wet.*, II, **54**(4), 1–46.

*Barkman, J. J. (1964). Over de biologie en oecologie der korstmossen. *Velewe* **8,** 1–18.

*Barkman, J. J. (1966*a*). Bibliographia phytosociologica cryptogamica, pars I: Epiphyta supplementum. *Excerpta Bot.*, B, **7,** 5–17.

*Barkman, J. J. (1966*b*). Menschlicher Einflusz auf die Epiphytenvegetation West-Europas. In: Tuxen, R. (ed.) *Anthropogene Vegetation, Bericht über das Internationale Symposium in Stolzen/Weser 1961 der Internationalen Vereinigung für Vegetationskunde*, 8–18. The Hague: Junk.

Barkman, J. J. (1969). The influence of air pollution on bryophytes and lichens. In: *Air Pollution, Proceedings of the first European Congress on the influence of air pollution on plants and animals, Wageningen 1968*, 197–209. Wageningen: Centre for Agricultural Publishing and Documentation.

Barkman, J. J., Rose, F. and Westhoff, V. (1969). Discussion in section 5: The effects of air pollution on non-vascular plants. In: *Air Pollution, Proceedings of the first European Congress on the influence of air pollution on plants and animals, Wageningen 1968*, 237–41. Wageningen: Centre for Agricultural Publishing and Documentation.

*Beschel, R. [E.] (1952). Flechten und Moose im St. Peter-Friedhof in Salzburg. *Mitt. naturw. ArbGemein. Haus Nat. Salzb., Bot.* **2,** 44–51.

Beschel, R. E. (1958). Flechtenvereine der Städte, Stadtflechten und ihr Wachstum. *Ber. Naturw.-med. Ver. Innsbruck* **52,** 1–158.

*Beschel, R. E. (1966). Lichens—age rivals of trees. *Young Naturalist, Ontario* **8**(7), 1, 3.

*Black, L. (1948). The ecology of a city park, Frick Park, Pittsburgh, Penna. *Bull. Pittsb. Univ.* **44**(6). [Not seen; cited by Sauberer (1951).]

Bortenschlager, S. and Schmidt, H. (1963). Luftverunreiningung und Flechtenverbreitung in Linz. *Ber. Naturw.-med. Ver. Innsbruck* **53,** 23–7.

*Bouly de Lesdain, M. (1948). Ecologie (Phanérogames—mousses—lichens) de quelques sites de Paris. *Encycl. biogéogr. ecol.* **4,** 1–88.

*Bowen, H. J. M. (1970*a*). Air pollution and its effects on plants. In: Perring, F. H. (ed.) *The flora of a changing Britain*, 119–27. London: Botanical Society of the British Isles.

Bowen, H. J. M. (1970*b*). Determination of sulphate ion by replacement of iodate in iodine-131 labelled barium iodate. *Analyst, Lond.* **95,** 665–7.

*Brightman, F. H. (1959). Some factors influencing lichen growth in towns. *Lichenologist* **1,** 104–8.

*Brightman, F. H. (1964). The distribution of the lichen *Lecanora conizaeoides* Cromb. in north Ireland. *Ir. Nat. J.* **14,** 258–62.

*Brightman, F. H. (1965). Some patterns of distribution of lichens in southern England. *SEast. Nat.* **69,** 10–17.

*Brightman, F. H. (1971). Lichens. *Bull. Kent Fld Club* **16,** 7–8.

Britzelmayer, M. (1875). Die Lichenen der Flora von Augsberg. *Ber. naturhist. Ver. Augsberg* **23,** 31–64.

Brodo, I. M. (1961*a*). Transplant experiments with corticolous lichens using a new technique. *Ecology* **42,** 838–41.

*Brodo, I. M. (1961*b*). A study of lichen ecology in central Long Island, New York. *Am. Midl. Nat.* **65,** 290–310.

Brodo, I. M. (1967). Lichen growth and cities: A study on Long Island, New York. *Bryologist* **69,** 427–49.

*Brodo, I. M. (1968). The lichens of Long Island, New York: A vegetational and floristic analysis. *Bull. N.Y. St. Mus.* **410,** i–x, 1–330.

*Brodo, I. M. (1971). Lichens and air pollution. *Conservationist, N.Y.* **26,** 22–6.

Clifton, M. (1969). The National Survey of air pollution in the United Kingdom. In: *Air Pollution, Proceedings of the first European Congress on the influence of air pollution on plants and animals, Wageningen 1968,* 303–13. Wageningen: Centre for Agricultural Publishing and Documentation.

*Codoreanu, V., Ţiu-Rovenţa, E. and Micle, F. (1961). Licheni corticoli din grădina botanică din Cluj. *Contrtiuni bot. Cluj* **1960,** 97–108.

*Coker, P. D. (1967). The effects of sulphur dioxide pollution on bark epiphytes. *Trans. Br. bryol. Soc.* **5,** 341–7.

Comeau, G. and LeBlanc, F. (1971). Influence de l'ozone et de l'anhydride sulfreux sur la régénération des feuilles de *Funaria hygrometrica* Hedw. *Naturaliste can.* **98,** 347–58.

*Comeau, G. and LeBlanc, F. (1972). Influence du fluor sur le *Funaria hygrometrica* et l'*Hypogymnia physodes*. *Can. J. Bot.* **50,** 847–56.

*Crombie, J. M. (1869). IV. Lichenes. In: Trimen, H. and Dyer, W. T. (ed.) *Flora of Middlesex,* 405–7. London: Hardwicke.

*Crombie, J. M. (1874). Nylander on the algo-lichen hypothesis, and on the nutrition of lichens, &c. *Grevillea* **2,** 145–52.

*Crombie, J. M. (1885). On the lichen-flora of Epping Forest and the causes affecting its recent diminution. *Trans. Essex Fld Club* **4,** 54–75.

*Degelius, G. (1961). The lichen flora of the botanic garden in Gothenburg (Sweden). *Acta Horti gothoburg.* **24,** 25–60.

DeSloover, J. R. (1964). Végétaux épiphytes et pollution de l'air. *Revue Quest. scient.* **25,** 531–61.

DeSloover, J. (1969). Pollutions atmosphériques et tolérance spécifique chez les lichens. *Bull. Soc. bot. Fr., Mém.* **1968,** 205–17.

*DeSloover, J. and Lambinon, J. (1965). Contribution à l'étude des lichens corticoles du bassin de la Dendre. *Bull. Soc. r. Bot. Belg.* **98,** 229–73.

DeSloover, J. and LeBlanc, F. (1968). Mapping of atmospheric pollution on the basis of lichen sensitivity. In: Misra, R. and Gopal, B. (ed.)

*Proceedings of the Symposium on recent advances in tropical ecology*, 42–56. Varanasi: The International Society for Tropical Ecology.

DeSloover, J. and LeBlanc, F. (1970). Pollutions atmosphériques et fertilité chez les mousses et chez les lichens épiphytiques. *Bull. Acad. Soc. lorr. Sci.* **9,** 82–90.

Domrös, M. (1966). Luftverunreinigung und Stadtklima im Rheinisch-Westfälischen Industriegebeit und ihre Auswirkung auf den Flechtenbewuchs der Bäume. *Arb. rhein. Landesk.* **23,** 1–132.

*Erichsen, C. F. E. (1906). Beiträge zur Flechtenflora der Umgegend von Hamburg und Holsteins. *Ver. Naturw. Ver. Hamb.*, III, **13,** 44–104.

*Erichsen, C. F. E. (1928). Die Flechten des Moränengebiets von Ostschleswig mit Berücksichtigung der angreuzenden Gebiete. *Ver. bot. Ver. Prov. Brandenb.* **70,** 128–223.

*Ericson, K. (1969). *Luftföroreningars inverkan på epifytiska lavar i trakten av Köping.* Thesis, Växtbiologiska Institutionen, Uppsala. [Not seen; cited by Skye (1969).]

*Eriksson, O. (1966). *Lavar och luftföroreningar i Sundsvallstrakten.* Thesis, Växtbiologiska Institutionen, Uppsala. [Not seen; cited by Skye (1969).]

Felföldy, L. (1942). A városi levegö hatása az epiphyton-zuzmóvegetációra Debrecenben. *Acta geobot. Hungar.* **4,** 332–49.

Fenton, A. F. (1960). Lichens as indicators of atmospheric pollution. *Ir. Nat. J.* **13,** 153–9.

*Fenton, A. F. (1962). *Les lichéns en tant qu'indicateurs du degre de pollution atmospherique: Observations faites à Belfast, Irlande du Nord.* Geneva: World Health Organization Report WHO/EBL/3. [Mimeographed.]

Fenton, A. F. (1964). Atmospheric pollution of Belfast and its relationship to the lichen flora. *Ir. Nat. J.* **14,** 237–45.

*Frey, E. (1958). Die anthropogenen Einflüsse auf die Flechtenflora und -vegetation in verschiedenen Gebieten der Schweiz, Ein Beitrag zum Problem der Ausbreitung und Wanderung der Flechten. *Ber. geobot. ForschInst. Rübel* **33,** 91–107.

*Gelting, P. (1951). Laver. In: Gelting, P., Jørgensen, C. A. and Køie, M. (ed.) *Vilde Planter i Norden. Sporenplanter. Mosser-Laver-Svampe-Alger*, 60–170. Copenhagen: Gads.

Gilbert, O. L. (1965). Lichens as indicators of air pollution in the Tyne Valley. In: Goodman, G. T., Edwards, R. W. and Lambert, J. M. (ed.) *Ecology and the Industrial Society*, 35–47. Oxford: Blackwell.

Gilbert, O. L. (1968*a*). Bryophytes as indicators of air pollution in the Tyne Valley. *New Phytol.* **67,** 15–30.

Gilbert, O. L. (1968*b*). Biological estimation of air pollution. In: Commonwealth Mycological Institute, *Plant pathologist's pocketbook*, 206–7. Kew: Commonwealth Mycological Institute.

Gilbert, O. L. (1968*c*). *Biological indicators of air pollution.* Ph.D. thesis, University of Newcastle upon Tyne.
Gilbert, O. L. (1969). The effect of $SO_2$ on lichens and bryophytes around Newcastle upon Tyne. In: *Air Pollution, Proceedings of the first European Congress on the influence of air pollution on plants and animals, Wageningen 1968*, 223–35. Wageningen: Centre for Agricultural Publishing and Documentation.
Gilbert, O. L. (1970*a*). Further studies on the effect of sulphur dioxide on lichens and bryophytes. *New Phytol.* **69,** 605–27.
Gilbert, O. L. (1970*b*). A biological scale for the estimation of sulphur dioxide pollution. *New Phytol.* **69,** 629–34.
Gilbert, O. L. (1970*c*). New tasks for lowly plants. *New Scientist* **46,** 288–9.
Gilbert, O. L. (1971*a*). Studies along the edge of a lichen desert. *Lichenologist* **5,** 11–17.
Gilbert, O. L. (1971*b*). The effect of airborne fluorides on lichens. *Lichenologist* **5,** 26–32.
*Gilbert, O. L. (1973). Reaction to air pollution. In: Ahmadjian, V. and Hale, M. E. (ed.) *The lichens*: in press. London and New York: Academic Press.
Granger, J.-M. (1970). Computer mapping as an aid in air pollution studies—Montreal region study. In: Goodrich, J. C. (ed.) *Laboratory for computer graphics and spatial analysis*, **2**(E), i–xii, 1–29, Cambridge, Mass.: Harvard University. [Mimeographed.]
Granger, J.-M. (1972). Computer mapping as an aid in air-pollution studies: Montreal region study. *Sarracenia* **15,** 43–83.
Griffith, J. L. (1966). *Some aspects of the effect of atmospheric pollution on the lichen flora to the west of Consett, Co. Durham.* M.Sc. thesis, University of Durham.
*Grindon, L. H. (1859). *The Manchester flora.* London: White.
*Hallberg, I. (1969). *Förändringar av lavfloran i Kvarntorpsområdet till följd av luftföroreningar.* Thesis, Växtbiologiska Institutionen, Uppsala. [Not seen; cited by Skye (1969).]
Harris, G. P. (1971). The ecology of corticolous lichens II. The relationship between physiology and the environment. *J. Ecol.* **59,** 411–52.
*Haselhoff, E. and Lindau, G. (1903). *Die Beschädigung der Vegetation durch Rauch.* Leipzig: Borntraeger.
Haugsjå, P. K. (1930). Über den Einfluß der Stadt Oslo auf die Flechtenvegetation der Bäume. *Nyt Mag. Naturvid.* **68,** 1–116.
Hawksworth, D. L. (1969). The lichen flora of Derbyshire. *Lichenologist* **4,** 105–93.
Hawksworth, D. L. (1971*a*). Lichens as litmus for air pollution: A historical review. *Int. J. Environ. Studies* **1,** 281–96.
Hawksworth, D. L. (1971*b*). *Lobaria pulmonaria* (L.) Hoffm. transplanted into Dovedale, Derbyshire. *Naturalist, Hull,* **1971**, 127–8.
*Hawksworth, D. L. and Rose, F. (1969). A note on the lichens and

bryophytes of the Wyre Forest. *Proc. Birmingham nat. Hist. Soc.* **21**, 191–7.

Hawksworth, D. L. and Rose, F. (1970). Qualitative scale for estimating sulphur dioxide air pollution in England and Wales using epiphytic lichens. *Nature, Lond.* **227**, 145–8.

*Hawksworth, D. L. and Walpole, P. R. (1966). The lichens of Bradgate Park, Leicestershire. *Trans. Leicester Lit. Phil. Soc.* **60**, 48–56.

*Hill, D. J. (1971). Experimental study of the effect of sulphite on lichens with reference to atmospheric pollution. *New Phytol.* **70**, 831–6.

*Høeg, O. A. (1934). Zur Flechtenflora von Stockholm. *Nyt Mag. Naturvid.* **75**, 129–36.

Hoffman, G. R. (1972). Bark samplers for use in air pollution-epiphytic cryptogam studies. *Bryologist* **74**, 490–3.

*Horwood, A. R. (1907). On the disappearance of cryptogamic plants. *J. Bot., Lond.* **45**, 334–9.

*Hue, l'Abbé (1893). Lichens des environs de Paris. *Bull. Soc. bot. Fr.* **40**, 165–85.

*Ingold, C. T. (1972). The advance of mycology. *Trans. Br. mycol. Soc.* **58**(2), *Suppl.*, 5–14.

Iserentant, R. and Margot, J. (1964). Studiecentrum voor regionale ontwikkeling, Rijksuniversiteit—Gent, 1964. In: Anselin, M. *et al.* (ed.) *Richtplan voor de ruimtelijke ordening en ontwikkeling van het Genste—meetjesland vlaamse Ardennen, land van waas.* Brussels: Minn. van Openbare Werken. [Mimeographed.]

Jones, E. W. (1952). Some observations on the lichen flora of tree boles, with special reference to the effect of smoke. *Revue bryol. lichén.* **21**, 96–115.

*Kajanus, B. (1911). Morphologische Flechtenstudien. *Ark. Bot.* **10**(4), 1–47.

*Kershaw, K. A. (1963). Lichens. *Endeavour* **22**, 65–9.

Kershaw, K. A. and Harris, G. P. (1971). Simulation studies and ecology: Use of the model. *Statistical Ecol.* **3**, 23–42.

*Klement, O. (1931). Zur Flechtenflora des Erzgebirges. Die Umgebung von Komotau. *Beih. bot. Zbl.* **48**(2), 52–96.

*Klement, O. (1956). Zur Flechtenflora des Kölner Domes. *Decheniana* **109**, 87–90.

*Klement, O. (1958). Die Flechtenvegetation der Stadt Hannover. *Beitr. Naturk. Niedersachs.* **11**(3), 56–60.

*Klement, O. (1966). Vom Flechtensterben im nördlichen Deutschland. *Ber. naturhist. Ges. Hannover* **110**, 55–66.

*Klement, O. (1971). Über Flechten der Eilenriede. *Beih. Ber. naturhist. Ges.* **7**, 139–42.

Kofler, L., Jacquard, F. and Martin, J.-F. (1969). Influence de fumées d'usines sur la germination des spores de certains lichens. *Bull. Soc. bot. Fr., Mém.* **1968**, 219–30.

*Kovanen, M. (1961). Turun kaupungin jäkäläksvillisuudesta. *Turun Ylioppilas* **8**, 135–52.

*Kozik, R. (1970). Porosty miasta Tarnowa i okolicy. *Fragm. flor. geobot.* **16,** 361–81.

*Krog, H. (1969). Luftforensningenes innvirkning på lavvehetasjonen. *Naturen* **1969,** 97–108.

*Krog, H. (1970). *Lav og luftforurensninger.* Oslo: Nork Institutt for Luftforskning.

Krusenstjerna, E. (1945). Bladmossvegetation och Bladmossflora i Uppsala-trakten. *Acta phytogeogr. suec.* **19,** 1–250.

Lange, O. L., Schultze, E.-D. and Koch, W. (1970). Experimentell-ökologische Untersuchungen an Flechten der Negev-Wüste II. $CO_2$ Gaswechsel und Wasserhaushalt von *Ramalina maciformis* (Del.) Bory am natürlichen Standort während der sommerlichen Trockenperiode. *Flora, Jena* **159,** 38–62.

*Laundon, J. R. (1956). The lichen ecology of Northamptonshire. In: *The first fifty years, A history of Kettering & District Naturalists Society & Field Club,* 89–96. Kettering: Kettering and District Naturalists Society and Field Club.

Laundon, J. R. (1967). A study of the lichen flora of London. *Lichenologist* **3,** 277–327.

*Laundon, J. R. (1968). A study of the lichen flora of London. *Smokeless Air* **145,** 168.

Laundon, J. R. (1970). London's lichens. *London Nat.* **49,** 20–69.

*Laundon, J. R. (1972). Value of fungi as indicators of pollution. *Int. J. Environ. Studies* **3,** 69–71.

LeBlanc, F. (1960) *Écologie et phytosociologie des épiphytes corticoles du sud du Québec.* Thesis, University of Montreal. [Not seen; cited by Barkman (1969) and LeBlanc (1961).]

LeBlanc, F. (1961). Influence de l'atmosphère polluée des grandes agglomérations urbaines sur les épiphytes corticoles. *Revue can. Biol.* **20,** 823–7.

*LeBlanc, F. (1969). Epiphytes and air pollution. In: *Air Pollution, Proceedings of the first European Congress on the influence of air pollution on plants and animals, Wageningen 1968,* 211–21. Wageningen: Centre for Agricultural Publishing and Documentation.

LeBlanc, F. (1971). Possibilities and methods for mapping air pollution on the basis of lichen sensitivity. *Mitt. forstl. BundVersAnst. Wien* **92,** 103–26.

LeBlanc, F., Comeau, G., and Rao, D. N. (1971). Fluoride injury symptoms in epiphytic lichens and mosses. *Can. J. Bot.* **49,** 1691–8.

LeBlanc, F. and DeSloover, J. (1970). Relation between industrialization and the distribution and growth of epiphytic lichens and mosses in Montreal. *Can. J. Bot.* **48,** 1485–96.

LeBlanc, F. and DeSloover, J. (1972). Effet de l'industrialisation et de l'urbanisation sur la végétation épiphyte de Montréal. *Sarracenia* **15,** 1–41.

LeBlanc, F. and Rao, D. N. (1966). Réaction de quelques lichens et mousses épiphytiques à l'anhydride sulfureux dans la région de Sudbury, Ontario. *Bryologist* **69**, 338–46.

LeBlanc, F. and Rao, D. N. (1972). Effects of sulfur dioxide on lichen and moss transplants. *Ecology*, in press.

LeBlanc, F., Rao, D. N. and Comeau, G. (1972*a*). The epiphytic vegetation of *Populus balsamifera* and its significance as an air pollution indicator in Sudbury, Ontario. *Can. J. Bot.* **50**, 519–28.

LeBlanc, F., Rao, D. N. and Comeau, G. (1972*b*). Indices of atmospheric purity and fluoride pollution pattern in Arvida, Quebec. *Can. J. Bot.* **50**, 991–8.

*Leighton, W. A. (1868). Notulae lichenologicae no. XXIII. *Ann. Mag. nat. Hist.*, IV, **2**, 245–9.

Lihnell, D. (1969). Sulphate contents of tree leaves as an indicator of $SO_2$ air pollution in industrial areas. In: *Air Pollution, Proceedings of the first European Congress on the influence of air pollution on plants and animals, Wageningen 1968*, 341–52. Wageningen: Centre for Agricultural Publishing and Documentation.

Lundström, H. (1968). Luftföroreningars inverkan på epifytfloran hos barrträd i Stockholmsområdet. *Stud. Forest. suec.* **56**, 1–55.

Mägdefrau, K. (1960). Flechtenvegetation und Stadtklima. *Naturw. Rdsch. Stuttg.* **13**, 210–14.

*Magnusson, B. (1969). *Luftföreningars inverkan på epifytiska lavar i Slite.* Thesis, Växtbiologiska Institutionen, Uppsala. [Not seen; cited by Skye (1969).]

*Martin, J.-F. and Jacquard, F. (1968). Influence des fumées d'usines sur la distribution des lichens dans la vallée de la Romanche (Isère). *Pollut. Atmospherique* **10**, 95–9.

*Mattick, F. (1937). Flechtenvegetation und Flechtenflora des Gebiets der Freien Stadt Danzig. *Ber. westpreuss. bot.-zool. Ver.* **59**, 1–54.

*Mazel, A. (1964). *Fluoruroses industrielles.* Thesis, University of Toulouse. [Not seen; cited by Martin and Jacquard (1968).]

Mellanby, K. (1967). *Pesticides and pollution.* London: Collins.

Moberg, R. (1968). Luftföroreningars inverkan på epifytiska lavar i Köpmanholmen. *Svensk bot. Tidskr.* **62**, 169–96.

Mrose, H. (1941). Die Verbreitung baumbewohnender Flechten in Abhängigkeit vom Sulfatgehalt der Niederschlagswässer. *Bioklim. Beibl.* **8**, 58–60.

Nash, T. H. (1971*a*). Lichen sensitivity to hydrogen fluoride. *Bull. Torrey bot. Club* **98**, 103–6.

*Nash, T. H. (1971*b*). *Effects of effluents from a zinc factory on lichens.* Ph.D. thesis, Rutgers University. [Not seen; cited by Nash, 1972.]

*Nash, T. H. (1972). Simplification of the Blue Mountain lichen communities near a zinc factory. *Bryologist* **75**, 315–24.

Natho, G. (1964*a*). Die Verbreitung der epixylen Flechten und Algen im Demokratischen Berlin. *Wiss. Z. Humboldt-Univ. Berl., math.-nat. R.* **13**, 53–75.

*Natho, G. (1964*b*). Zur Verbreitung rindenbewohnender Flechten in Kleinstädten-Ostseebad Kühlungsborn. *Wiss. Z. Humboldt-Univ. Berl., math.-nat. R.* **13,** 639–43.

Natho, G. (1965). Flechtenentwicklung in Städten (Ein Überblick). *Drudea, Berlin* **4,** 33–44.

Nienburg, W. (1919). Studien zur Biologie der Flechten. I. II. III. *Z. Bot.* **11,** 1–38.

Nordforsk (1971). Use of lichens as air pollution indicators. *Scand. Res. Inf. Notes* **6,** 12.

Nylander, W. (1866). Les lichens du Jardin du Luxembourg. *Bull. Soc. bot. Fr.* **13,** 364–72.

*Nylander, W. (1874). On Dr. H. A. Weddell's remarks in 'Grevillea'. *Grevillea* **3,** 17–22.

*Paulson, R. (1919). The lichen flora of Hertfordshire. *Trans. nat. Hist. Soc. Herts.* **17,** 83–96.

Pišút, I. (1962). Bemerkungen zur Wirkung der Exhalationsprodukte auf die flechtenvegetation in der Umgebung von Rudňany (Nordostslowakei). *Biológia, Bratisl.* **17,** 481–94.

*Pišút, I. (1971). Verbreitung der Arten der flechtengattung *Lobaria* (Schreb.) Hue in der Slowakei. *Acta rer. nat. Mus. Nat. Slov., Bratisl.* **17,** 105–30.

*Pišút, I. and Jelínková, E. (1971). Über die Artberechtigung der Flechte *Lecanora conizaeoides* Nyl. ex Cromb. *Preslia* **43,** 254–7.

*Piterans, A. V. (1968). Vliyaniya superfosfatnogo zavoda na razvitie lishaĭnikov. In: Nakhutsrishviti, I. G. (ed.) *Materialȳ III Zakavkazskoĭ Konferentsii po sporovȳm rasteniyam,* 251–3. Tbilisi.

Pyatt, F. B. (1969). *Atmospheric pollution in South Wales in relation to the growth and distribution of lichens.* Ph.D. thesis, University of Wales.

Pyatt, F. B. (1970). Lichens as indicators of air pollution in a steel producing town in South Wales. *Environ. Pollut.* **1,** 45–56.

*Rao, D. N. and LeBlanc, F. (1966). Effects of sulfur dioxide on the lichen algae, with special reference to chlorophyll. *Bryologist* **69,** 69–75.

Rao, D. N. and LeBlanc, F. (1967). Influence of an iron-sintering plant on corticolous epiphytes in Wawa, Ontario. *Bryologist* **70,** 141–57.

Richardson, D. H. S. (1967). The transplantation of lichen thalli to solve some taxonomic problems in *Xanthoria parietina* (L.) Th. Fr. *Lichenologist* **3,** 386–91.

Rose, F. (1970). Lichens as pollution indicators. *Your Environ.* **1,** 185–9.

Rose, F., Hawksworth, D. L. and Coppins, B. J. (1970). A lichenological excursion through the north of England. *Naturalist, Hull* **1970,** 49–55.

*Rožková, A. and Kmoch, M. (1956). Vymezení zakouřených částí Plzně pomocí lišejníků. *Živa* **42,** 1–3.

Rydzak, J. (1954). Rozmieszczenie i ekologia porostów miasta Lublina. *Annls Univ. Mariae Curie-Skłodowska,* C, **8,** 233–356.

Rydzak, J. (1956–9). Wpływ małych miast na florę porostów. *Annls Univ.*

*Mariae Curie-Skłodowska*, C, **10,** 1–32, 33–66, 157–75, 321–98; **11,** 25–50, 51–72; **13,** 275–323.
Rydzak, J. (1969). Lichens as indicators of the ecological conditions of the habitat. *Annls Univ. Mariae Curie-Skłodowska*, C, **23,** 131–64.
Rydzak, J. (1970). Flora i ekologia porostów drzew przydrożnych. *Annls Univ. Mariae Curie-Skłodowska*, C, **25,** 149–57.
*Rydzak, J. and Krysiak, K. (1968). Flora porostów Tomaszowa Mazowieckiego. *Annls Univ. Mariae Curie-Skłodowska*, C, **22,** 169–94.
*Rydzak, J. and Krysiak, K. (1970). Lichen flora of Tomaszów Mazowiecki. *Vegetatio* **21,** 375–97.
Rydzak, J. and Piórecki, J. (1971). Stan flory porostów w okolicach Tarnobrzeskiego zagłębiasi arkowego. *Annls Univ. Mariae Curie-Skłodowska*, C, **26,** 343–52.
*Rydzak, J. and Sałata, B. (1970). Badania nad stanem ilościowyn flory porostów nadrzewnych Puszczy Soiskiej. *Annls Univ. Mariae Curie-Skłodowska*, C, **25,** 159–65.
Rydzak, J. and Stasiak, H. (1971). Badania nad stanem flory porostów w rejonie przemysłu azotowego w Puławach. *Annls Univ. Mariae Curie-Skłodowska*, C, **26,** 329–42.
Sauberer, A. (1951). Die Verteilung rindenbewohnender Flechten in Wien, ein bioklimatisches Großstadtproblem. *Wett. Leben* **3,** 116–21.
*Saunders, P. J. W. (1970). Air pollution in relation to lichens and fungi. *Lichenologist* **4,** 337–349.
*Savidge, J. P. (1963). Climate. In: Savidge, J. P. (ed.) *Travis's flora of south Lancashire*, 29–59. Liverpool: Liverpool Botanical Society.
*Saxen, W. (1953). Flechten und Klima im Lande Schleswig. *Die Heimat* **60,** 173–5. [Not seen; cited by Barkman (1962).]
Schinzel, A. (1957). Lichen growth and air pollution. In: World Health Organization, *Conference on public health aspects of air pollution in Europe, Milan 1957*, 96–102. Copenhagen: World Health Organization. [Mimeographed.]
Schmid, A. B. (1956). *Die epixyle Flechtenvegetation von München*. Thesis, University of Munich. [Mimeographed.]
*Schofield, E. and Hamilton, W. L. (1970). Probable damage to tundra biota through sulphur dioxide destruction of lichens. *Biological Conservation* **2,** 278–80.
Schönbeck, H. (1969). Eine methode zur Erfassung der biologischen Wirkung von Luftverunreinigungen durch transplantierte Flechten. *Staub* **29,** 14–18.
Schubert, R. and Fritsche, W. (1965). Beitrag zur Einwirkung von Luftverunreinigungen auf xerische Flechten. *Arch. NatSchutz* **52,** 107–10.
*Schulz, K. (1931). Die Flechtenvegetation der Mark Brandenburg. *Beih. Feddes Repert.* **67,** 1–192.
Sernander, R. (1912). Studier öfvar lafvarnes biologi I. Nitrofila lafvar. *Svensk bot. Tidskr.* **6,** 803–83.

Sernander, R. (1926). *Stockholms natur*. Uppsala: Almqvist and Wiksells.
Skye, E. (1958). Luftföroreningars inverkan på busk- och bladlavfloran kring skifferoljeverket i Närkes Kvarntorp. *Svensk bot. Tidskr.* **52,** 133–90.
Skye, E. (1964). Epifytfloran och luftföroreningarna. *Svensk natur.* **1964,** 327–32.
Skye, E. (1965). Botanical indicators of air pollution. *Acta phytogeogr. suec.* **50,** 285–7.
*Skye, E. (1967). Lavar mäter lortluft. *Forskning och Framsteg, Stockholm* **2,** 3–6. [Not seen; cited by Skye (1969).]
Skye, E. (1968). Lichens and air pollution. *Acta phytogeogr. suec.* **52,** 1–123.
*Skye, E. (1969). Användandet av lavar som indikatorer och testorganismer på luftföroreningar. *Nordisk Hygienisk Tidskr.* **50,** 115–34.
*Skye, E. and Hallberg, I. (1969). Changes in the lichen flora following air pollution. *Oikos* **20,** 547–52.
*Smith, A. L. (1919). Lichens of the Baslow foray. *Trans. Br. mycol. Soc.* **6,** 252.
*Sowter, F. A. (1950). *The cryptogamic flora of Leicestershire and Rutland —Lichenes.* Leicester: Leicester Literary and Philosophical Society.
*Sowter, F. A. and Hawksworth, D. L. (1970). Leicestershire and Rutland cryptogamic notes, I. *Trans. Leicester Lit. Phil. Soc.* **64,** 89–100.
Spenling, N. (1971). Flechten und Flechtengesellschaften des Waldviertels. *Herzogia* **2,** 161–230.
*Steiner, M. (1957). Rindenepiphyten als Indikatoren des Städtklimas. In: Vogler, P. and Kühn, E. (ed.) *Medizin und Städtebau, ein Handbuch für gesundheitlichen Städtebau,* 119–24. Munich, Berlin, *etc.*: Urban and Schwarzenberg.
Steiner, M. and Schulze-Horn, D. (1955). Über die Verbreitung und Expositionsabhängigkeit der Rinden-epiphyten im Stadtgebiet von Bonn. *Decheniana* **108,** 1–16.
*Stirton, J. (1874). Lichens, the peculiarities of their structure and development. *Trans. Glasgow Fld Nat.* **2,** 32.
Tallis, J. H. (1964). Lichens and atmospheric pollution. *Advmt Sci., Lond.* **21,** 250–2.
*Tobler, F. (1921). Die Wolbecker Flechten-Standorte. *Hedwigia* **63,** 7–10.
*Tobler, F. (1925). *Biologie der Flechten.* Berlin: Borntraeger.
Trass, H. (1968*a*). Indeks samblikur ühmituste kasutamiseks õhu saastatuse määramisel. *Eesti Loõdus* **11,** 628.
*Trass, H. (1968*b*). Samblikud—õhu saastatuse inditaatorid. *Eesti Loõdus* **11,** 80–3.
*Trass, H. (1968*c*) *Analiz likhenoflory Estonii.* Avtoreferat dissertatzii, Tartu State University. [Not seen; reference supplied by Dr Ahti.]
Trass, H. (1971). Poleotolerantnost' lishaĭnikov. In: Vimba, E. (ed.) *Mater. VI Simpos. Mikol. i Likhenol. Pribalt. respubl.* **1,** 66–70. Riga.

*Trümpener, E. (1926). Über die Bedeutung der Wasserstoffionenkonzentration für die Verbreitung von Flechten. *Beih. bot. Zbl.* **42,** 321–54.

*Ubisch, H. von and Nilsson, J. (1966). *Luftföroreningsundersökning i Stockholm, Redogörelse för verksamhetsåren och eldningssäsongerna 1963/4 och 1964/5.* Stockholm: National Institute of Public Health. [Not seen; cited by Skye (1968).]

Vaarna, V. V. (1934). Helsingin kaupungin puiden ja pensaiden jäkäläkasvisto. *Ann. bot. Soc. zool.-bot. fenn. 'Vanamo'* **5**(6), 1–32.

Vareschi, V. (1936). Die Epiphytenvegetation von Zürich. (Epixylenstudien II.). *Ber. schweiz. bot. Ges.* **46,** 445–88.

Vareschi, V. (1953). La influencia de los bosques y parques sobre el aire de la cuidad de Caracas. *Acta cient. venez.* **4,** 89–95.

Villwock, I. (1962). Der Stadteinfluß Hamburgs auf die Verbreitung epiphytischer Flechten. *Ab. Verh. naturw. Ver. Hamburg,* II, **6,** 147–66.

Warren Spring Laboratory (1969–71). *The investigation of air pollution, National Survey, Smoke and sulphur dioxide.* Stevenage, Herts.: Department of Trade and Industry.

*Weddell, H. A. (1869). Les lichens des promenades publiques et, en particulier, du Jardin de Blossac, à Poitiers. *Bull. Soc. bot. Fr.* **16,** 194–203.

*Weddell, H. A. (1873). Nouvelle revue des lichens du Jardin public de Blossac, à Poitiers. *Mém. Soc. natn. Sci. nat. math. Cherbourg* **17,** 353–73.

*Weddell, H. A. (1874). Remarks on a paper published (Jan. 1874) by Dr. W. Nylander in the 'Flora', and lately reissued in 'Grevillea'. *Grevillea* **2,** 182–5.

*Wheldon, J. A. and Travis, W. G. (1915). The lichens of south Lancashire. *J. Linn. Soc.* (*Bot.*) **43,** 87–136.

*Wilmanns, O. (1966). Anthropogener Wandel der Kryptogamen-Vegetation in Südwestdeutschland. *Ber. geobot. ForschInst. Rübel* **37,** 74–87.

*Wirth, V. (1968). Soziologie, Standortsökologie und Areal des *Lobarion pulmonariae* im Südschwarzwald. *Bot. Jb.* **88,** 317–65.

Zurzycki, J. (1949). Études sur la flore des lichens de Cracovie et de ses environs. *C. r. mens. Séanc. Cl. Sci. math. nat. Acad. pol. Sci. Lett.* **1949** (3/5), 18.

*Zwackh-Holzenhausen, W. R. von (1883). *Die Lichenen Heidelbergs nach dem Systeme und den Bestimmungen Dr. William Nylander's.* Heidelberg: Weiss.

# 4: Detailed Mapping in South-East England

F. ROSE

In the course of studies on the distribution, ecology and phytosociology of epiphytic lichens in south-east England, several species have been mapped in detail down to one kilometre square units of the Ordnance Survey National Grid. An attempt has been made to survey all parts of the area covered by the base map used in Figs. 1–6 (i.e. Kent, Surrey and Sussex together with adjacent parts of Berkshire, Buckinghamshire and Hampshire) with equal intensity. Preliminary observations indicated that trees in densely built-up parts of the London conurbation only rarely had any epiphytic lichens apart from *Lecanora conizaeoides* and intensive field-work in these areas was consequently limited to open spaces and parks. The outer southern suburban areas were, however, given special attention.

This work, carried out in 1966–72, has revealed some interesting distribution patterns. It soon became clear that many species characteristic of mature, well-lit trees of *Acer pseudoplatanus*, *Fraxinus* and *Quercus* in wholly rural parts of the area disappeared as the London conurbation was approached, and that different species were lost at very different distances from the southern edge of the London conurbation. Similar, but less extreme, patterns are encountered in the environs of other moderately sized towns, the industrial parts of the Thames estuary, the lower Medway valley, and the Adur estuary west of Brighton, and around isolated industrial plants in east Kent. The loss of epiphytic species, both in built-up and industrial areas and rural country surrounding them, correlates with mean winter sulphur dioxide levels of air pollution at all volumetric recording stations in the area. Most of the species would be expected in rural areas on general habitat grounds, and no correlations with other factors likely to cause their absence have been found. Thus it appears very probable, particularly when one considers also the data from transplant and laboratory experiments (ch 3, 13, 14), that differences in sulphur dioxide concentrations are the principal cause of the distribution patterns found in this area.

Examples of maps constructed for particular species are presented as Figs. 1–6.

In order to simplify the figures, all localities examined with negative results have been excluded. Literature and herbarium sources have been examined and older reports obtained from these are indicated by **bold** open circles. Unfortunately species which were formerly common were rarely given precise localities in literature references, but enough localized reports have been traced to make it clear that recessions in the distribution of these species have occurred from the London conurbation and other areas now affected by significant levels of sulphur dioxide.

More detailed discussions of the past and present distributions of species treated in this chapter in England and Wales are presented in chapter 16.

## Maps of particular species

### *Parmelia caperata* (Fig. 1)

*Parmelia caperata*, a characteristic species of well-lit trees with moderately acidic bark (e.g. *Fraxinus*, *Quercus*) in areas of England with mean winter sulphur dioxide levels below *c* 55 $\mu g/m^3$ (ch 16, Fig. 6), is not found within a radius of about 32 km (20 miles) of the centre of London on the south side, except in a single site. This station is in the bottom of a sheltered valley at High Elms Park, near Orpington, about 24 km from the centre of London.

Last century it was known from several sites nearer to London, for example at Bexley and at Swanscombe Wood, Kent (Holmes, 1878). The Swanscombe locality is still fairly rural although now close to the lower Thames industrial zone. More recent declines in this species since 1930–57 have been noted to the south of the London conurbation (ch 16, p. 349) and it is also approaching extinction in Windsor Great Park. Fig. 1 shows the almost total absence of *P. caperata* in a broad belt along the Thames Valley both to the west of London up to Reading, and east of London to near Faversham and Whitstable.

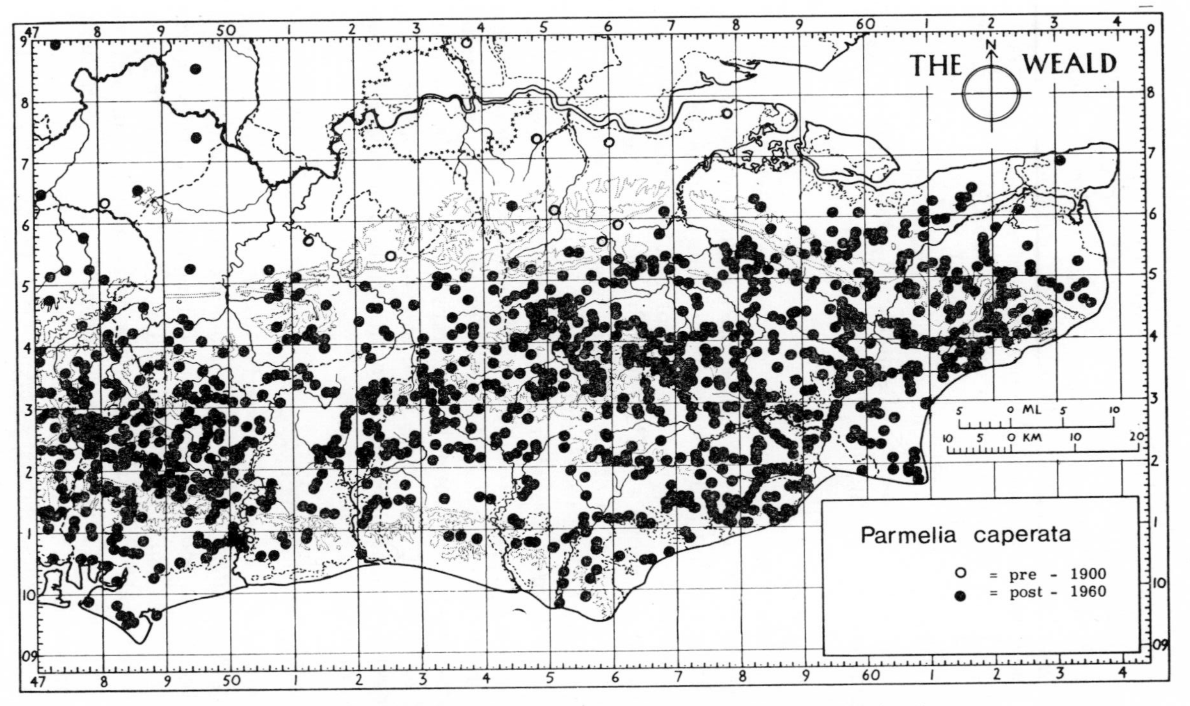


Fig. 1 Distribution of *Parmelia caperata* in south-east England

Other gaps in the distribution correlate well with: (*a*) the Richborough Power Station (61/34-62-) to the north of Sandwich, east Kent; (*b*) the paper and cement works of the Medway valley (51/74-58-) near Maidstone; (*c*) the drainage of polluted air from the small town of Tonbridge (51/60-46-) into the flat, low-lying, inversion-prone Medway valley to its east; and (*d*) the industrial area to the west of Brighton (50/25-05-). In these four areas apparently suitable trees are plentiful, but the gaps seen on the South Downs and the Sussex coastal plain can, however, be correlated with the absence of suitable trees rather than sulphur dioxide pollution of the air.

*Usnea* spp. (Fig. 2)

The genus *Usnea* (mostly *U. subfloridana*) shows a similar pattern to that of *Parmelia caperata* but does not approach as closely to London and is now absent from an area 48 km (30 miles) south from the centre of London. Compared with *P. caperata* it also shows a similar but wider zone of absence through the area to the south of the Thames west and east of London. In its nearest localities to the Thames Valley axis it is always stunted, confined to sheltered woodland sites, and represented only by *U. subfloridana*. Further to the south and east in Sussex and south and east Kent, the genus occurs in luxuriant stands, in more open sites, and is also represented by *U. ceratina*, *U. fragilescens*, *U. glabrescens*, *U. intexta* and *U. rubiginea*. In more remote sites several species of this genus often occur in close association in the same habitats.

*Anaptychia ciliaris* (Fig. 3)

In contrast to the two species so far discussed *Anaptychia ciliaris* is largely confined to very well-lit boles of trees with bark of a higher pH. It most commonly occurs on *Acer campestre*, *A. pseudoplatanus* and *Ulmus* spp., but is also found on *Fraxinus* and more rarely *Quercus* trees whose barks have become eutrophiated by animal excreta in parks and pastures. Because of these habitat restrictions this species does not show the same density of sites as the less habitat-demanding *Parmelia caperata*. The present inner limit to London of *Anaptychia ciliaris*, however, corresponds closely with that of *P. caperata*, and under field

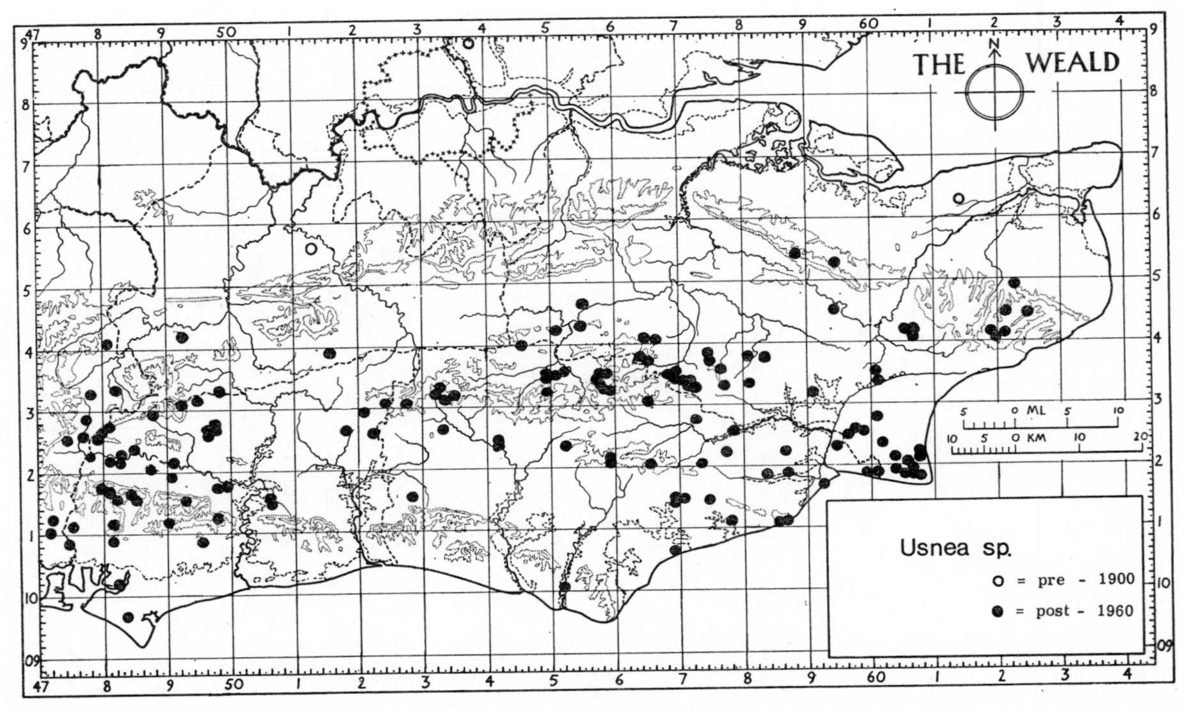


Fig. 2 Distribution of *Usnea* species in south-east England

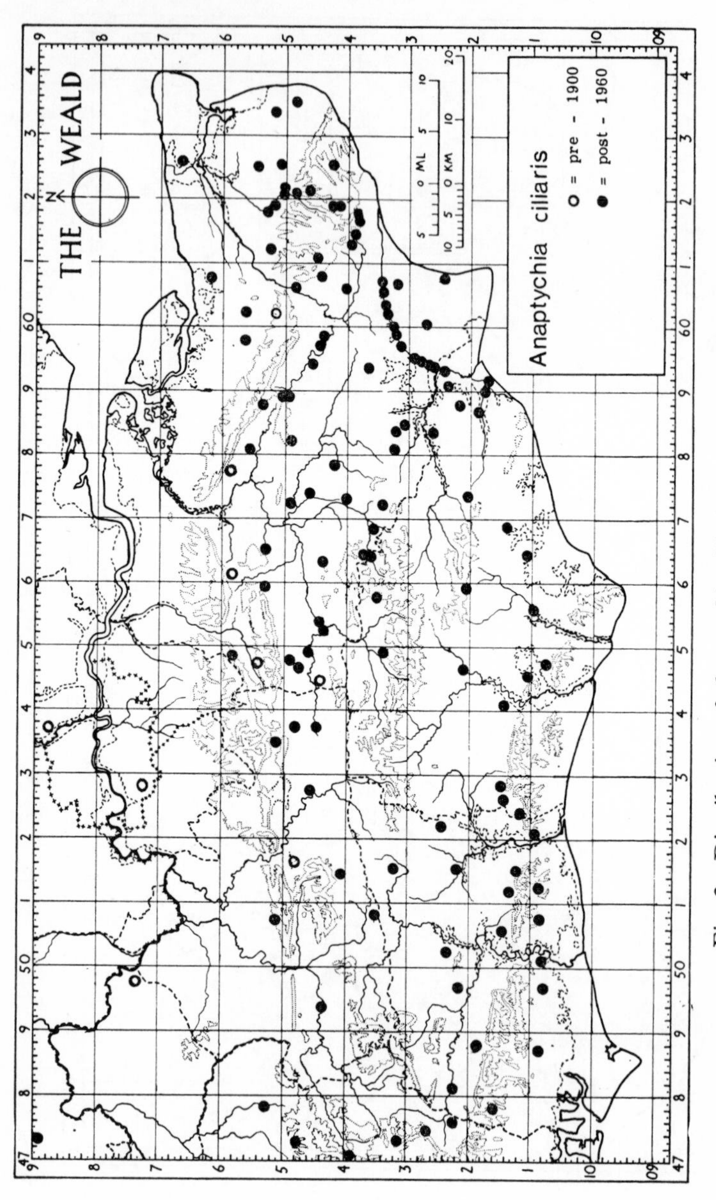

Fig. 3 Distribution of *Anaptychia ciliaris* in south-east England

conditions these species are affected by similar mean sulphur dioxide levels.

Today *Anaptychia ciliaris* is only found with ascocarps beyond about 56 km (35 miles) from the centre of London, although in the early nineteenth century specimens with ascocarps were found within 8 km of the centre of London at Tooting and Walthamstow.

*Parmelia perlata* (Fig. 4)

*Parmelia perlata*, which normally occurs with *P. caperata* in areas of England with mean winter sulphur dioxide levels below about 40 $\mu g/m^3$ (ch 16, Fig. 5) has a distribution in south-east England very similar to that of *Usnea* spp., appearing for the first time at a distance of about 48 km (30 miles) to the south of the centre of London, and at decreasing distances from the Thames Valley to the east and west of London.

*Lobaria* spp. (Fig. 5)

*Lobaria* species are characteristic of ancient undisturbed forests and parklands and usually occur on well-lit mature trees which, in south-east England, are often somewhat sheltered. *L. pulmonaria* was formerly widespread in England (ch 16, Fig. 3) but has declined drastically. Where the habitat has remained unchanged (e.g. Epping Forest) air pollution is clearly the cause, but its reduction to only three extant localities in south-east England is also due to the destruction, alteration of management methods, and possibly also drainage, of ancient woodlands. The species is certainly very sensitive to sulphur dioxide as transplant and laboratory experiments have shown (ch 3, 14) and it is interesting that in its extant Sussex sites (Eridge Park, Eastdean Park Wood) it is restricted to deep, sheltered valleys where levels would be expected to be lowered (ch 2, 3).

The other *Lobaria* species have also declined. *L. laetevirens* and *L. scrobiculata* are restricted to single localities of the same type as *L. pulmonaria*. *L. amplissima* is now extinct in south-east England and has even been lost from Eridge Park where both *L. laetevirens* and *L. pulmonaria* still persist in a very limited area.

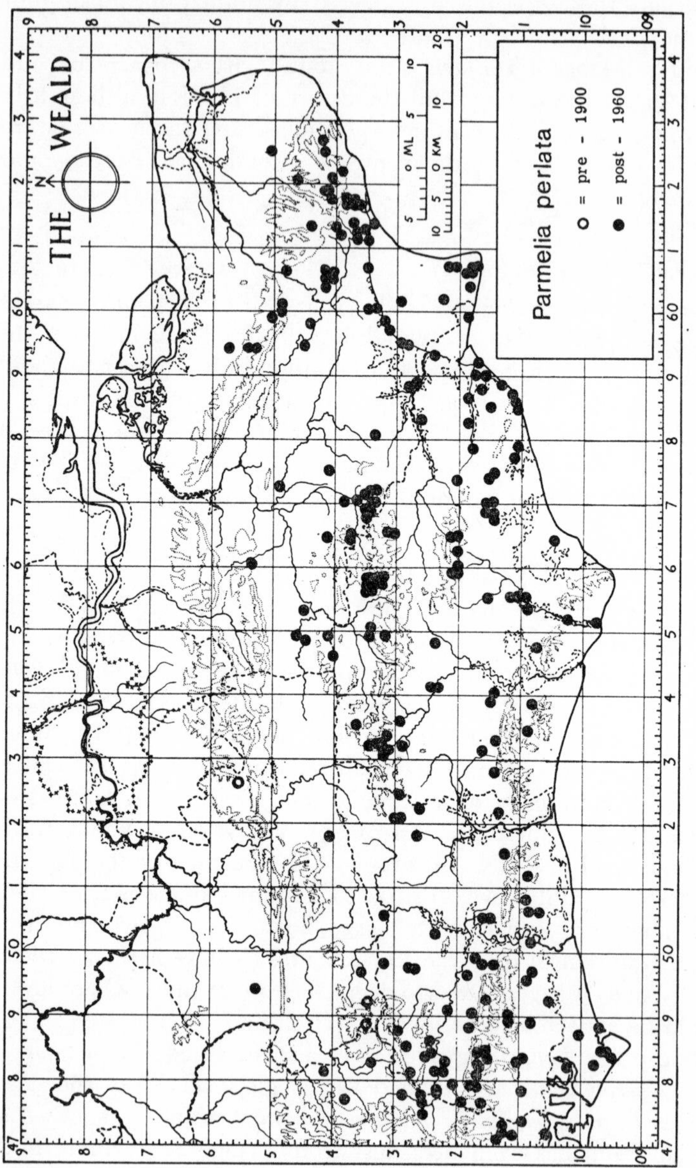


Fig. 4 Distribution of *Parmelia perlata* in south-east England

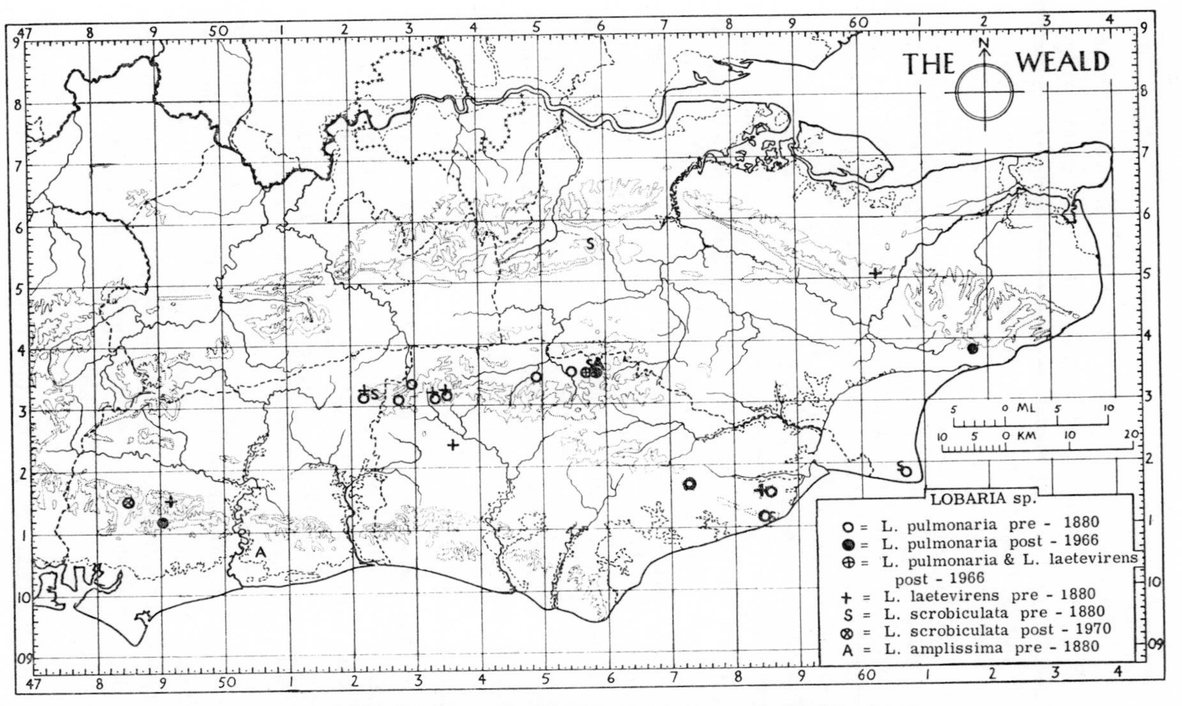


Fig. 5 Distribution of *Lobaria* species in south-east England

*Inner limits* (Fig. 6)

Fig. 6 summarizes, by plotting contours, the inner limits of some species already discussed together with that of the more sulphur dioxide-tolerant *Hypogymnia physodes*. *Hypogymnia physodes* comes much closer to the built-up and industrial zones than the other species treated in this chapter and even enters sparsely built-up residential areas south of London, just as it does to the north of that city. From Fig. 6 it is clear that the best correlations between the limits of particular species are with the positions of sources of sulphur dioxide emissions, particularly large industrial plants and oil- and coal-fired power stations. London Heathrow and Gatwick airports are indicated by 'A' and 'G', respectively. Gatwick airport does not appear to have any marked effect to date, but it is tempting to explain the absence of many epiphytic species from otherwise non-industrial parts of south-east Berkshire and north-west Surrey by the much larger airport at Heathrow (A). Another factor which may be important in this area, however, is the topography which makes this region prone to atmospheric inversions and consequently increased sulphur dioxide pollution of the air under certain atmospheric conditions (Lamb, 1970).

## Discussion

The distribution patterns of many epiphytic lichens in south-east England, maps of some of which are presented here, correlate very well with mean winter sulphur dioxide levels. Attempts to demonstrate correlations with other factors such as rainfall have met with little success. It is therefore clear that distribution maps of this type, particularly where the inner limits of species are considered, provide an indication of the mean sulphur dioxide levels in the air. Examples of the correlation between the lichen vegetation according to the scheme of Hawksworth and Rose (1970), and volumetric gauge readings of sulphur dioxide values are mentioned in chapter 3, Table 2.

Species distribution maps of the type presented here of necessity omit data on the frequency of the species. While they are necessary in order to establish the relative tolerance of particular species, they are clearly less satisfactory than zone-maps,

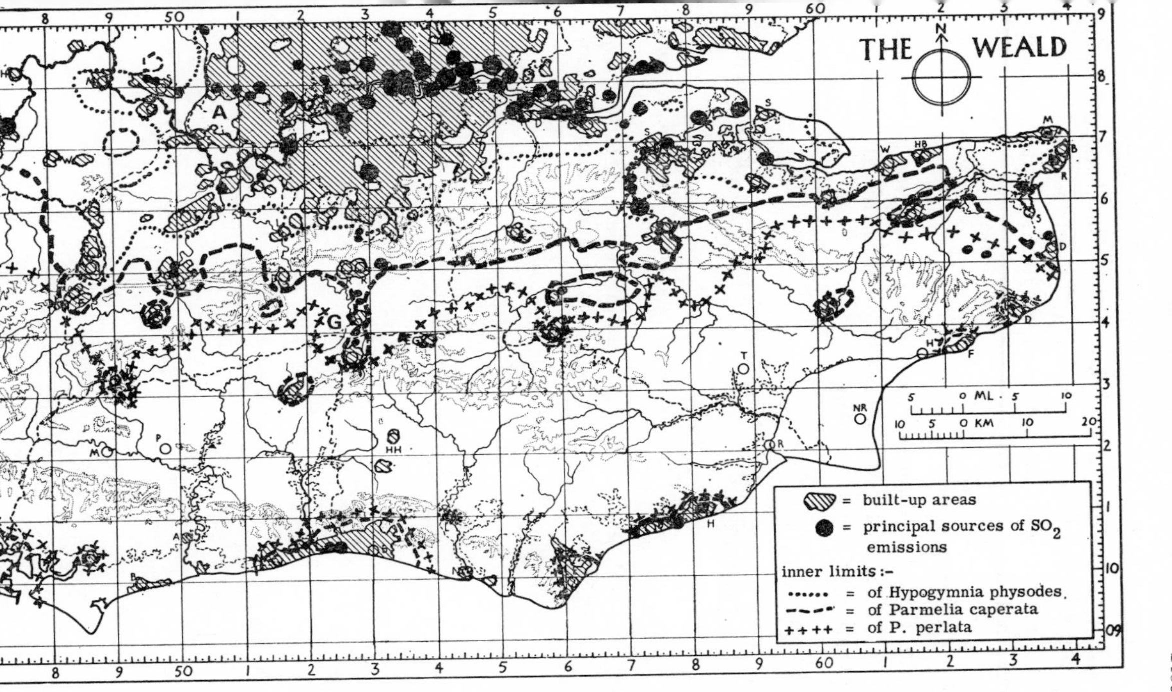


Fig. 6 Built-up areas, principal sources of sulphur dioxide emissions, and the inner limits of *Hypogymnia physodes*, *Parmelia caperata* and *P. perlata* in south-east England; the sizes of the dots indicating sulphur dioxide emission sources are proportional to the size of the source (after Rose, 1970)

which consider many species and their frequency, for the practical assessment of mean sulphur dioxide levels on the basis of the lichen vegetation. A zone-map for south-east England based on the scales they have worked out has been published by Hawksworth and Rose (1970, p. 147).

## Acknowledgements

I am grateful to the editors of *Your Environment* for permission to use Fig. 6, and to Dr D. L. Hawksworth for his assistance in the preparation of my manuscript.

## References

Hawksworth, D. L. and Rose, F. (1970). Qualitative scale for estimating sulphur dioxide air pollution in England and Wales using epiphytic lichens. *Nature, Lond.* **277,** 145–8.

Holmes, E. M. (1878). A cryptogamic flora of Kent, Lichens. *J. Bot., Lond.* **16,** 117–20, 209–12, 329–45, 373–6.

Lamb, H. H. (1970). Our changing climate. In: Perring, F. H. (ed.) *The flora of a changing Britain*, 11–24. London: Botanical Society of the British Isles.

Rose, F. (1970). Lichens as pollution indicators. *Your Environment* **1,** 185–9.

# 5: Distribution of some Epiphytic Lichens around an Oil Refinery at Fawley, Hampshire

D. I. MORGAN-HUWS and F. N. HAYNES

This chapter describes a study made in 1966 of the epiphytic lichen vegetation in the area surrounding the large Esso oil refinery at Fawley, on the western shores of Southampton Water (Figs. 1 and 2), Hampshire, England.

A small works (the 'old' refinery), on low ground adjacent to the shore, dates from 1921 and remains a small part of the present-day complex (the 'new' refinery), dating from 1952 (Fig. 2). The site of the refinery was previously part of the Cadland Estate. Before the erection of the 'new' refinery the north-eastern part of the site was mainly woodland and parkland, whilst the south-western part was mainly agricultural land similar to that of the rural area which lies beyond the refinery's landward boundary today.

The rural area beyond the refinery is mixed agricultural land on which significant residential development has occurred around the villages of Newtown, Holbury, Blackfield and Fawley since 1952. The area to the north-east of the refinery's seaward boundary, and beyond Southampton Water, is mixed agricultural and horticultural land on which extensive encroachment by residential development has taken place in the last fifty years, resulting in an intricate pattern of 'ribbon development' over much of the area.

There is no record of the lichen vegetation of the Fawley area prior to the building of the refinery but there is no reason to doubt that it was similar to that still present to the west of Fawley; i.e. the area around Norleywood west of the Beaulieu river which is similar in both land-use and its position in relation to the sea (Fig. 1).

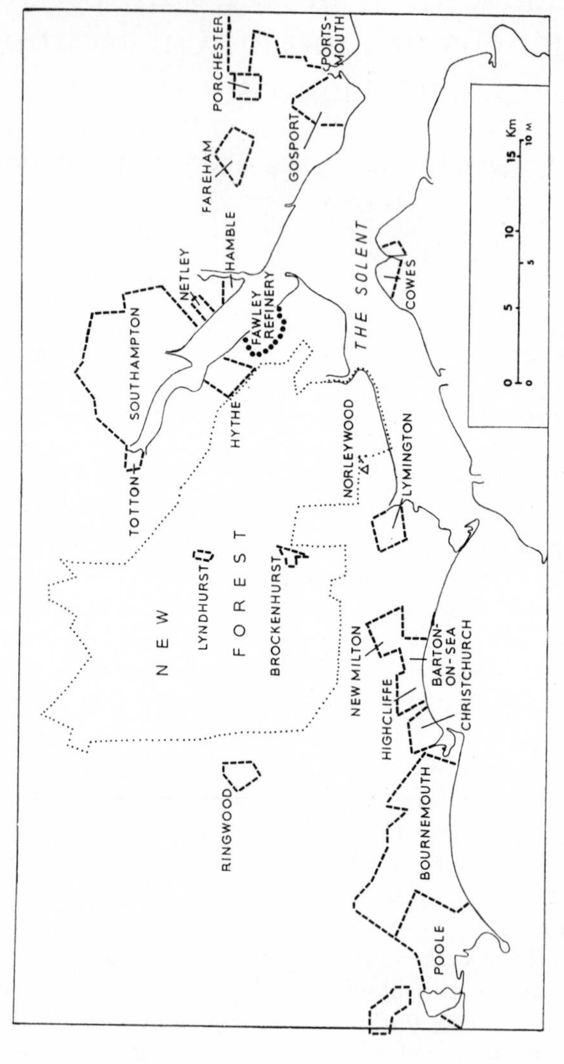


Fig. 1 Map of south-west Hampshire

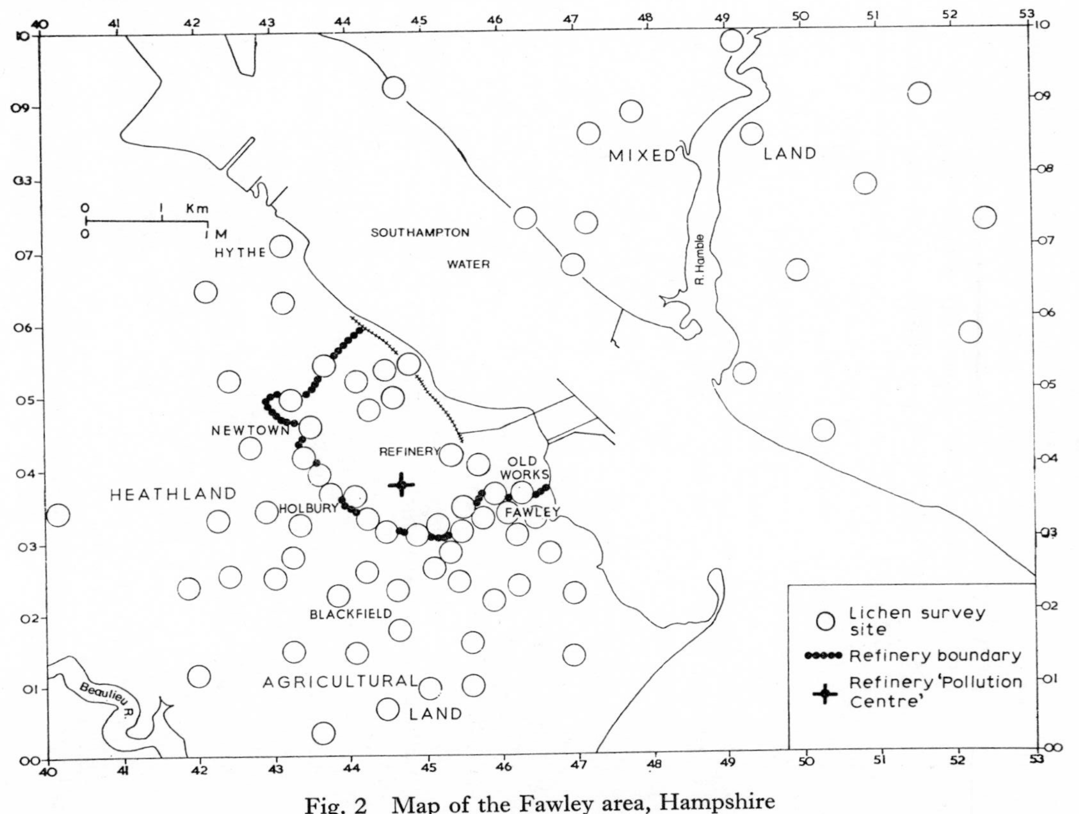


Fig. 2 Map of the Fawley area, Hampshire

## Climate and Air Pollution

The area surrounding the landward boundary of the refinery and that to the north-east beyond Southampton Water are both characterized by their proximity to the sea and their generally flat topography which rarely exceeds 40 m (130 ft) in altitude. The close proximity to the sea results in a significant maritime influence and the annual rainfall is low and about 760 mm (30 in) throughout the area of the survey. A feature of coastal districts is the influence of maritime air-masses which give rise to a very high frequency of relative humidities between 95 and 100 per cent (Oliver, 1959). Although the coastal climate in this particular area is not so extremely maritime as that of south-west Britain, this influence further asserts itself by the penetration of Southampton Water through the area. The prevailing wind is south-westerly and from the sea, and sea breezes help to maintain the maritime influence during calm dry summer periods.

In urban areas, such as Southampton, the major pollutants released into the air are smoke (particulate matter) and sulphur dioxide. In the survey area, domestic pollution from the villages and areas of 'ribbon development' contributes to the background pollution on top of which that of the refinery is imposed.

An oil refinery is a complex industrial plant which releases a number of pollutants into the air of which sulphur dioxide is the most important (Sutton, 1968). A large amount of fuel is used by a refinery in the process of refining crude oil and the bulk of the sulphur dioxide released comes from the furnace stacks with a further contribution from the sulphur-recovery plant. At Fawley there is a cluster of major furnace stacks, varying between 30 m (100 ft) and 50 m (160 ft) in height, and located in a central area of the refinery. The refinery's 'pollution centre' is defined as being the central point of this cluster of stacks.

As a consequence of high-temperature fuel combustion in furnaces, little smoke is released from the furnace stacks and only a small amount from the flares. Therefore, the refinery is a major emitter of sulphur dioxide but not of smoke. Air pollution measurements at sites around the refinery (see below) reveal sulphur dioxide concentrations similar to those in many urban areas (*see* Warren Spring Laboratory, 1964–71), but smoke concentrations well below those usually present in urban areas.

## Methods

### *Lichen survey*

For comparative purposes the lichen vegetation of a common and constant substrate and standard habitat was investigated (*see* ch 3). Trees occur frequently throughout the area and the commonest is the pedunculate oak, *Quercus robur*. The lichen community which typically occurs on the trunk of this oak in this area belongs to the *Physodion* (more particularly to the union *Parmelietum revolutae* var. *caperatosum*; *see* Hawksworth, 1982) which is gradually replaced by *Conizaeoidion* (union *Lecanoretum pityreae*) towards the refinery boundary.

The survey was restricted to the following eleven species or species groups which constituted the bulk of the lichen vegetation on oak: *Evernia prunastri*, *Hypogymnia physodes*, *Lecanora conizaeoides*, *Parmelia caperata*, *P. glabratula* group (including *P. subaurifera*), *P. perlata* group (including *P. reticulata*), *P. saxatilis*, *P. subrudecta*, *P. sulcata*, *Ramalina* spp. (mainly *R. farinacea*), and *Usnea* spp. (mainly *U. subfloridana* but including some *U. ceratina*).

In order to ensure that the trunks used for sampling were subject to comparable environmental conditions trees were only surveyed if they were well-established (trunk diameter greater than 0.5 m at breast height), erect, undamaged, and free-standing (*see* ch 3). The south-west-facing half-sector of the trunk was examined to a height of 2 m above ground level. This portion of the trunk typically carried the entire macrolichen flora of the trunk.

Skye (1958), in his study of the large oil-shale works at Kvarntorp in a rural area of Sweden, used sites each comprising a small number of neighbouring trees. It was decided to adopt a similar type of site for the present study, and in an area where pollution changes might be abrupt it seemed desirable to select a large number of small sites. Any disadvantages due to the restricting of examination to a small number of trees per site should be offset by the large number and close proximity of these sites (Fig. 2).

The presence or absence of the lichen species was noted for each trunk examined and a distinction made between occurrences on the main trunk and on the tree base. A minimum of four trees was examined at each site.

*Air pollution survey*

Smoke and sulphur dioxide levels were measured at numerous stations throughout the area surveyed, and determined using the methods of the Warren Spring Laboratory employed in the 'U.K. National Survey of Air Pollution' (*see* Clifton, 1969). The annual average daily sulphur dioxide levels are presented in the form of 'contours' in Fig. 10.

## Results

*Distribution patterns*

The results of the field survey are presented in Figs. 3–8. The lichen distribution shows a general pattern with species becoming excluded from the area close to the refinery. Some species tend to become restricted to the base or butt roots of the trunk near their inner limit of distribution.

The distribution of *Lecanora conizaeoides* (Fig. 3) is unique amongst the species studied. It occurs at every site including those within the refinery boundary.

*Hypogymnia physodes* (Fig. 4) occurs at approximately 50 per cent of the sites within the refinery boundary and appears to be the most tolerant foliose lichen to pollution from the refinery.

*Evernia prunastri* (Fig. 5) and *Parmelia sulcata* both occur at a few sites within the refinery boundary and form a small group of species slightly less tolerant than *H. physodes*. All these three macrolichens occur in over 50 per cent of the sites examined to the north-east of Southampton Water.

*Parmelia caperata* (Fig. 6), the *P. glabratula* group, *P. subrudecta* and *Ramalina* spp., are excluded from a number of sites in an approximate 1 km belt beyond the landward boundary of the refinery and all four species show a marked decline in the area to the north-east of Southampton Water where they occur at less than 30 per cent of the sites. These four species appear to be less tolerant than *E. prunastri* and *P. sulcata*.

*Usnea* spp. (Fig. 7) show a somewhat complicated distributional

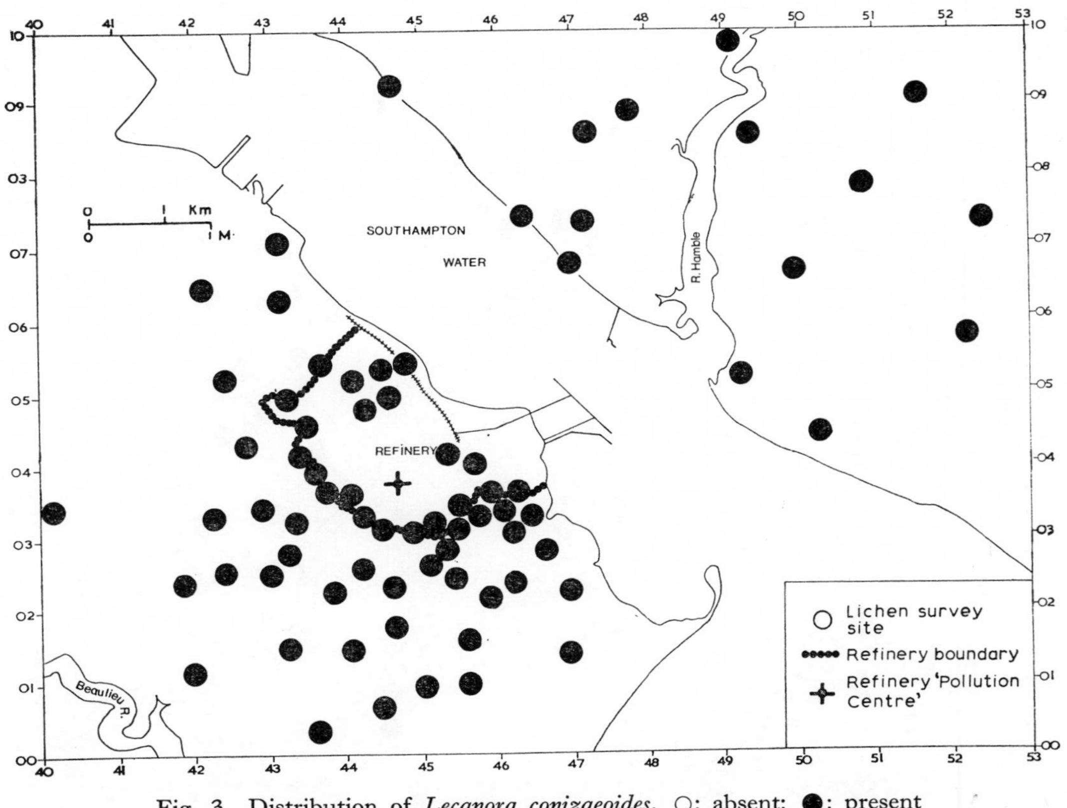


Fig. 3 Distribution of *Lecanora conizaeoides*. ○: absent; ●: present

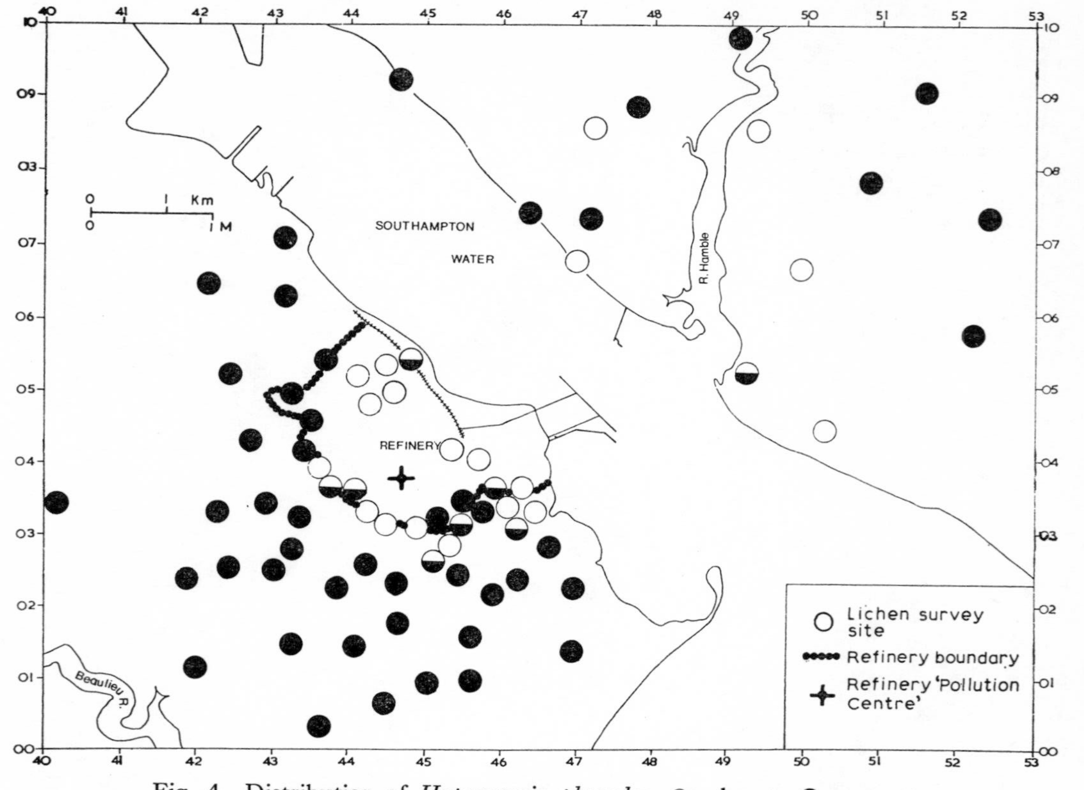


Fig. 4 Distribution of *Hypogymnia physodes*. ○: absent; ●: present; ◐: present, but only on the base

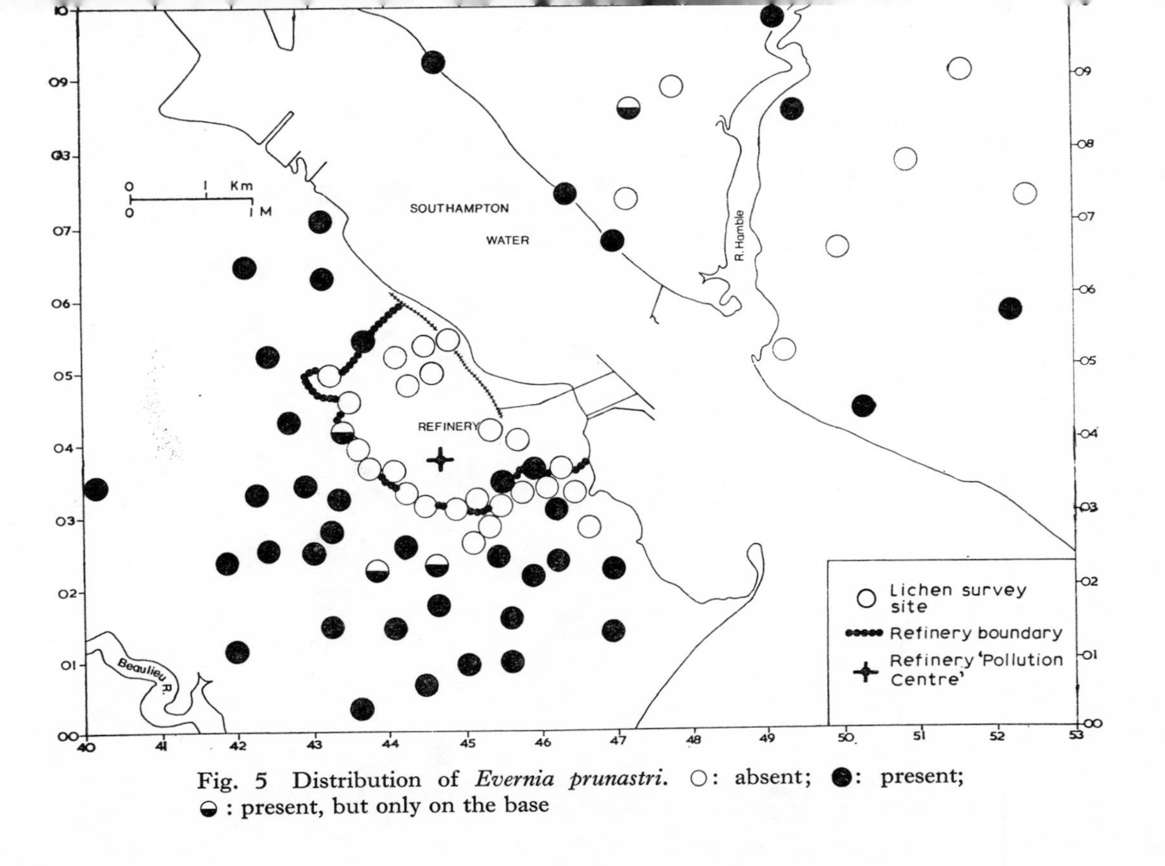


Fig. 5 Distribution of *Evernia prunastri*. ○: absent; ●: present; ◒: present, but only on the base

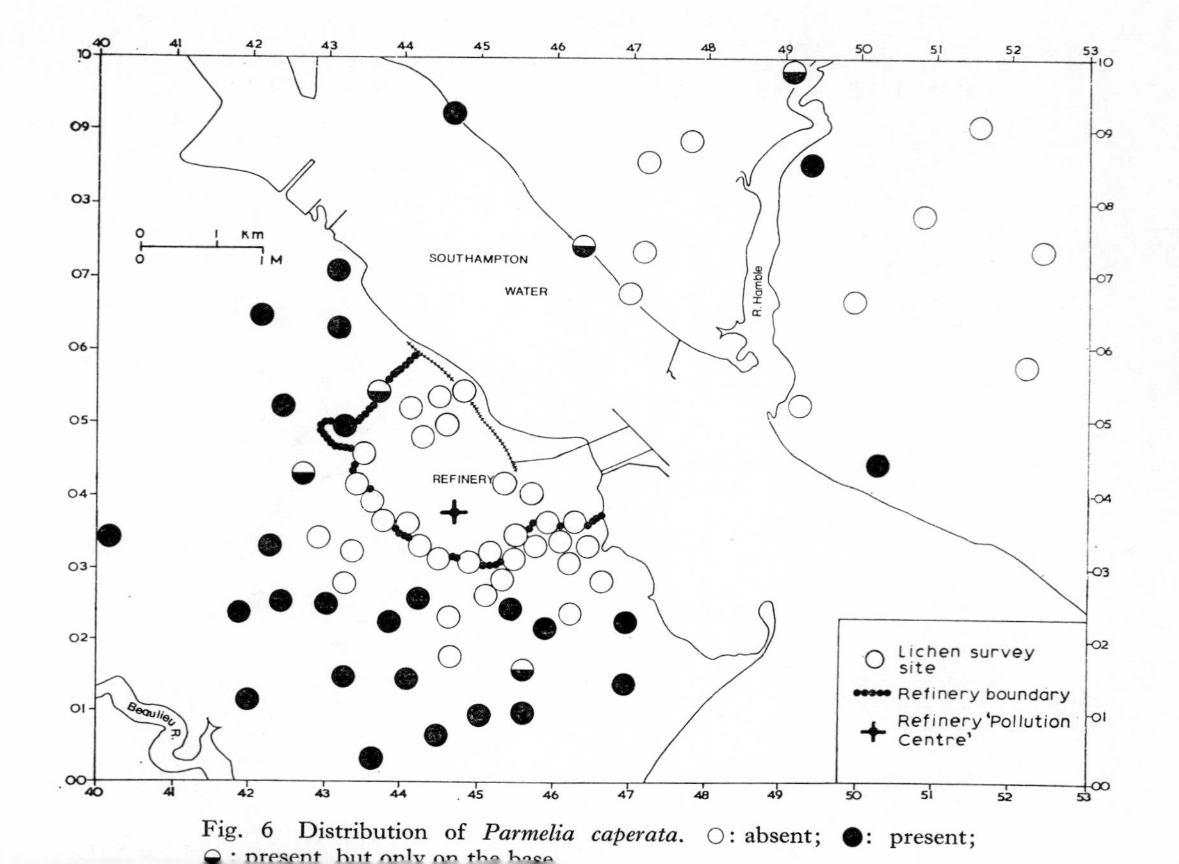


Fig. 6 Distribution of *Parmelia caperata*. ○: absent; ●: present;
◐: present, but only on the base

pattern intermediate between the last group and the next. Like the following group *Usnea* spp. are generally excluded from a belt of about 2 km to the south of the refinery (an area of arable farming as well as pasture), but like the previous group they approach the western boundary of the refinery. *Usnea* spp. were found in only one site to the north-east of Southampton Water.

The *Parmelia perlata* group (Fig. 8) and *P. saxatilis* are generally excluded from a 2 km belt beyond the landward boundary of the refinery, except to the north-west. Both species are almost entirely absent from the area to the north-east of Southampton Water. Unlike *P. perlata*, *P. saxatilis* is absent even at peripheral sites to the south of the refinery in an area of arable farming but does occur relatively close to the boundary at one site in the vicinity of some gravel workings. It seems probable that some factor other than air pollution is affecting the distribution of *P. saxatilis* in this area and it is consequently not discussed further in this paper.

Clearly, all species except *L. conizaeoides* show a concentric pattern of exclusion related to the position of the 'new' refinery and more locally to that of the 'old' refinery. Land-use probably has a modifying influence on the distribution of some species but there can be no doubt that the oil refinery is the main causal factor of the distribution patterns found. The various species discussed are arranged in order of their tolerance to air pollution from the refinery in Table 1.

*Table 1 Order of species tolerance*

| Range of tolerance | | Species |
|---|---|---|
| *Most tolerant* | 1 | *Lecanora conizaeoides* |
| ↓ | 2 | *Hypogymnia physodes* |
| | 3 | *Evernia prunastri* and *Parmelia sulcata* |
| | 4 | *P. caperata*, *P. glabratula* group, *P. subrudecta* and *Ramalina* spp. |
| | 5 | *Usnea* spp. |
| *Least tolerant* | 6 | *P. perlata* group |

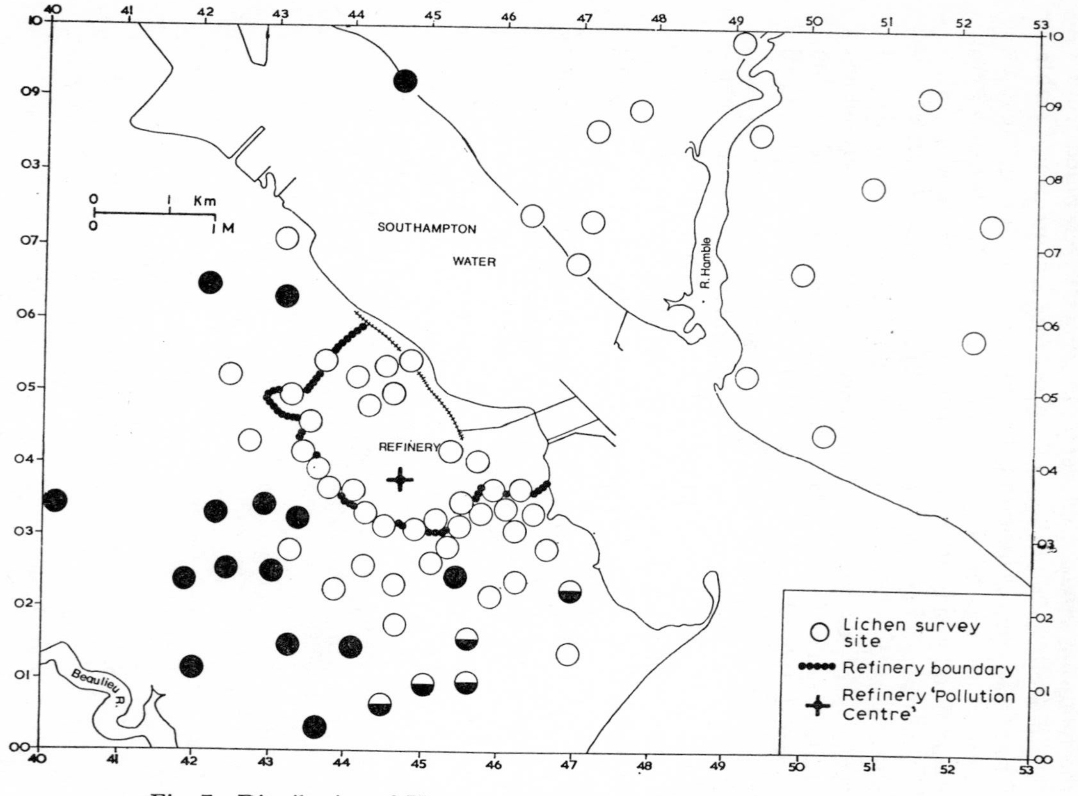


Fig. 7 Distribution of *Usnea* spp. ○ : absent; ● : present; ◒ : present, but only on the base

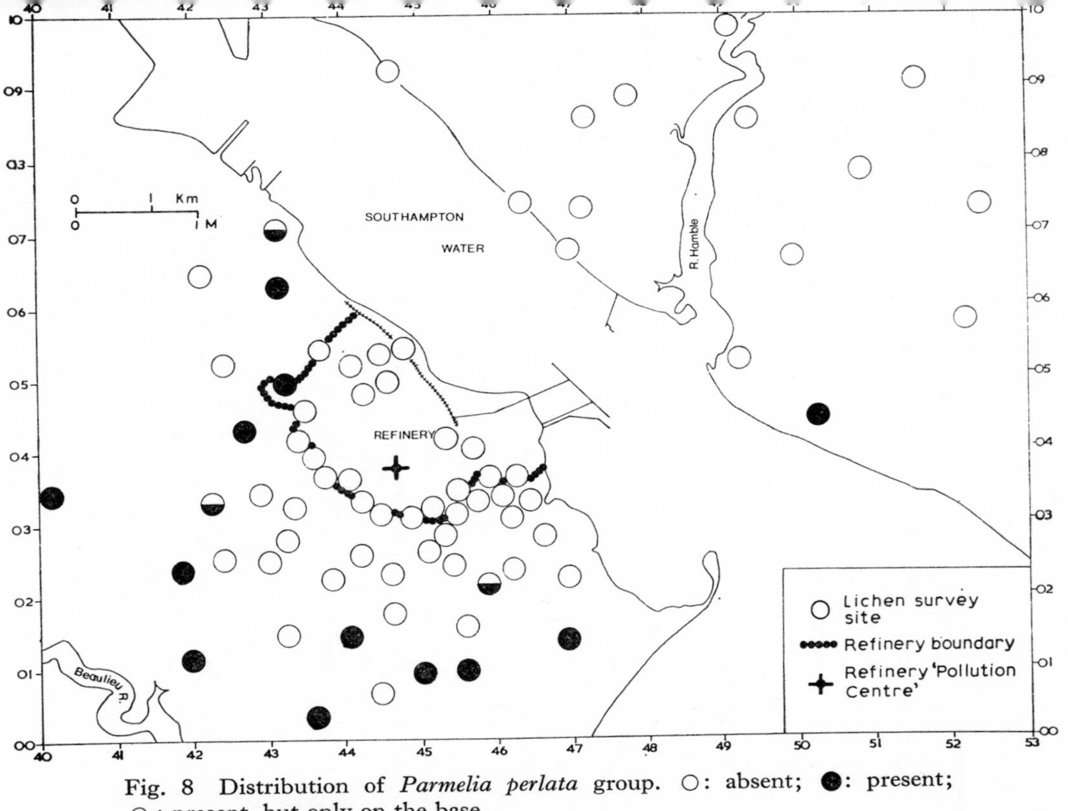


Fig. 8 Distribution of *Parmelia perlata* group. ○: absent; ●: present; ◒: present, but only on the base

*Zonal patterns*

Differential species tolerance (Table 1) is summarized in Fig. 9 where the three most significant inner limits of distribution are shown.

The innermost contour delimiting zone I represents the approximate inner limit of *E. prunastri* and *P. sulcata* so that within this zone only *L. conizaeoides* and *H. physodes* occur. The next contour is the limit of *P. caperata*, the *P. glabratula* group, *P. subrudecta* and *Ramalina* spp., and in zone II which it delimits *E. prunastri* and *P. sulcata* occur in addition to *L. conizaeoides* and *H. physodes*. The third contour represents the inner limit of *P. perlata* and delimits zone III.

Beyond these three zones is a region in which all the species studied occur and, on the basis of presence or absence, can be considered as relatively unaffected by the refinery (zone IV).

These four zones are defined on the basis of the presence or absence of particular species at a site and take no account of the abundance of a species (e.g. as determined from percentage cover), nor of its luxuriance (e.g. size of specimens), both of which can be expected to reveal a more detailed picture of zonation (Morgan-Huws, 1971; ch 3).

None the less, presence or absence is a practical and definitive tool for recognizing the broad picture of air pollution effects around such an isolated industrial plant.

**Discussion**

*Factors affecting zonation*

Any influence the refinery may have on the relative humidity of the air in this maritime area could only occur within the boundary of the works and would not have any effect at a distance of over 2 km to the west and south of the refinery boundary. Differences in climatic factors of this type clearly cannot account for the concentric zonal pattern found although air pollution from an isolated source such as the refinery might be expected to give rise to such a pattern.

The small amount of smoke released by the refinery was reflected by the very low smoke levels recorded at pollution recording gauges on the boundary of the refinery and on the

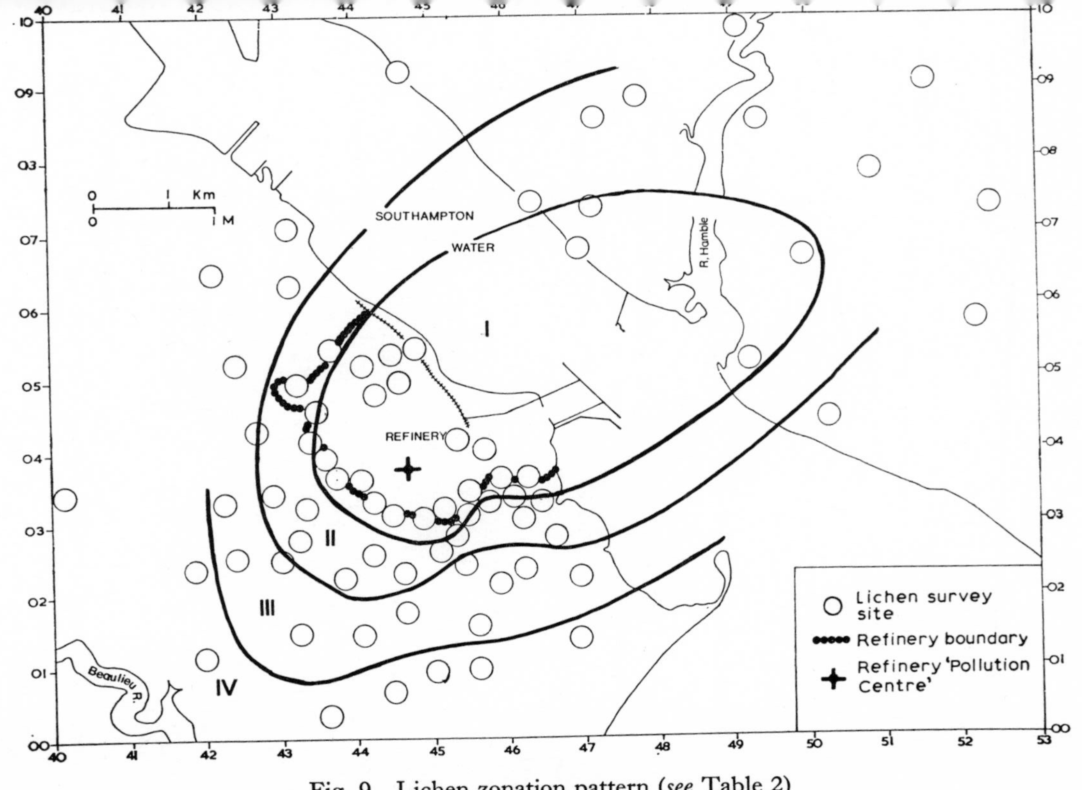


Fig. 9 Lichen zonation pattern (*see* Table 2)

opposite shore of Southampton Water. Smoke does not, therefore, appear to be the primary factor causing the zonation of lichens near the refinery (*see* ch 8).

Sulphur dioxide, however, is released in substantial quantities by the refinery and the levels monitored on the boundary of the refinery and to the north-east of Southampton Water reflect this high emission. In Fig. 10, on the basis of sulphur dioxide data obtained from many recording gauges in the area, the approximate position of the annual average daily sulphur dioxide contours for 70 $\mu g/m^3$ and 40 $\mu g/m^3$ are drawn. The displacement of these contours to the north-east reflects the high proportion of the prevailing south-westerly winds.

*Relation of zones to sulphur dioxide levels*

In Table 2 a comparison is made between the lichen zones recognized (Fig. 9) and the annual average daily sulphur dioxide levels (Fig. 10). Zone I appears to coincide closely with the 70 $\mu g/m^3$ contour and therefore this zone can be considered as having experienced more than 70 $\mu g/m^3$ of sulphur dioxide. The outer boundary of zone II coincides approximately with the 40 $\mu g/m^3$ contour to the west and south of the refinery and this zone can be considered as having experienced between 40 and 70 $\mu g/m^3$ of sulphur dioxide. The outer boundary of zone III lies in an area where there were relatively few air pollution monitoring stations and is tentatively considered as having experienced 30–40 $\mu g/m^3$ of sulphur dioxide. The relatively unaffected area (zone IV) can be considered as having experienced less than 30 $\mu g/m^3$ of sulphur dioxide.

Thus it is clear that the pattern of lichen zonation is closely associated with the site of the refinery and sulphur dioxide would appear to be the primary causal factor for the pattern of lichen zonation.

The emissions of sulphur dioxide from the refinery have remained fairly constant throughout the period 1952–66, when this study was made. An equilibrated response by the lichen vegetation following the sudden introduction of an emission source of appreciable levels of sulphur dioxide might be expected to take a considerable period of time (*see* ch 3, 16). Further studies to establish whether such an equilibrium has been attained at this

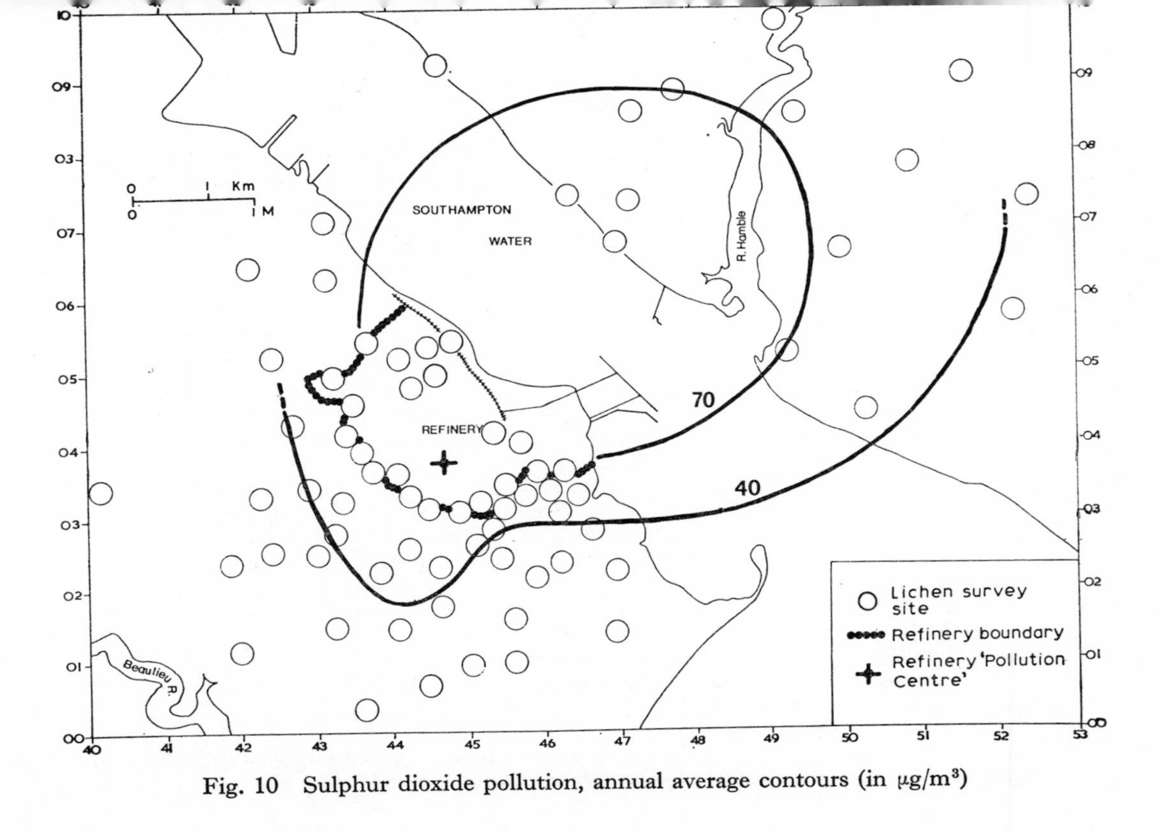


Fig. 10 Sulphur dioxide pollution, annual average contours (in $\mu g/m^3$)

*Table 2* *The presence of certain lichens on oak trunks and mean annual sulphur dioxide levels in the Fawley area compared with the data of Hawksworth and Rose* (*1970*)

| *Fawley survey* Zone | *Fawley survey* Lichen vegetation | Mean annual sulphur dioxide in μg/m³ | *Hawksworth and Rose* (1970) Zone | *Hawksworth and Rose* (1970) Mean winter sulphur dioxide in μg/m³ |
|---|---|---|---|---|
| I | *Lecanora conizaeoides*, *Hypogymnia physodes* (both frequent); *Evernia prunastri*, *Parmelia sulcata* (both occasional) | >70 | 4–5 | *c* 60–>70 |
| II | *L. conizaeoides*, *H. physodes*, *E. prunastri* and *P. sulcata* (all frequent); *P. caperata*, *P. glabratula* group, *P. subrudecta*, *Ramalina* spp. (all occasional) | 40–70 | 5–6 | *c* 50–60 |
| III | *L. conizaeoides*, *H. physodes*, *E. prunastri*, *P. sulcata*, *P. caperata*, *P. glabratula* group, *Ramalina* spp. (all frequent); *Usnea* spp. (becoming frequent) | 30–40 | 7 | *c* 40 |
| IV | *L. conizaeoides* (becoming less frequent); all other species listed for zone III (all frequent); *P. perlata* group (occasional) | <30 | 8 | *c* 35 |

site cannot, unfortunately, be envisaged owing to the increase in sulphur dioxide emissions from the refinery since 1967 and the added contribution of sulphur dioxide emissions from the recently commissioned oil-fired power station at Calshot, 3 km south-east of Fawley.

Ranwell (1961) reported that on a field meeting of the British Lichen Society in October 1960, the Whitley Wood and Gritnam Wood area of the New Forest, 15–16 km (9–9.5 miles) west-north-west of Fawley, smelt of oil fumes and that there was '. . . wholesale death of the larger fruticose and foliose lichens . . . ' In 1972 these woods contained 112 and 83 corticolous species, respectively, in communities belonging to zone 9 of Hawksworth and Rose (1970), and showed no sign of air pollution damage (F. Rose, unpublished). It is evident that some factor other than air pollution was responsible for this observation and that the smell of hydrocarbons (which may not have been accompanied by high sulphur dioxide levels) was entirely fortuitous.

Since this study was made, Gilbert (1970) and Hawksworth and Rose (1970; *see* ch 3) have related the lichen vegetation on trees in England and Wales to mean annual and mean winter sulphur dioxide levels, respectively. The zones in the scale of Hawksworth and Rose (1970) and the mean winter sulphur dioxide levels to which they correspond are compared with the data from the Fawley survey in Table 2. Bearing in mind that mean winter sulphur dioxide levels tend to be slightly higher than mean annual levels the correspondence between the Fawley data and their scale is striking.

**Conclusions**

A direct relationship is indicated between the annual average sulphur dioxide levels and the zonation of the lichen vegetation of oak trunks in the area around the Esso oil refinery at Fawley. There is no evidence to indicate that air humidity has any effect on the zonation patterns.

The empirical expression of 'presence or absence' gives the distributional limits of the individual species which in turn enables a series of zones to be delimited. A consideration of the relative luxuriance of the lichen vegetation would allow a more critical analysis of the total extent of the affected area to be made.

The different levels of tolerance to sulphur dioxide for the species discussed are similar to those found in a more general survey of the lichens of oak trunks in the south-west of Hampshire, and in other parts of England and Wales by Gilbert (1970) and Hawksworth and Rose (1970). The Fawley study reflects the influence of sulphur dioxide around urban areas where it is typically accompanied by much higher smoke levels implying that smoke may not be a factor contributing to the limitation of the lichen vegetation in such areas.

**Acknowledgement**

We are grateful to Dr F. Rose for allowing us to quote some of his unpublished data.

## References

Clifton, M. (1969). The National Survey of air pollution in the United Kingdom. In: *Air Pollution, Proceedings of the first European Congress on the influence of air pollution on plants and animals, Wageningen 1968*, 303–13. Wageningen: Centre for Agricultural Publishing and Documentation.

Gilbert, O. L. (1970). A biological scale for the estimation of sulphur dioxide pollution. *New Phytol.* **69,** 629–34.

Hawksworth, D. L. (1972). The natural history of Slapton Ley Nature Reserve IV. Lichens. *Field Studies* **3,** 535–78.

Hawksworth, D. L. and Rose, F. (1970). Qualitative scale for estimating sulphur dioxide air pollution in England and Wales using epiphytic lichens. *Nature, Lond.* **227,** 145–8.

Morgan-Huws, D. I. (1971). *Lichens and Air Pollution.* Ph.D. Thesis, University of Leicester.

Oliver, J. (1959). The climate of the Dale peninsula, Pembrokeshire. *Field Studies* **1,** 40–56.

Ranwell, D. S. (1961). Field meeting at Lyndhurst. *Lichenologist* **1,** 275–6.

Skye, E. (1958). Luftföroreningars inverkan på busk- och bladlavfloran kring skifferoljeverket i Närkes Kvarntorp. *Svensk bot. Tidskr.* **52,** 133–90.

Sutton, P. (1968). Air pollution in petroleum refining—part 2. *Chem. Process Engng* **1968,** 96–100.

Warren Spring Laboratory (1964–71). *The investigation of air pollution, National Survey, Smoke and sulphur dioxide.* Stevenage, Herts.: Department of Trade and Industry.

# 6: Urban Lichen Studies

J. R. LAUNDON

The scarcity of lichens in towns is a well-known phenomenon. Most urban lichen studies have been carried out with a view to explaining this poverty. Urban work is important, not only because of the ever-increasing quantity of land being given over to building development, but because towns have an influence on the lichen flora throughout much of western Europe, rural areas included, and it therefore has a relationship to general studies of ecology and distribution. Moreover, some of the most important present-day economic effects concerning lichens are associated with the urban environment, namely their use as indicators of air pollution, and their growth on surfaces causing discoloration and spoilage.

## Changes in urban air pollution

There is no detailed account of the lichen flora of any town or city prior to 1866. It is probable that in medieval towns in western Europe the lichen flora was different from that which occurred in the surrounding woodland and fields. Air pollution was reported from cities as early as 1273, when the burning of coal in London was prohibited as being 'prejudicial to health' (National Society for Clean Air, 1968, p. 46). Thus it is likely that pollution was already having some effect on the lichen flora at this time, and causing some species on tree bark to be less abundant. Even comparatively unpolluted small towns in medieval times would have had a marked effect on the lichen flora. The trees, which grew in back gardens and sometimes formed small areas of woodland within the city walls, would have had nitrophilous lichens upon their boles, such as species of *Buellia*, *Physcia* and *Xanthoria*. Nitrophilous lichens are those that are confined to habitats rich in nitrogenous matter. By contrast, in woodland outside the towns nitrophobous lichens would have predominated, as they do today. Town buildings would have provided habitats for saxicolous lichens, again chiefly nitrophilous species. In lowland Europe before man started to use stone for building purposes, these species would have been largely absent because of the lack of rock outcrops. They must have spread chiefly from mountain areas or rocky coasts to colonize buildings in towns and villages. Unfortunately there is no information to judge their progression.

With the coming of the Industrial Revolution, towns made rapid growth because of the huge increases in population, and the urban areas as we know them today came into being. Industrial processes, together with the fuel burnt by domestic users, led to considerable increases in air pollution, the most widespread and important forms of which were smoke, grit, and sulphur dioxide. This pollution was far more deleterious to lichens than the destruction of woods, fields, heaths, and other favourable habitats which disappeared beneath the bricks and mortar. The pattern of pollution changes during the nineteenth century is illustrated by the lichen studies of Forster and Crombie from Epping Forest (*see* ch 16) and Walthamstow, the latter only 11 km (7 miles) from the centre of London. Forster recorded such sensitive lichens as *Anaptychia ciliaris*, *Arthonia radiata*, *Arthopyrenia* spp., *Candelaria concolor*, *Graphis scripta*, *Lecanora pallida*, *Lecidella elaeochroma*, *Opegrapha atra*, *Phaeographis dendritica*, *Thelotrema lepadinum* and *Usnea* spp. from Walthamstow, with many species from Hoe Street, then undeveloped, which proved that the lichen flora was unaffected by pollution at the time of collecting, namely the late eighteenth century (Laundon, 1970, p. 27). In 1885 Crombie reported that the lichen flora of Walthamstow had declined markedly due to the spread of pollution, whilst 'about Hoe Street . . . where numerous species were collected by Forster . . . we would at present vainly search for any in a fully-developed condition' (Crombie, 1885, p. 74). From this and other evidence it can be established that pollution first spread beyond the built-up areas of towns in England to affect lichens in rural areas around the middle of the nineteenth century.

In most other towns and cities throughout Europe the surrounding epiphytic lichen vegetation suffered as industrialization occurred and urban expansion took place. Schmid (in Mägdefrau, 1960, p. 211) illustrates the extension of pollution damage around München, Germany, between 1890 and 1956, during which time the area of epiphytic damage increased six-fold (Fig. 1).

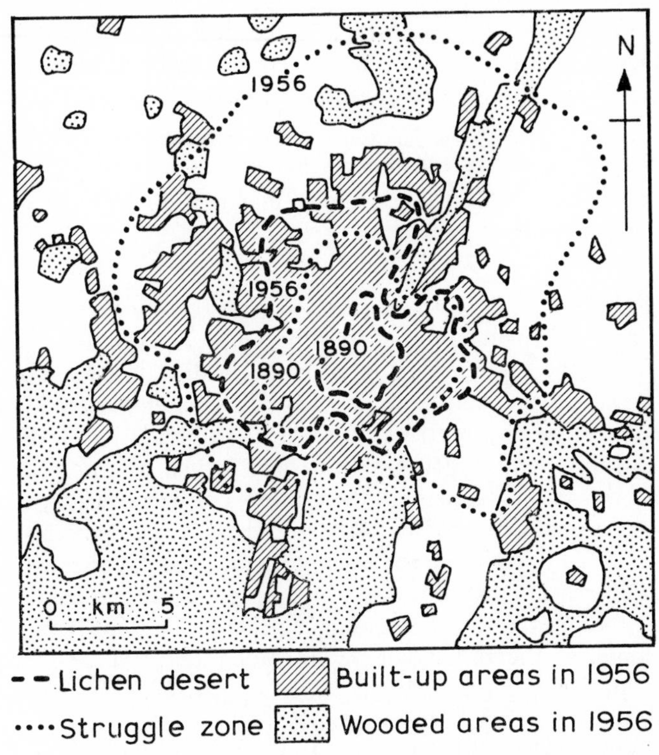


Fig. 1 Extension of pollution damage in München, Germany, between 1890 and 1956 (after Mägdefrau, 1960, p. 211)

In more recent times significant changes in pollution levels have taken place in towns. In England, forests of chimneys pouring out black smoke are now a thing of the past. In London the concentration of smoke has declined by three-quarters between 1954 and 1967, from a mean winter concentration of 400 $\mu g/m^3$ to 100 $\mu g/m^3$ (Craxford and Weatherley, 1968, p. 12), and there has been a marked, though lesser, decline in smoke concentrations throughout the country. On the other hand sulphur dioxide emissions and average concentrations in London have declined only slightly between 1954 and 1967 (Craxford and Weatherley, 1968, Table 4 and Fig. 6), whilst emissions in the country as a whole have increased but urban concentrations have fallen. Many other towns show changes comparable to London (*see* ch 16). As it is sulphur dioxide which is harmful to lichens it is not surprising that there has been no recorded marked improvement in the lichen flora of any urban area to date.

## History of urban studies

Most urban lichen studies belong to fairly distinct categories. These are outlined below.

### *Early investigations*

The first urban lichen study published was Nylander's (1866) account of the lichens which grew in the Jardins du Luxembourg, in the heart of the 'left bank' of Paris. This paper was read before its publication at a meeting of the Société Botanique de France on 13 July 1866, and in the discussion which followed Cosson declared that the decrease in the numbers of lichens in cities was due to the production of dark smoke and gaseous emissions which make the air unsuitable for their growth. The paper itself consisted chiefly of a list of species, including habitat and frequency, which occurred in the gardens, ecological observations being little developed at the time. The list included *Parmelia acetabulum*, some species of *Physcia* and *Xanthoria parietina*.

Between Nylander's account in 1866 and Sernander's observations in 1912 and 1926, urban lichen studies made little progress. Arnold (1891–1901) published a detailed account of the lichen flora of München and its surroundings, but the statement by Barkman (1958, p. 116), implying that he carried out transplant experiments, appears to be unsubstantiated. Later Nienburg (1919) drew attention to the fact that many of the lichens in towns were nitrophilous.

### *Zonation*

In 1926 Sernander (1926, p. 160), developing his earlier concepts, concluded that in towns there were three zones of lichen development which could be recognized. In city centres, around gas-manufacturing works, railway stations (steam trains were in service) and large industrial plants, there was a lichen desert ('lavöknen'). Here, Sernander wrote, the trunks of trees are nearly bare, or more precisely their bark is more or less soaked with soot; in the outer part of the zone especially if the climate is damp the bark is covered mainly with green algae—only on stones are there some solitary nitrophilous lichens. Sernander's second zone is a struggle zone ('kampzonen') which occurs outside the lichen desert, where the trunks are beginning to become colonized with lichens, including nitrophilous species, but they are not abundant; on outcrops of rock the nitrophilous lichens have a denser cover. Sernander's third zone is a normal zone ('normalzonen') where lichens are abundant on the trunks of trees and outcrops of rocks.

Sernander's observations evidently created a considerable interest in the distribution of lichens around cities, to judge from the number of studies which appeared in later years, complete with maps of both the distribution of individual species, and/or the zones themselves. Haugsjå's (1930) paper on Oslo was the earliest, providing the first maps of lichens around a city, twenty in all. The maps show the inner limit of each species as well as its inner limit of normal development, together with the limits of the struggle zone as defined by Sernander.

Four years later Vaarna (1934) published a survey of Helsinki, on similar lines to Haugsjå's work on Oslo. Maps of fifteen species were produced, showing their inner limit in relation to the city plan. Subsequently many authors have mapped the distribution of different lichens in built-up areas or have produced zone-maps based on Sernander's concepts (Fig. 2). Hawksworth (1971; ch. 3) gives a fine summary of these publications. These maps are very useful in providing a guide to the severity, extent, and pattern of sulphur dioxide pollution within urban areas, and make possible comparisons at different intervals of time (Fig. 1), as well as comparisons between different cities (Fig. 2). It appears likely that the mapping of urban lichens, particularly of important indicator species, to demonstrate pollution patterns will continue. Vareschi's (1953) study of Caracas even prompted him to suggest an ideal city plan for the minimization of pollution damage, based on a continuous zone of parks stretching through the centre

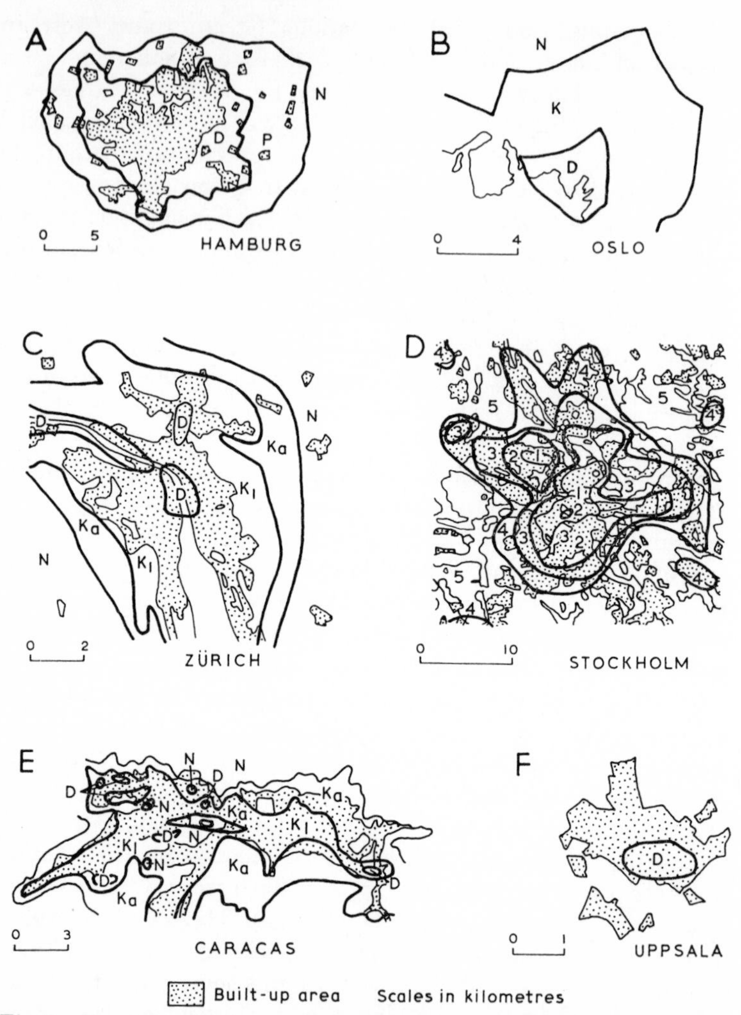


Fig. 2 Examples of lichen zonation patterns in towns. A: Hamburg (after Villwock, 1962, p. 158); B: Oslo (after Haugsjå, 1930, Tafel I); C: Zürich (after Vareschi, 1936, p. 479); D: Stockholm (after Skye, 1968, p. 24); E: Caracas (after Vareschi, 1953, p. 93); F: Uppsala (after von Krusenstjerna, 1945, p. 101)

D: lichen desert; K: struggle zone; $K_i$: inner struggle zone; $K_a$: outer struggle zone; N: normal zone; P: pioneer zone; 1–5: zones from lichen desert (1) to normal (5). For definitions of zones, see text and papers cited. This figure is reproduced with permission from Hawksworth (1971, p.283) in the direction of the prevailing winds. No new town appears to have deliberately adopted Vareschi's plan.

*Aridity*

From 1866 until 1954, it had been assumed by most lichenologists that air pollution was the cause of lichen poverty in urban areas. Then Rydzak (1954) reported on a study of Lublin in Poland, and concluded that dryness and not air pollution was the cause of the impoverishment of the lichen flora. He later (*see* Rydzak, 1959) studied twenty-five small towns in Poland in which there was little obvious pollution and came to the same conclusion. Rydzak and Krysiak (1970) then published a study of an industrial area to contrast with the 'clean' towns of the earlier work, and found a 'comparatively good' lichen flora. This was regarded as further evidence that toxic gases do not affect lichens and that the conclusion supported the 'Drought Hypothesis'.

The only major study to support Rydzak's views was Beschel's (1958) detailed account of five Austrian towns, which concluded that aridity was the main cause of the lichen poverty.

Rydzak's observations have been useful in drawing attention to the importance of the effects of low humidity in towns, and for indicating that sulphur dioxide has less effect where the climate is more continental. He has also brought controversy into urban lichenology which has been beneficial in promoting more study and research. Against this, his claims have been harmful to conservationists and others concerned about air pollution. However, Dr Rydzak's claims do not stand up to scientific scrutiny (see the detailed account in ch 7). In brief, this is because sulphur dioxide levels for his towns are not given and no explanation is offered for the poverty of the lichen flora around isolated factories in rural areas where low humidity does not occur. Nor do his claims account for areas of high humidity in urban surroundings, such as a forested uninhabited island in Montreal, reported upon by Rao and LeBlanc (1966, p. 69) or Farm Bog, on London's Wimbledon Common, mentioned by Laundon (1967, p. 283), not having a rich epiphytic flora, as they would if dryness were the overriding factor. Indeed the work of Skye (1958, p. 159, Fig. 6; 1964, p. 330), Gilbert (1965, p. 42) and others have shown that sulphur dioxide is the main pollutant affecting lichens, and dryness is of secondary importance. Nevertheless, lichens which can tolerate polluted air are often best developed where moisture is at a maximum, such as at the base of trees.

*Scales*

Observations in urban areas at sites where pollution levels are known has enabled lichenologists to construct scales relating lichen development on tree boles to pollution levels. The first scale published for England appeared in Jones (1952, p. 115). Outside the zone where lichens were absent, Jones noted that three zones could be related to decreasing pollution. The first was of *Lecanora conizaeoides* alone, the second with *Hypogymnia physodes* and *Parmelia* spp. entering, and the third with *Evernia* and *Ramalina* occurring together with the other species. More sophisticated scales have since been published, the most interesting of which are by Barkman (1963), by Hawksworth and Rose (1970) and by Gilbert (1970*a*).

Barkman's (1963) scale was included in his study of central Limburg, Belgium. Fifteen types of epiphytic vegetation were recognized and mapped, and these were placed in order of richness, but were not directly related to sulphur dioxide levels. This study was commissioned by the authority for the planning of Limburg and from the epiphytic vegetation the whole area was classified into three categories (Barkman, 1969, p. 205), the first with little pollution where more factories could still be built, the second with moderate pollution where new factories should be prohibited, and the third with heavy pollution where factories and mines should be closed or more stringent measures should be taken to reduce the emission of pollution. This survey demonstrates the practical value of the use of a scale based on lichen development, and the way it can be used in planning for the location of housing and industry. To obtain the same results by measuring directly the pollution in the air would involve a very expensive and time-consuming operation, at many times the cost of Barkman's survey and involving years rather than weeks of work.

Hawksworth and Rose's (1970) scale gives eleven zones, with a corresponding scale for eutrophiated bark. The scale ranges from epiphytes absent at zone 0 to *Teloschistes flavicans* communities, etc., at zone 10 with 'pure' air. The scale has been applied to Leicester and shows that in the city centre epiphytes are either absent (zone 0) or *Pleurococcus* is confined to the base of trees (zone 1). Zone 2 with *Pleurococcus* extending up the trunks and *Lecanora conizaeoides* occurring at the base corresponds to *c* 150 $\mu g/m^3$ of sulphur dioxide for the winter months, and extends over most of the built-up area outside the centre. Zone 3 with *L. conizaeoides* extending up the trunks, corresponds to *c* 125 $\mu g/m^3$ and occurs in the outer suburbs and over the surrounding countryside. Macrolichens, *Hypogymnia* and *Parmelia* spp., come in at the base of trees to denote zone 4, which corresponds to a sulphur dioxide level of *c* 70 $\mu g/m^3$, and which occurs only in scattered rural areas of Leicestershire and not in the urban part at all. The application of this scale provides a cheap and quick method of assessing air pollution levels in both urban and rural areas.

Gilbert's (1970*a*) scale differs from that of Hawksworth and Rose in being based on communities rather than individual species. It also includes acid stonework and calcareous stonework, including asbestos cement roofs, in addition to tree boles.

*Modifying factors*

Apart from scales, the most important new work on urban lichenology concerns factors modifying the effects of pollution. Gilbert (1970*b*) gives an excellent summary in which he cites shelter, pH, nutrients, and the age of the substratum as being the chief factors which modify the effects of sulphur dioxide in towns. Water relations are considered to be unimportant. The age of the substratum is perhaps the most interesting of these modifying factors. The importance of age was first demonstrated by Laundon (1967, p. 298) who found that, amongst other evidence, *Caloplaca heppiana* occurred on over 80 per cent of limestone memorials erected in the eighteenth century at Mitcham churchyard in London, compared with none on those dating from the twentieth century, and attributed the lack of recent colonization to rising levels of pollution during the nineteenth century. It is now apparent that relict lichen communities exist on a larger scale than has been realized hitherto. They probably occur in rural areas as well as in towns. Morgan-Huws (1970) has indicated that the disappearance of some lichens from parts of the New Forest could be due to regeneration failure from propagules under increasing pollution. Gilbert (1971*a*) considers that local populations of rare species (e.g. *Lobaria* spp.; *see* ch 4 and 16) are unable to colonize new sites because pollution has depressed their vigour. The relict status of colonies of *Parmelia saxatilis* near Blyth in Northumberland was demonstrated by Gilbert (1971*b*, p. 14) by means of chart quadrats over six years. Thus much of our interesting lichen flora may be of a relict nature and at risk, and there is a danger of further extinctions of populations over the next few decades.

Laundon's work on churchyards stressed the importance of this habitat for lichens. In London, two-thirds of the present lichen flora occurs in churchyards and cemeteries (Laundon, 1970, Table 2), chiefly on old limestone memorials in churchyards. Indeed, two-thirds of the London flora is found on calcareous stone. The richness of the lichen flora on this substratum in towns is due to the high pH value which indirectly reduces the toxic effect of sulphur dioxide by altering the ionic form in which sulphur dioxide is present (Gilbert, 1970*b*, p. 614; ch 2). In many continental European towns saxicolous lichens are often less evident because the old churches usually abut directly on to the street and there are no old memorials to provide relict lichen habitats. Occasionally the old walls of the churches themselves have a reasonable lichen flora. In continental Europe memorials such as headstones are a comparatively recent phenomenon, and they are usually confined to cemeteries, which have a rather poor saxicolous flora.

### *Other investigations*

In addition to the types of study already mentioned, there are a few other investigations which have recently been carried out in urban areas but which have attracted less interest. Corticolous transplants were undertaken by Brodo (1961, 1967), who studied damage in relation to distance from the urban area by means of photography. Schönbeck (1969) fixed plants of *Hypogymnia physodes* on to boards which he placed in different parts of the Ruhr, and recorded the effects of pollution on the plants by means of photography, in order to assess the level of pollution in different areas.

The sociology of lichens in urban areas was studied by Beschel (1958) for Austrian towns, and by Laundon (1967, pp. 290–301) for London. Urban communities were used by Gilbert (1970*a*) as pollution indicators.

The level of air pollution has been expressed quantitatively as an 'Index of Atmospheric Purity' by DeSloover and LeBlanc (1968, p. 50) from studies of epiphytic vegetation in the Dendre region of Belgium, and by LeBlanc and DeSloover (1970) from Montreal. Some criticisms of this method are given by Hawksworth (1971, p. 289; ch 3) and by LeBlanc (1971, p. 114).

## Toxitolerant species

At present work is being carried out on the taxonomy, history and distribution of the more important toxitolerant species growing in towns.

*Lecanora conizaeoides* is the most toxitolerant species which occurs on trees, extending further into the centres of towns than any other corticolous lichen. Studies of its distribution show that it is abundant in a continuous zone of pollution, in both rural and urban habitats, across the western part of the North European Plain from east Wales through England, Belgium, the Netherlands, northern Germany and Denmark. Elsewhere it is largely restricted to urban and industrial centres. It has recently been found in North America, where it has been accidentally introduced, and where it may possibly spread. Once established, it smothers all tree trunks, branches and twigs to form the community *Conizaeoidion* (*see* Laundon, 1967, p. 292). The history of the spread of this lichen is being studied by the examination of historical collections. It is absent from all the eighteenth- and early nineteenth-century collections examined to date: Acharius, Borrer, Dillenius, Forster, Linnaeus, J. E. Smith, etc. The earliest British specimen appears to be that collected by the Reverend Andrew Bloxam 'at the bottom of a fir in plantation Appleby road' at Twycross in Leicestershire (BM). Later Bloxam collected further material from Twycross (BM) and the adjoining Gopsall Park (BM). Unfortunately these collections are undated but were collected some time between 1839 and 1871 when Bloxam was Vicar of Twycross (Rev. J. A. MacDonogh, present Vicar of Twycross, *in litt.*). The oldest specimens are labelled *Lecanora varia* var. *conizaea*, a combination which was made in 1861, and it is therefore likely that they were collected at about this time. It is evident that *L. conizaeoides* was absent or very rare in Britain before the middle of the nineteenth century. By 1870, however, it was becoming widespread, for during the eighteen-sixties or thereabouts it was collected from localities as far afield as Buxton in Derbyshire, the New Forest in Hampshire, as well as from localities near London, Manchester, etc. (all BM). Thus it spread rapidly with the rise of background air pollution during the major impact of the Industrial Revolution. It seems assured of a good future. The British distribution of this species is also discussed in chapter 16.

Another lichen which has more recently become common in urban areas is *Stereocaulon pileatum*. This species had been found only in Highland Britain until I collected it on fencing at Box Hill Station, West Humble, Mickleham, Surrey, in 1955 (BM). Since that date it has been collected in a number of urban areas in lowland Britain, usually on town walls of acid stone. It is locally abundant and is spreading.

The most common urban lichen is *Lecanora dispersa* which grows on calcareous stone. It even tolerates localities with the highest recorded sulphur dioxide levels, such as the City of London and the centre of New York. It is remarkable for its variation which is currently being studied. In rural areas, where it is also abundant, it has a whitish thallus and gives calcareous buildings and walls an attractive weathered appearance. In urban areas this same species has a blackish thallus, thus giving calcareous stone and cement a dirty aspect. This dark form is called *L. dispersa* f. *dissipata* and it occurs even in small towns where there is no soot deposit. As the plant is generally common in towns, and attractively coloured whitish and orange-lobed and foliose lichens are scarce or absent, the lichen disfigures concrete, cement and asbestos cement, thus making surfaces look unsightly. Therefore the lichen acts as a spoilage agent, and is worthy of the attention of workers on biodeterioration. With the present extensive use of concrete in town building and architecture, the discoloration of surfaces by lichen growth is a matter of visual and aesthetic importance.

## Summary

Urban lichen studies have been chiefly concerned with the impoverished lichen flora of towns and cities, and the reasons for this poverty. Air pollution has generally been blamed for this scarcity. Pollution was reported as early as 1273, but it did not become widespread until the middle of the nineteenth century. There has been no recorded marked improvement in the lichen flora of any urban area to date, because of the maintenance of high levels of sulphur dioxide.

The history of urban studies may be categorized into early investigations, zonation, aridity, scales, modifying factors, and other investigations; studies of these are outlined. The use of scales based on lichen development for estimating the level of pollution is of considerable importance.

Work is now being carried out on the taxonomy, history and distribution of the more important toxitolerant lichens. *Lecanora conizaeoides* was not found in Britain until *c* 1860, yet was becoming widespread by 1870. *Stereocaulon pileatum* was not collected in Lowland Britain until 1955, but is already locally abundant in a number of urban areas. In towns *Lecanora dispersa* has a blackish thallus which disfigures calcareous surfaces and acts as a spoilage agent.

## Acknowledgements

I thank Dr D. L. Hawksworth, Mr P. W. James and Mr R. Ross for reading the manuscript and for their helpful suggestions. I am especially grateful to Dr Hawksworth for providing the illustrations and for allowing me to make extensive use of his bibliography (Hawksworth, 1971). Thanks are extended to Reverend J. A. MacDonogh for informing me of the dates when Andrew Bloxam was Vicar of Twycross.

## References

Arnold, F. (1891–1901). Zur Lichenflora von München. *Ber. Bayer. bot. Ges.* **1–2, 5–8** [as supplements].

Barkman, J. J. (1958). *Phytosociology and Ecology of Cryptogamic Epiphytes.* Assen, Netherlands: Van Gorcum.

Barkman, J. J. (1963). De epifyten-flora en -vegetatie van Midden—Limburg (België). *Verh. K. ned. Akad. Wet.* II, **54**(4), 1–46.

Barkman, J. J. (1969). The influence of air pollution on bryophytes and lichens. In: *Air Pollution, Proceedings of the first European Congress on the influence of air pollution on plants and animals*, 197–209. Wageningen: Centre for Agricultural Publishing and Documentation.

Beschel, R. (1958). Flechtenvereine der Städte, Stadtflechten und ihr Wachstum. *Ber. naturw.-med. Ver. Innsbruck* **52,** 1–158.

Brodo, I. M. (1961). Transplant experiments with corticolous lichens using a new technique. *Ecology* **42,** 838–41.

Brodo, I. M. (1967). Lichen growth and cities: a study on Long Island, New York. *Bryologist* **69,** 427–49.

Craxford, S. R. and Weatherley, M.-L. P. M. (1968). *Air Pollution in Great Britain.* Stevenage: Warren Spring Laboratory.

Crombie, J. M. (1885). On the lichen-flora of Epping Forest, and the causes affecting its recent diminution. *Trans. Essex Fld Club* **4,** 54–75.

DeSloover, J. and LeBlanc, F. (1968). Mapping of atmospheric pollution on the basis of lichen sensitivity. In: Misra, R. and Gobal, B. (ed.) *Proceedings of the Symposium on Recent Advances in Tropical Ecology,* 42–56. Varanasi: International Society for Tropical Ecology.

Gilbert, O. L. (1965). Lichens as indicators of air pollution in the Tyne Valley. In: Goodman, G. T., Edwards, R. W. and Lambert, J. M. (ed.) *Ecology and the Industrial Society,* 35–47. Oxford: Blackwell.

Gilbert, O. L. (1970*a*). A biological scale for the estimation of sulphur dioxide pollution. *New Phytol.* **69,** 629–34.

Gilbert, O. L. (1970*b*). Further studies on the effect of sulphur dioxide on lichens and bryophytes. *New Phytol.* **69,** 605–27.

Gilbert, O. L. (1971*a*). Lichen conservation research. *Br. Lichen Soc. Bull.* **28,** 11.

Gilbert, O. L. (1971*b*). Studies along the edge of a lichen desert. *Lichenologist* **5,** 11–17.

Haugsjå, P. K. (1930). Über den Einfluß der Stadt Oslo auf die Flechtenvegetation der Bäume. *Nyt Mag. Naturvid.* **68,** 1–116.

Hawksworth, D. L. (1971). Lichens as litmus for air pollution: a historical review. *Int. J. Environ. Studies* **1,** 281–96.

Hawksworth, D. L. and Rose, F. (1970). Qualitative scale for estimating sulphur dioxide air pollution in England and Wales using epiphytic lichens. *Nature, Lond.* **227,** 145–8.

Jones, E. W. (1952). Some observations on the lichen flora of tree boles, with special reference to the effect of smoke. *Revue bryol. lichén.* **21,** 96–115.

Krusenstjerna, E. von (1945). Bladmossvegetation och bladmossflora i Uppsala-traken. *Acta phytogeogr. suec.* **19,** 1–250.

Laundon, J. R. (1967). A study of the lichen flora of London. *Lichenologist* **3,** 277–327.

Laundon, J. R. (1970). London's lichens. *Lond. Nat.* **49,** 20–69.
LeBlanc, F. (1971). Possibilities and methods for mapping air pollution on the basis of lichen sensitivity. *Mitt. forstl. BundVersAnst. Wien* **92,** 103–26.
LeBlanc, F. and DeSloover, J. (1970). Relation between industrialization and the distribution and growth of epiphytic lichens and mosses in Montreal. *Can. J. Bot.* **48,** 1485–96.
Mägdefrau, K. (1960). Flechtenvegetation und Stadtklima. *Naturw. Rdsch., Stuttg.* **13,** 210–14.
Morgan-Huws, D. I. (1970). News. *Int. Lichenological Newsl.* **4**(2), 5–6.
National Society for Clean Air (1968). *Clean Air Yb.* **1968–1969.**
Nienburg, W. (1919). Studien zur Biologie der Flechten. I. II. III. *Z. Bot.* **11,** 1–38.
Nylander, W. (1866). Les lichens du Jardin du Luxembourg. *Bull. Soc. bot. Fr.* **13,** 364–72.
Rao, D. N. and LeBlanc, F. (1966). Effects of sulfur dioxide on the lichen alga, with special reference to chlorophyll. *Bryologist* **69,** 69–75.
Rydzak, J. (1954). Rozmieszczenie i ekologia porostów miasta Lublina. *Annls Univ. Mariae Curie-Skłodowska,* C, **13,** 275–323.
Rydzak, J. (1959). Influence of small towns on the lichen vegetation. Part VII. *Annls Univ. Mariae Curie-Skłodowska,* C, **13,** 275–323.
Rydzak, J. and Krysiak, K. (1970). Lichen flora of Tomaszów Mazowiecki. *Vegetatio* **21,** 375–97.
Schönbeck, H. (1969). Eine Methode zur Erfassung der biologischen Wirkung von Luftverunreinigungen durch transplantierte Flechten. *Staub* **29,** 14–18.
Sernander, R. (1926). *Stockholms Natur.* Uppsala: Almquist and Wiksells.
Skye, E. (1958). Luftföroreningars inverkan på busk- och bladlavfloran kring skifferoljeverket i Närkes Kvarntorp. *Svensk bot. Tidskr.* **52,** 133–90.
Skye, E. (1964). Epifytfloran och luftföroreningarna. *Svensk Naturv.* **1964**, 327–32.
Skye, E. (1968). Lichens and air pollution. *Acta phytogeogr. suec.* **52,** 1–123.
Vaarna, V. V. (1934). Helsingin kaupungin puiden ja pensaiden jäkäläkasvisto. *Annls bot. Soc. zool.-bot. fenn. Vanamo* **5**(6), 1–32.
Vareschi, V. (1936). Die Epiphytenvegetation von Zürich. (Epixylenstudien II.) *Ber. schweiz. bot. Ges.* **46,** 445–88.
Vareschi, V. (1953). La influencia de los bosques y parques sobre el aire de la ciudad de Caracas. *Acta cient. venez.* **4**, 89–95.
Villwock, I. (1962). Der Stadteinfluß Hamburgs auf die Verbreitung epiphytischer Flechten. *Abh. Verh. naturw. Ver. Hamburg.* II, **6,** 147–166.

# 7: The 'Drought Hypothesis'

B. J. COPPINS

In the last decade most lichenologists have considered that sulphur dioxide in the air is the main factor limiting the lichen flora and vegetation in urban areas and large rural regions surrounding them (Hawksworth, 1971). This view accords with both field correlations with sulphur dioxide levels (ch 3) and experimental data (ch 13, 14). The late Dr Jan Rydzak and some of his students, however, have dissented from this view and in a long series of papers have repeatedly rejected claims of the sensitivity of lichens to the levels of sulphur dioxide normally found in towns and around isolated industrial plants. Rydzak considered the zonation patterns seen in urban lichen floras to be due to adverse micro-climatic conditions, particularly the lowering of humidity, increased temperature and an increased frequency of drying/wetting regimes. He terms this theory the 'Drought Hypothesis' which he does not define explicitly but which is based on his 'Ecological Hypothesis', '. . . the occurrence and distribution of the individual lichen species, as of all organisms, underlies the basic influence of a complex of numerous macro- and micro-climatic, edaphic, geographical, historical and other factors, which form the ecological conditions of the habitat under natural conditions, and under those modified by human activity' (Rydzak, 1969).

Many workers have commented on errors in Rydzak's interpretations of various data (e.g. Barkman, 1958, 1961, 1969; Skye, 1958, 1968; Brodo, 1967; Laundon, 1967; Savidge, 1963; LeBlanc, 1961; LeBlanc and Rao, 1966; DeSloover and LeBlanc, 1968; Gilbert, 1970 and Hawksworth, 1971) but no comprehensive review of the points he raises has previously been presented.

## Rydzak's arguments

Rydzak's main objections to the 'Toxic Gas Hypothesis' are reviewed in his second paper on the lichens of Lublin (Rydzak,

1969). These are discussed here in the order in which he presents them in this paper.

(1) Rydak notes that over 100 lichen species are known in cities and considers that any assumption that these species are toxi-tolerant is groundless. However, if one examines the list of 44 epiphytic taxa he recorded in Lublin (Rydzak, 1969) and Tomaszów Mazowiecki (Rydzak and Krysiak, 1968, 1970), all but three of them (*Physcia aipolia*, *Ramalina fraxinea* and *Usnea hirta*) can be regarded as toxitolerant. If a comparison is made with the scale of Hawksworth and Rose (1970; *see* also ch 3, Table 1) the remaining 41 appear in the more polluted zones of this scale (i.e. $<5$). Furthermore, the above three species were very rare, had low percentage covers and were either in the extremities of, or outside, the built-up areas.

Rydzak presumed that if the species seen in towns were toxi-tolerant they would not be inhibited from covering open surfaces of tree trunks, and would therefore not be largely confined to crevices and bases of the trunks. He suggests that this behaviour is a result of more favourable water regimes, and provides protection from insolation and wind. While this explanation may be partially true for some species it must also be borne in mind that the wind carries sulphur dioxide with it. This observation may alternatively be explained in the following manner:

(*a*) As the pollution source is approached the more toxiphobic species become confined to bark crevices and lower parts of the trunk, leaving only the more tolerant species inhabiting the open surfaces. The more sensitive species are consequently less exposed to impaction by air pollutants.

(*b*) Further towards the source higher levels of air pollution will occur in sheltered niches and consequently the more sensitive species then disappear. The pollution levels higher up the trunks may also become too high for the more tolerant species to occur on the open surfaces and these in turn become confined to crevices and tree bases.

(*c*) Finally, close to the pollution source, sulphur dioxide levels in the air may become so high that the shelter afforded by bark crevices and tree bases becomes insufficient, and all species may disappear.

Geiger (1969) observed that the air velocity over a tree is greatest at the middle bole and lowest at the tree base. This results in the middle bole being exposed to a greater volume of air than the tree base, and hence a greater quantity of air-borne pollutants. Gilbert (1968) demonstrated that much lower levels of sulphur dioxide occurred at ground level than at about six inches above it. Gilbert (1970) has also shown that microhabitats more favourable to epiphytes in urban and polluted situations, such as nutrient streaks and tree bases, have a higher pH and a more effective buffer capacity. He further gave evidence to show that the water relations of a microhabitat had little effect on survival, except where a continual seepage of alkaline water (e.g. from nutrient streaks on tree trunks) maintained the pH at a sufficiently high level (*c* pH 4) to prevent sulphur dioxide in solution being in its most toxic form of undissociated sulphurous acid. All of these data are more compatible with the 'Toxic Gas Theory' than the 'Drought Hypothesis'.

(2) The tolerance to sulphur dioxide of saxicolous species on alkaline substrates in urban areas is well known (Hawksworth, 1971). Such substrates neutralize the dissolved acidic toxic gases by maintaining a pH of about 4 or above resulting in the ionization of sulphurous acid to progressively less toxic forms of bisulphite, sulphite and sulphate (Gilbert, 1970). The toxicity of sulphur dioxide in solution to mosses and lichens has been shown to be pH-dependent by Gilbert (1968), Baddeley, Ferry and Finegan (1971) and Hill (1971). Rydzak states that gases act directly on the cells of the thallus so that the substrate cannot neutralize the sulphur dioxide although he gives no evidence for this supposition. The course of uptake of sulphur dioxide into the lichen thallus has not been closely investigated. However, the knowledge that the strongly polar sulphur dioxide molecule is readily adsorbed onto liquid and solid surfaces, and the probability that most of the uptake occurs when the lichen thallus is moist, renders Rydzak's suggestion untenable. It is more reasonable to suppose that most of the sulphur dioxide passes into solution before entering the cells of the mycobiont and phycobiont (*see* ch 2). Lichen thalli are known to be most active physiologically when fully hydrated, and this aspect of their physiology is discussed further in chapter 12.

(3) The annual coal consumption of Lublin had nearly trebled

from 130 000 tons in 1948 to 370 000 tons in 1966 resulting in the release of 11 000 tons of sulphur dioxide into the air per annum. Rydzak stated that this increased sulphur dioxide output had not affected the lichen flora of the north-eastern and eastern parts of the town in spite of the prevailing south-westerly and westerly winds. However, this conclusion does not seem to be substantiated by his own data (Rydzak, 1969, pp. 156–64, Table 3). The flora of the west and south-west parts of the city (away from the prevailing wind) is significantly better developed than that of the north-east part. The more sensitive corticolous species (*Parmelia glabratula*, *Physcia aipolia*, *Pseudevernia furfuracea* and *Ramalina fraxinea*) are restricted to the south and west and other slightly less sensitive ones (e.g. *Candelariella xanthostigma*, *Evernia prunastri*, *Lecanora carpinea* and *Parmelia exasperatula*) are more frequent and better developed in these areas as opposed to the north-east. On pp. 143–4 of the same paper Rydzak states that the epiphytic flora of trees in a cemetery in the north-east part of the city had declined since his earlier studies in 1948, although he makes no attempt to explain this. As sulphur dioxide pollution is the major environmental factor likely to have significantly changed at this site it would seem reasonable to infer that this was the cause.

Rydzak goes on to say that corticolous lichens are very rare in his sectors C4, D4, E4 and F4 although there are no major industrial plants in this part of the town. However, it is not surprising that the floras are poor here as these sites are in the most densely built-up areas in the town centre where sulphur dioxide pollution from domestic sources is probably very significant. Furthermore, toxic gases from the industrial sites will not remain around the factories but will be dispersed into other parts of the town and also beyond its limits. This effect will be especially pronounced in the case of pollution emitted from tall chimneys.

Rydzak acknowledged that in the eighteen years between 1948 and 1966 there had been a considerable decline in the lichen flora with a reduction in vitality of individuals, diversity of species and percentage cover. Ten epiphytic species (19 per cent of the original total) had completely disappeared and at least four of them, *Anaptychia ciliaris*, *Candelaria concolor*, *Ramalina fastigiata* and *R. pollinaria*, can be regarded as relatively toxiphobic (*cf* Hawksworth and Rose, 1970). Apart from the role of habitat destruction Rydzak implies that the decline is due solely to urban growth and industrial development resulting in a change of the town climate. As he places most emphasis on changes in relative humidity it is surprising that his own data (his Table 5 and Fig. 2) do not support this conclusion. His figures show no persistent downward trend in relative humidity values, only the expected minor fluctuations from year to year. Rydzak's monthly data are converted to yearly averages and presented in Table 1.

*Table 1 Annual average values of relative humidity at two meteorological stations (UMCS and PIHM) in Lublin, Poland (after Rydzak, 1969, p. 136)*

| Site | Year | | | | | | | | | | | | | | |
|---|---|---|---|---|---|---|---|---|---|---|---|---|---|---|---|
| | '52 | '53 | '54 | '55 | '56 | '57 | '58 | '59 | '60 | '61 | '62 | '63 | '64 | '65 | '66 |
| UMCS | 79 | 77 | 80 | 79 | 79 | 77 | 82 | 77 | 80 | 76 | 81 | 78 | 77 | 78 | 80 |
| PIHM | 79 | 78 | 79 | 80 | 80 | 78 | 83 | 79 | 82 | 80 | 83 | 79 | 78 | 80 | 79 |

(4–6) Rydzak considers that normal vegetation is found on the outskirts of large towns but in the centre of small towns (Rydzak, 1956–9), where the air contains only traces of sulphur dioxide, the lichen flora is poor. Such a statement is obviously unsatisfactory as no major town or city in Europe appears to have completely unaffected lichen vegetation in its suburbs. The flora in the outskirts of Lublin (population: 207 000) cannot be considered normal, and neither is that around the smaller industrial town of Tomaszów Mazowiecki (population: 53 000). Similarly, Fenton (1960) found that relatively unaffected lichen communities were absent on roadside trees up to about 2 km south of Belfast. In a transect west of Newcastle, Gilbert (1969) found that *Evernia prunastri* only approached normal development at about 15 km from the city outskirts. Brodo (1966) states that the effect of New York on lichen vegetation can be seen up to 64 km from that city. Also, one has to travel some 15–25 km south from the edge of the London suburbs to find well-developed epiphytic communities containing such species as *Parmelia perlata* and *Usnea subfloridana* (*cf* ch 4).

In the case of small towns, nowhere in any of his numerous examples does Rydzak present sulphur dioxide data to substantiate his view. Also, he fails to establish in physico-chemical terms what a 'trace amount of sulphur dioxide' is. In small towns domestic fuel consumption, together with consumption by light industry and public buildings, can well be expected to produce sufficient amounts of sulphur dioxide to affect the epiphytic vegetation (*see* Table 2 and compare with sulphur dioxide values in the scale of Hawksworth in chapter 3).

It is also interesting to note that in this Table, the mean winter sulphur dioxide levels for 1968–70 in Tonbridge and Omagh were 67 $\mu g/m^3$ and 60 $\mu g/m^3$ respectively, although Tonbridge has a population of more than 20 000 more than that in Omagh. Large towns are not always as large sources of sulphur dioxide as small ones and consequently some (e.g. Plymouth) have much better lichen vegetation near their centres than smaller ones (e.g. Barnstaple). This observation is clearly in accord with the 'Toxic Gas Hypothesis'. Although locally high levels of sulphur dioxide can be reached in small towns, the total sulphur dioxide output of such a small town may be fairly low and from relatively low-level chimneys, resulting in a steep gradient in sulphur dioxide levels, and consequently of the lichen vegetation, away from the town centre.

(7) Rydzak puts forward as evidence against the 'Toxic Gas Hypothesis' the statement '. . . in London, where the mean annual sulphur dioxide concentration is 0.14 ppm in some districts, numerous lichen habitats have been found'. However, if one examines the data on London (Chandler, 1965; Laundon, 1967; Weatherley and Gooriah, 1968; ch 6), this statement is seen to be very misleading. Mean annual sulphur dioxide concentrations as high as *c* 400 $\mu g/m^3$ (0.14 ppm) are of very rare occurrence and only arise in the central part of the city and in the immediate vicinity of large industrial plants. Most of the city, within a radius of 16 km of the centre, experiences mean annual levels of 100–250 $\mu g/m^3$ (0.04–0.09 ppm). The inner part of London, where the mean annual sulphur dioxide concentration is 286 $\mu g/m^3$ (0.10 ppm) or more, possesses only about thirteen species. Of these only *Lecanora dispersa* is common, occurring on calcareous rocks and walls, and even *Lecanora conizaeoides* is

*Table 2* *Mean winter sulphur dioxide levels in the central parts of relatively isolated small and medium-sized towns in England and Northern Ireland (data from Warren Spring Laboratory, 1964–71)*

| Town | County | Population | Mean winter $SO_2$ ($\mu g/m^3$) | | | | | | | |
|---|---|---|---|---|---|---|---|---|---|---|
| | | (approx.) | 1963 | 1964 | 1965 | 1966 | 1967 | 1968 | 1969 | 1970 |
| Eastbourne | Sussex | 65 630 | 126 | 107 | 120 | 92 | 94 | 90 | N | N |
| Tonbridge | Kent | 28 230 | N | N | N | N | N | 70 | 75 | 56 |
| Portadown | Co. Armagh | 18 605 | N | 81 | 94 | 82 | 92 | 76 | 98 | 65 |
| Stroud | Gloucs. | 18 350 | N | 76 | 89 | 83 | 61 | N | 47 | N |
| Lurgan | Co. Armagh | 17 873 | 90 | N | 44 | N | 48 | N | 91 | 53 |
| Haywards Heath | Sussex | 14 373 | 105 | 102 | N | 76 | 73 | 76 | N | N |
| Newry | Co. Down | 12 450 | N | 67 | 74 | N | N | 159 | 81 | N |
| Omagh | Co. Tyrone | 8 109 | N | N | N | N | N | 60 | 63 | 56 |

N: data not available

scarce. Within a radius of 16 km from the centre of London 71 species have been recorded since 1950. This seemingly large total is put into perspective when it is considered that it represents the flora of an area of 805 $km^2$ and that totals of this kind can be listed from a number of individual artificial habitats, especially churchyards, to the south of London. Furthermore, only some 15 epiphytic species are currently represented in the London flora and only one, *Lecanora conizaeoides*, is widely distributed. The remainder are very local or rare and some (e.g. *Chaenotheca ferruginea*, *Hypogymnia physodes* and *Ochrolechia androgyna*) may now be extinct.

Following his 'observations' on London, Rydzak makes a further statement which contradicts his own views. With reference to the paper of Brodo (1967), he states, '. . . in New York, with the sulphur dioxide concentration averaging 0.17 ppm, scarce lichen vegetation has been found as far as about 30 km from the centre of Brooklyn'. It is difficult, perhaps, to interpret what he means by this, but the fact that the lichen vegetation is still poorly developed at such a distance from the city indicates that air pollution is the main detrimental factor. Indeed, from his studies, Brodo (1967) concludes '. . . city-induced drought is regarded as acting on pollution-tolerant lichens close to a city centre with air pollution acting over much greater distances in decreasing lichen diversity and cover.'

(8) Rydzak correctly states that some writers believe that lichens are killed by prolonged exposure to toxic gases resulting in the concentration of toxic compounds in their thalli. He then argues '. . . in this connection, it is hard to explain why young thalli of various species do not abound in towns'. However, he fails to mention that many authors also believe that pollution is effective in inhibiting, either directly or indirectly, the production and establishment of diaspores (*cf* ch 3, 6, 15, 16). Margot has demonstrated with *Hypogymnia physodes* that the proportion of viable to non-viable soredia (i.e. those with or without phycobiont cells) is reduced by exposure to sulphur dioxide.

(9) Rydzak adapts some data from the papers of Pišút (1962) and Skye (1958) and attempts to show that their data do not support the 'Toxic Gas Hypothesis'. The work by Skye is the more comprehensive of the two and involves a study of epiphytic

vegetation around an isolated oil-shale works at Kvarntorp in Sweden. He found a good correlation between sulphur dioxide pollution patterns and lichen distribution (*cf* ch 3, Fig. 4). Rydzak states that at distances of 4.5–8 km from the works, Skye found a normal vegetation at a sulphur dioxide concentration averaging 10–30 $\mu$g S/$m^3$ (20–60 $\mu$g $SO_2/m^3$). However, these pollution levels are not particularly excessive (*cf* Hawksworth and Rose, 1970), although at the site 8 km from the works Skye notes some pollution damage. Rydzak comments that Skye recorded *Alectoria fuscescens* at a distance of 5.4 km from the works where the mean annual sulphur dioxide concentration is estimated to be 35 $\mu$g S/$m^3$ (70 $\mu$g $SO_2/m^3$), although he fails to point out that Skye records the *Alectoria* at this site as being damaged. Furthermore, the figure of '35 $\mu$g S/$m^3$' given by Rydzak is almost certainly misleading, because Skye, in fact, does not give sulphur dioxide data for the vicinity of this site, which lies to the north-west of the works. The sulphur dioxide data that Skye gives are for a transect to the east of the works in the direction of the prevailing wind. At a distance of 5.4 km east of the works a mean annual sulphur dioxide concentration of 35 $\mu$g S/$m^3$ can be expected from Skye's Fig. 6 and this is clearly where Rydzak arrived at this figure. From the wind diagram (Skye, 1958, Fig. 2) it is seen that south-easterly winds are only half as frequent as westerly winds. Therefore, the site 5.4 km north-west of the works was probably significantly less polluted than the equivalent site to the east. Hawksworth and Rose (1970) are of the opinion that *A. fuscescens* can tolerate average winter levels of about 50–60 $\mu$g $SO_2/m^3$ in the British Isles and this is in close agreement with the situation found at Kvarntorp.

Rydzak continues his argument by saying that if a normal vegetation could exist at the sulphur dioxide concentrations given by Skye, then it is difficult to understand, from the viewpoint of the 'Toxic Gas Hypothesis', why the influence of New York is felt as far as 64 km from the centre of the city. On the contrary, if we consider that New York is an enormous sulphur dioxide source with a population of over eight million people, this phenomenon is readily explained by the 'Toxic Gas Hypothesis'. Brodo (1967) states that 32 million tons of coal are consumed in the city annually. This can be expected to result in the emission of about 600 000 tons of sulphur dioxide per annum. In addition to this, large quantities of sulphur dioxide will be produced from oil-burning central heating systems etc. Clearly, much of this is carried many miles from the city and substantial amounts of sulphur dioxide can be expected in the air even 30–40 miles away. Unfortunately, Brodo gives no sulphur dioxide data for these distant areas but if it is assumed that average winter levels of the order of 40–70 $\mu g/m^3$ are experienced then some detrimental effects on lichen communities can be expected. Variations of climatic factors such as relative humidity and temperature, are far less likely to be responsible for damage to the lichen flora at such a distance from the city, especially in a coastal situation such as Long Island.

(10) Pearson and Skye (1965) and Rao and LeBlanc (1966) demonstrated experimentally the toxic effects of sulphur dioxide on lichens. Rydzak regards their experiments as of limited value owing to the exceedingly high concentrations of sulphur dioxide used (5–100 000 ppm in air) and at the time of writing this criticism was perfectly valid. However, more recent experimental evidence, using sulphur dioxide concentrations corresponding, it is believed, to those likely to occur in polluted areas in nature, shows not only that lichens are affected, but that the degree of physiological response in different species correlates with field observations on their relative tolerances to known sulphur dioxide levels (*see* ch 13, 14).

(11) Rydzak considers experiments involving the transplanting of lichens into urban or other polluted areas (Brodo, 1961; Rao and LeBlanc, 1966) as unimportant, and believes that they only serve to indicate that the organisms cannot survive in the unfavourable conditions of a new habitat. Such comment indicates the cautions to be borne in mind in such work, but certainly does not discredit their results. Also, since these experiments were carried out, the transplant technique has been developed, and later results obtained illustrate beyond any reasonable doubt the sensitivity of lichens to air pollution. Transplant experiments are discussed further in chapter 3.

Following these various arguments, Rydzak (1954, 1969, p. 151) presents a diagram to explain the paucity of urban lichen floras (Fig. 1). He considers that the 'heat-island' effect of the town

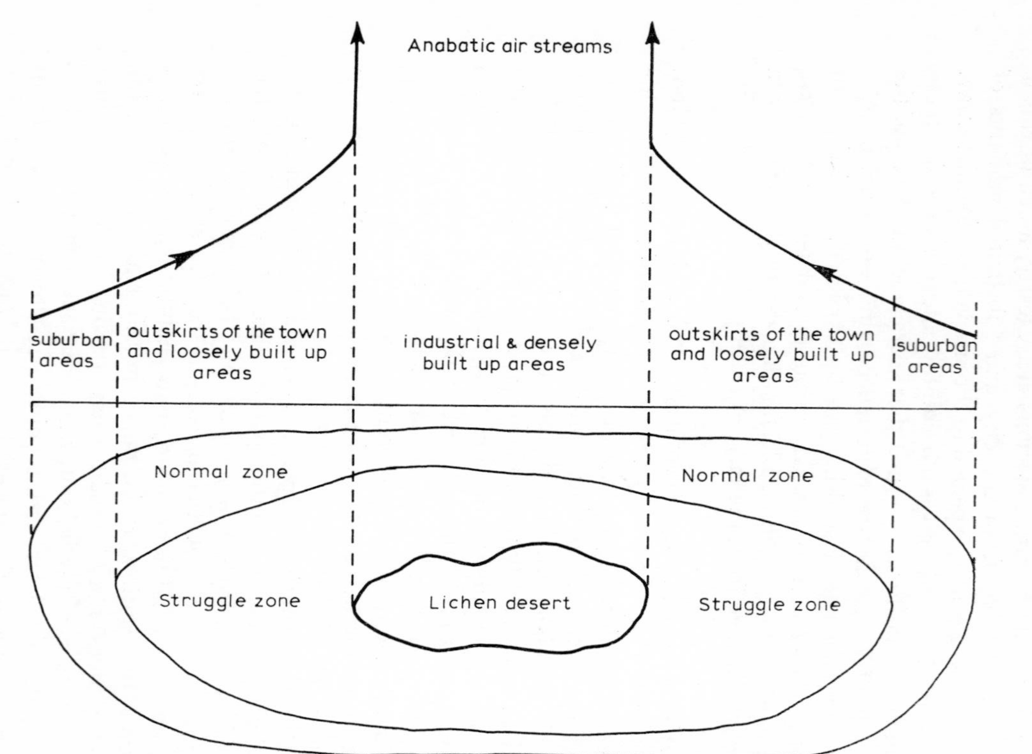


Fig. 1 Hypothetical correlation between the distribution of lichens in an urban area and anabatic air streams resulting from temperature increases from suburban areas towards the

centre results in '. . . convection air currents which hinder the formation of dew needed by lichens'. However, he gives no evidence to support the construction of this diagram. If such a phenomenon does occur it could only do so during anticyclonic weather over major conurbations when thermal inversions often result, thus preventing any massive upflow of air. Furthermore, the phenomenon could not be applicable to the small-town situation, especially in the absence of heavy industry, because sufficient heat could not be generated. The diagram is also erroneous in describing the flora of suburban areas as 'normal' (see points 4–6 above). Finally, if Rydzak's theory were correct, it would presumably involve a large influx of cooler, more humid air from the city environs, resulting in a higher relative humidity and hence a more favourable climate for lichen growth.

**Other considerations**

Apart from the points discussed above a number of other relevant factors require consideration.

According to the 'Drought Hypothesis' it is the dryness of the urban environment which is harmful to lichens, but the following findings are contrary to this view. Savidge (1963, p. 57) reports the death of epiphytes during prolonged periods of smog when sulphur dioxide concentrations were especially high and the relative humidity was 90–100 per cent. Rao and LeBlanc (1966) found that damage to lichens by sulphur dioxide was enhanced at high humidities, and Margot (ch 15) has shown that the soredia of *Hypogymnia physodes* are much more sensitive at higher relative humidities. Coker (1967) and Syratt and Wanstall (1969) found the same to be true for bryophytes. Barkman (1969) states that lichen deserts around towns are rather larger in the humid climates of the Netherlands and England than in the more continental climates of eastern Sweden, Poland, Hungary and Austria.

In his detailed studies in Stockholm Skye (1968) found no correlation between relative humidity or precipitation in the city and the development of the lichen flora. He found that '. . . it is only the chemical composition of the air that differs drastically from the normal conditions'. However, Steiner and Schulze-Horn (1955) did show a correlation between relative humidity and field observations on lichens, although there may have been a better correlation with sulphur dioxide levels had data been available.

Good correlations have been demonstrated between such criteria as lichen vegetation development and sulphur dioxide levels (*see* ch 3), and lichen distribution, sulphur dioxide levels and sulphate contents of tree leaves (Lihnell, 1969). Also correlation has been shown to exist between experimentally applied physiologically-damaging concentrations of sulphur dioxide in solution and the known tolerances of species to sulphur dioxide in the field (*see* ch 13, 14).

According to the 'Drought Hypothesis' a marked improvement of the lichen vegetation can be expected in humid parts of cities, but this is not found to be so. Laundon (1967), for example, reported that trees in semi-natural woodland at Farm Bog, Wimbledon, London, an area with soil which is permanently wet and where the trees are sheltered in a ravine, contained no more species than he found in other much drier woods in the area. Chandler (1962) recorded relative humidity and temperature along a north-east to south-west line across London during calm anticyclonic conditions at night. Under these conditions the differences in relative humidity and temperature between the city centre and the surrounding rural areas are found to be at a peak. He found that areas just outside the conurbation had a relative humidity of 95–100 per cent and the city centre one of about 75–85 per cent. According to the 'Drought Hypothesis', a poor lichen flora would be expected in the central part of the city and indeed this is found to be so. Also, a much improved lichen flora would be expected in the suburban parks and in the surrounding rural districts. However, this is not found to be the case and the epiphytic flora of these areas is still very poor and only corresponds to zone 3 of the scale of Hawksworth and Rose (1970).

To obtain reliable field evidence that lichens are sensitive to sulphur dioxide and that they can be used as indicators of this pollutant, situations are required where, apart from sulphur dioxide, environmental changes resulting from urbanization, especially relative humidity, are kept to a minimum. Such situations have been documented and involve investigations around isolated industrial plants in rural areas. Some examples are Skye (1958) around the oil-shale works at Kvarntorp in Sweden, Pišút

(1962) around the industrial plant at Rudňany, Czechoslovakia, Piterans (1968) around a superphosphate factory in the USSR, and Moberg (1968) around a sulphate pulp factory at Köpmanholmen on the Bothnian coast of Sweden. All these workers found a deteriorated lichen flora around these industrial sites and concluded that air pollution, particularly sulphur dioxide, was the cause.

Rydzak and Piórecki (1971) studied a similar situation in the Tarnobrzeg sulphur basin in Poland. It is apparent that here they found the effects of sulphur dioxide less easy to accommodate and they admitted that in the vicinity of the main industrial centre at Machów high concentrations of sulphur dioxide had a damaging effect on lichens. They attempted to show that no correlation existed between sulphur dioxide levels in the surrounding areas and the state of the lichen vegetation. However the sulphur dioxide data presented were inadequate and only in the form of maxima, an unsatisfactory form of measurement for these purposes (*cf* ch 2, 3). Furthermore, no lichenological data were given for the seemingly less-polluted area to the south-west (Fig. 2). The situation they found does not differ from that expected according to the 'Toxic Gas Hypothesis' and the lichen flora was severely affected in a large area around the industrial region. From their data the lichen flora can be seen to reach only a semblance of normality some 8 km south-east and 16 km north-east of Machów (Fig. 2).

Kozik (1970) studied the small industrial town of Tarnow in southern Poland. He found that in spite of the favourable high humidity, lichens were abnormally developed and he attributed this effect to air pollution.

The lichen flora has markedly declined in very humid situations some miles from urbanization and heavy industry, where significant levels of sulphur dioxide in the air are known to occur. Examples are seen in Derbyshire, England, in dales whose woodland floors have remained wet, and on trees in valleys in areas dominated by blanket peat bogs (*see* Hawksworth, 1969). That rural areas can experience significantly high levels of sulphur dioxide is demonstrated in chapter 3, Table 2.

If rural areas experience a marked lowering of relative humidity due to the influence of nearby urbanization, as is suggested by

Rydzak, then xerophytic species could be expected to survive or even increase their abundance. However, this is not the case and many xerophytic as well as hygrophytic species are detrimentally affected. For example, many of the species now extinct or very

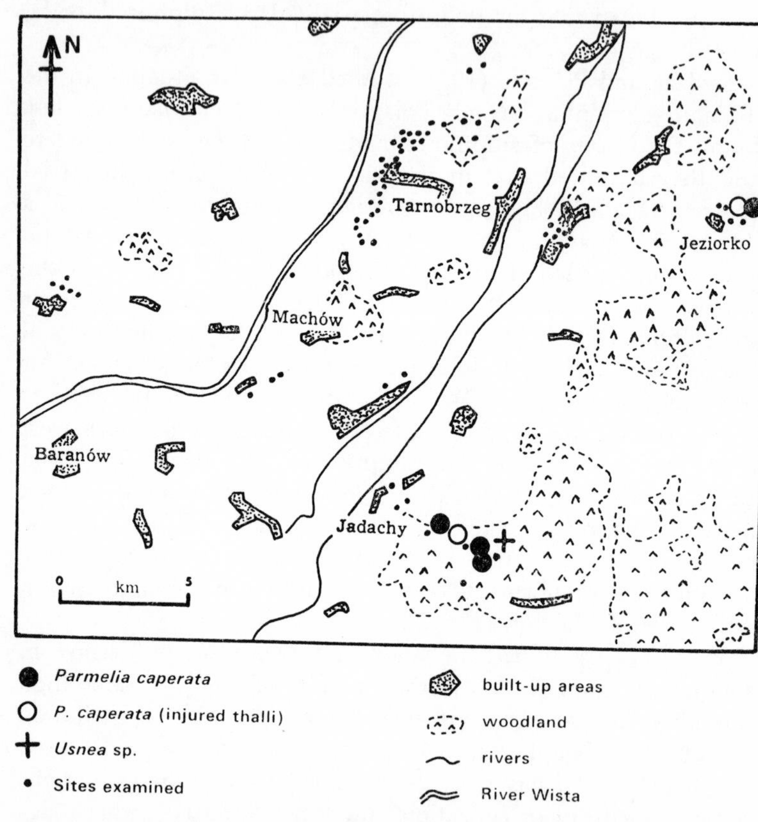


Fig. 2 Distribution of two moderately sulphur dioxide sensitive lichen species in the Tarnobrzeg Sulphur Basin, Poland (from data of Rydzak and Piórecki, 1971, p. 344 and Table 2)

scarce, but formerly widespread, in the Netherlands are xerophytes (Barkman, 1958, p. 298). The same can be said for many species in the Midland counties of England (*cf* chapter 16, Table 3). Finally, there appears to be no meteorological or climatological evidence to support Rydzak's view that cities influence the climate of surrounding rural areas in this way.

## Conclusions

A study of the arguments put forward in favour of the 'Drought Hypothesis' reveals that they include many statements which cannot be substantiated by field and laboratory investigations. Other observations with respect to lichen distribution, not considered by Rydzak, which cannot be explained by his hypothesis, are also discussed. It is clear that the presence of sulphur dioxide in the air can better explain the changes which have occurred in the lichen vegetation in both urban areas and the rural areas surrounding them.

As suggested by Brodo (1967), city-induced drought may have some effect on those species able to withstand the current sulphur dioxide levels in city centres, but this is not likely to be important in suburban and rural areas surrounding them. In the absence of experimental data this must remain hypothetical at present, although some data (see ch 15) provide a tentative indication of some correlation between relative humidity and sulphur dioxide effects under experimental conditions. On meteorological grounds such effects can only be expected in the largest cities of the world and are unlikely to be relevant in small towns, or near isolated industrial plants. Such effects would, in any case, be limited to the most hygrophilous species able to survive the prevailing sulphur dioxide levels.

## Acknowledgements

I would like to acknowledge the assistance of Dr D. L. Hawksworth who made a number of references available to me, prepared Figs. 1–2, and made many helpful suggestions. I would further like to thank Dr F. Rose and Miss J. Emberlin-Hasker for their helpful comments during the preparation of this chapter.

This work was prepared during the tenure of a grant from the Natural Environment Research Council.

## References

Baddeley, M. S., Ferry, B. W. and Finegan, E. J. (1971). A new method of measuring lichen respiration: Response of selected species to temperature, pH and sulphur dioxide. *Lichenologist* **5,** 18–25.

Barkman, J. J. (1958). *Phytosociology and ecology of cryptogamic epiphytes.* Assen, Netherlands: Van Gorcum.

Barkman, J. J. (1961). De verarming van de cryptogamen-flora in ons land gedurende de laaste honderd jaar. *Natura, Amst.* **58,** 141–51.

Barkman, J. J. (1969). The influence of air pollution on bryophytes and lichens. In: *Air Pollution, Proceedings of the first European Congress on the influence of air pollution on plants and animals, Wageningen 1968,* 197–209. Wageningen: Centre for Agricultural Publishing and Documentation.

Brodo, I. M. (1961). Transplant experiments with corticolous lichens using a new technique. *Ecology* **42,** 838–41.

Brodo, I. M. (1967). Lichen growth and cities: A study on Long Island, New York. *Bryologist* **69,** 427–49.

Chandler, T. J. (1962). Temperature and humidity traverses across London. *Weather* **17,** 235–42.

Chandler, T. J. (1965). *The climate of London.* London: Hutchinson.

Coker, P. D. (1967). The effects of sulphur dioxide pollution on bark epiphytes. *Trans. Br. bryol. Soc.* **5,** 341–7.

DeSloover, J. and LeBlanc, F. (1968). Mapping of atmospheric pollution on the basis of lichen sensitivity. In: Misra, R. and Gopal, B. (ed.) *Proceedings of the symposium on Recent Advances in Tropical Ecology,* 42–56. Varanasi: The International Society for Tropical Ecology.

Fenton, A. F. (1960). Lichens as indicators of atmospheric pollution. *Ir. Nat. J.* **13,** 153–9.

Geiger, R. (1965). *The climate near the ground.* Cambridge, Mass.: Harvard University Press.

Gilbert, O. L. (1968). Bryophytes as indicators of air pollution in the Tyne valley. *New Phytol.* **67,** 15–30.

Gilbert, O. L. (1969). The effect of $SO_2$ on lichens and bryophytes around Newcastle upon Tyne. In: *Air Pollution, Proceedings of the first European Congress on the influence of air pollution on plants and animals, Wageningen 1968,* 223–35. Wageningen: Centre for Agricultural Publishing and Documentation.

Gilbert, O. L. (1970). Further studies on the effect of sulphur dioxide on lichens and bryophytes. *New Phytol.* **69,** 605–27.

Gilbert, O. L. (1971). Studies along the edge of a lichen desert. *Lichenologist* **5,** 11–17.

Hawksworth, D. L. (1969). The lichen flora of Derbyshire. *Lichenologist* **4,** 105–93.

Hawksworth, D. L. (1971). Lichens as litmus for air pollution: A historical review. *Int. J. Environ. Studies* **1,** 281–96.

Hawksworth, D. L. and Rose, F. (1970). Qualitative scale for estimating sulphur dioxide air pollution in England and Wales using epiphytic lichens. *Nature, Lond.* **227**, 145–8.

Hill, D. J. (1971). Experimental study of the effect of sulphite on lichens with reference to atmospheric pollution. *New Phytol.* **70**, 831–6.

Kozik, R. (1970). Porosty miasta Tarnowa i okolicy. *Fragm. flor. geobot.* **16**, 361–81.

Laundon, J. R. (1967). A study of the lichen flora of London. *Lichenologist* **3**, 277–327.

LeBlanc, F. (1961). Influence de l'atmosphère polluée des grandes agglomérations urbaines sur les épiphytes corticoles. *Revue can. Biol.* **20**, 823–7.

LeBlanc, F. and Rao, D. N. (1966). Réaction de quelques lichens et mousses épiphytiques à l'anhydride sulfureux dans la région de Sudbury, Ontario. *Bryologist* **69**, 338–46.

Lihnell, D. (1969). Sulphate contents of tree leaves as an indicator of $SO_2$ air pollution in industrial areas. In: *Air Pollution, Proceedings of the first European Congress on the influence of air pollution on plants and animals, Wageningen 1968*, 341–52. Wageningen: Centre for Agricultural Publishing and Documentation.

Moberg, R. (1968). Luftföroreningars inverkan på epifytiska lavar i Köpmanholmen. *Svensk bot. Tidskr.* **62**, 169–96.

Pearson, L. and Skye, E. (1965). Air pollution affects pattern of photosynthesis in *Parmelia sulcata*, a corticolous lichen. *Science, N.Y.* **148**, 1600–2.

Pišút, I. (1962). Bemerkungen zur Wirkung der Exhalationsprodukte auf die flechtenvegetation in der Umgebung von Rudňany (Nordostslowakei). *Biológia, Bratisl.* **17**, 481–94.

Piterans, A. V. (1968). Vliyaniya superfosfatnogo zavoda na razvitie lishaĭnikov. In: Nakhutsrishviti, I. G. (ed.) *Materialȳ III Zakavkazskoĭ Konferentsii po sporovȳm rasteniyam*, 251–3. Tbilisi.

Rao, D. N. and LeBlanc, F. (1966). Effects of sulfur dioxide on the lichen algae, with special reference to chlorophyll. *Bryologist* **69**, 69–75.

Rydzak, J. (1954). Rozmieszczenie i ekologia porostów miasta Lublina. *Annls Univ. Mariae Curie-Skłodowska*, C, **8**, 233–356.

Rydzak, J. (1956–9). Wpływ małych miast na florę porostów. *Annls Univ. Mariae Curie-Skłodowska*, C, **10**, 1–32, 33–66, 157–75, 321–98; **11**, 25–50, 51–72; **13**, 275–323.

Rydzak, J. (1969). Lichens as indicators of the ecological conditions of the habitat. *Annls Univ. Mariae Curie-Skłodowska*, C, **23**, 131–64.

Rydzak, J. and Krysiak, K. (1968). Flora porostów Tomaszówa Mazowieckiego. *Annls Univ. Mariae Curie-Skłodowska*, C, **22**, 169–94.

Rydzak, J. and Krysiak, K. (1970). Lichen flora of Tomaszow Mazowiecki. *Vegetatio* **21**, 375–97.

Rydzak, J. and Piórecki, J. (1971). Stan flory porostów w okolicach tarnobrzeskiego zagłębia siarkowego. *Annls Univ. Mariae Curie-Skłodowska*, C, **26**, 343–52.

Savidge, J. P. (1963). Climate. In: Savidge, J. P. (ed.) *Travis's flora of south Lancashire*, 29–59. Liverpool: Liverpool Botanical Society.

Skye, E. (1958). Luftföroreningars inverkan på busk- och bladlavfloran kring skifferoljeverket i Närkes Kvarntorp. *Svensk bot. Tidskr.* **52,** 133–90.

Skye, E. (1968). Lichens and air pollution. *Acta phytogeogr. suec.* **52,** 1–123.

Steiner, M. and Schulze-Horn, D. (1955). Über die Verbreitung und Expositionsabhängigkeit der Rinden-epiphyten im Stadtgebiet von Bonn. *Decheniana* **108,** 1–16.

Syratt, W. J. and Wanstall, P. J. (1969). The effect of sulphur dioxide on epiphytic bryophytes. In: *Air Pollution, Proceedings of the first European Congress on the influence of air pollution on plants and animals, Wageningen 1968*, 79–85. Wageningen: Centre for Agricultural Publishing and Documentation.

Warren Spring Laboratory (1964–71). *The investigation of air pollution, National Survey, smoke and sulphur dioxide.* Stevenage, Herts.: Department of Trade and Industry.

Weatherley, M.-L. P. M. and Gooriah, B. D. (1969). *National Survey of smoke and sulphur dioxide, Draft report on the Greater London area.* Stevenage, Herts.: Ministry of Technology, Warren Spring Laboratory.

# 8: The Effect of Air Pollutants other than Hydrogen Fluoride and Sulphur Dioxide on Lichens

P. W. JAMES

In addition to their well-known and relatively widely documented sensitivity to sulphur dioxide and hydrogen fluoride air pollution (*see* ch 3, 4, 5 and 9), lichens also appear to indicate comparable modes of behaviour towards other forms of air pollutants. The air pollutants for which there is more than circumstantial evidence may be listed as follows: 1) heavy metal fallout, especially of copper, cadmium, iron, lead, manganese, nickel and zinc, chiefly as a result of smoke particulates from the partial combustion of coal and oil, but also from smelting processes and vehicle exhausts; 2) radionuclide fallout of long-life nuclides such as caesium-137 ($^{137}Cs$) and strontium-90 ($^{90}Sr$) and their uptake and assimilation in those biological food chains which include the ingestion of lichens by mammals; 3) ionizing radiation; 4) mechanical effects of the deposition of particulate smoke emissions as well as airborne dust from quarry workings and road usage; 5) farming techniques utilizing artificial fertilizers, fungicidal sprays and selective weed killers (Barkman, 1961). There is no information of the effect on lichens of other pollutants, such as ozone, nitrogen dioxide and hydrogen sulphide (*see* Nash, ch 10). The data on pollution by ammonia and potassium nitrate (saltpetre) emissions recorded by Rydzak and Stasiak (1971) are considered unreliable due to the high mean sulphur dioxide concentrations also recorded in the same area.

The most detailed information on this group of pollutants is available on radioactive nuclides. This is probably due to their direct association with man as a result of fallout from nuclear detonations and subsequent incorporation into his body via certain food chains. There is also preliminary evidence which suggests that zoning patterns of lichens may occur and be related to certain types and concentrations of heavy metal fallout around sources of pollution. Apart from the heavy metal content of its particulate fraction, the effect of smoke on lichens has been found to be much less deleterious than was previously thought (Almborn, 1943; Jones, 1952). This is due to the fairly recent recognition and separation of the effect of sulphur dioxide which nearly always accompanies smoke emission. The effect of modern farming techniques and the consequent total depletion of the lichen vegetation, or at least an enhanced eutrophication, in rural areas is an important aspect which has received very little attention.

## Heavy metal pollution

The predisposition for inorganic cation uptake from their substrate and atmosphere in excess of their biological requirements is a well-known characteristic of many lichens. These accumulations, which are a feature of many lichens inhabiting natural, relatively unpolluted environments, may become significant in areas of either rich natural mineral deposits or where there is a heavy metal fallout pollution either due to smelting and other industrial processes, or from combustion engine exhausts, as well as from the wholesale partial combustion of coal and oil.

In an important germinal paper dealing with spectrographic analysis of the trace element content of various groups of plants in Finland and including 16 lichens, Lounamaa (1956) noted particularly large accumulations of zinc (3000–10 000 ppm), especially in *Umbilicaria pustulata* growing on siliceous rocks. This pattern of accumulation of zinc was closely mirrored by cadmium which, in *U. pustulata*, reached maximum concentrations of 30–3000 ppm, three times as great as in other lichens on siliceous rocks. Chromium, at 300–1000 ppm, was strikingly concentrated by lichens growing on ultrabasic rocks whilst nickel reached a content of 600 ppm in *Parmelia centrifuga* growing on serpentine rock. Manganese was not noticeably accumulated but 10 000 ppm were concentrated in lichens growing on rodonite indicating a greatly exaggerated uptake on a manganese-rich substrate. The lead content of the lichens tested was remarkably high, ranging from 300–3000 ppm on samples taken from siliceous rock; the values for samples from ultrabasic rock were much lower. 3000–6000 ppm of lead were recorded from lichens on lead-rich rocks of the Orijarvi mining area. The copper content of lichens was normally low but rose to 3000 ppm in mining areas rich in the metal. Tin, only exceptionally noted in higher plants, occurred in significant amounts (up to 100 ppm) in lichens. Lounamaa emphasizes the significant amounts of gallium, yttrium, tin and lead in his samples. The nature of the substrate, according to him, is accountable for the differences in lichen content; thus the chromium, manganese, cobalt and nickel content of lichens is consistently higher on ultrabasic rocks whereas lead, zinc and cobalt have greater accumulations in thalli on siliceous rock. The substrate appeared to have little effect on the uptake of boron, copper, molybdenum and silver. The conclusions to be drawn from this evidence suggest that lichens are conspicuously different from all other plants in regard to their trace element concentrations and that the majority of the elements studied occurred in lichens in greater concentrations than in other plants. Boron and manganese, the latter element with notable exceptions, were the only metals accumulated in lichens in smaller quantities than in other plants. Manganese occurred in smaller amounts in the lichen than in the substrate, and cobalt, nickel, molybdenum and silver were present in equivalent amounts in other plants in the same habitat. Zinc, cadmium, tin and lead were strikingly concentrated, especially in certain lichens such as representatives of the genera *Umbilicaria* and *Stereocaulon*. Chromium, gallium, yttrium, and zirconium occurred in generally higher concentrations in lichens than in other plants but not exceeding the content of the substrate.

A spectrographic examination of the lichens associated with sandstone rocks of different age and strata in Colorado (LeRoy and Koksoy, 1962) revealed high accumulations of strontium, vanadium, yttrium, appreciable amounts of molybdenum and zinc and detected the presence of beryllium (*see* Table 1). Accepting that the source of the metal in the lichens was derived from the substrate, the authors postulated that lichens might be considered as possible indicators for mineral exploration. Subbotina and Timoféeff-Ressovsky (1961), using radioactive tracers, recorded strong absorption of cerium, zinc, and to a lesser extent,

*Table 1 Summary of the spectrographic analyses of trace elements in lichen species from sandstones of the Morrison (Jurassic) and Dakota (Cretaceous) formations cropping out in Turkey Creek, Jefferson County, and 10 miles west of Denver, Colorado (in ppm) (after Leroy and Koksoy, 1962)*

| | Sample | % Ash | Cu | Cr | Pb | Mo | Ni | Ag | Sr | Sn | U | V | Zn | Be |
|---|---|---|---|---|---|---|---|---|---|---|---|---|---|---|
| *Dakota (Lower Cretaceous)* | R | — | 10 | <10 | 30 | <10 | <10 | <1 | <20 | <10 | <1 | <10 | 200 | <1 |
| | LB | 5.9 | 500 | 150 | 500 | 20 | 100 | 7 | 1000 | 30 | 3.1 | 70 | 1000 | 1 |
| | LG | 10.0 | 200 | 150 | 1500 | 10 | 20 | 7 | 5000 | 10 | 1 | 50 | 300 | <1 |
| | R | — | 30 | <10 | 15 | <10 | <10 | <1 | 50 | <10 | <1 | <10 | 200 | <1 |
| | LB | 3.6 | 1000 | 150 | 1000 | 50 | 100 | 7 | 5000 | 50 | 11 | 70 | 1500 | 1 |
| | LG | 12.0 | 200 | 50 | 500 | 20 | 20 | 5 | 5000 | 10 | 2 | 50 | 300 | <1 |
| | SO | 6.4 | 300 | 150 | 1000 | 30 | 30 | 7 | 2000 | 20 | 3 | 70 | 500 | <1 |
| | R | — | 50 | <10 | 15 | <10 | <10 | <1 | 20 | <10 | <1 | <10 | 200 | <1 |
| | LG | 14.4 | 200 | 50 | 1000 | 15 | 15 | 5 | 5000 | 10 | 1.5 | 50 | 200 | <1 |
| | SG | 15.0 | 100 | 30 | 1000 | 10 | 15 | 5 | 2000 | 10 | 1 | 50 | 200 | <1 |
| *Morrison (Jurassic)* | R | — | 10 | 10 | 50 | <10 | <10 | <1 | 20 | <10 | <1 | 10 | 200 | <1 |
| | LB | 4.1 | 500 | 150 | 30 | 50 | 50 | 5 | 1500 | 30 | 10 | 70 | 500 | 3 |
| | R | — | 70 | 10 | 10 | <10 | <10 | <1 | 50 | <10 | <1 | 10 | 200 | <1 |
| | LB | 4.0 | 700 | 100 | 500 | 50 | 50 | 7 | 1500 | 30 | 13 | 50 | 2000 | 1 |
| | LG | 12.7 | 150 | 50 | 1000 | 15 | 15 | 5 | 5000 | 10 | 1 | 50 | 200 | <1 |

LB: *Umbilicaria hyperborea*; LG: *Parmelia conspersa*; SG: *Lecanora rubina*; SO: *Xanthoria (Caloplaca) elegans*; R: rock iron, caesium, strontium and cobalt. Comparable values for metal contents of bark substratum and corticolous lichens have been reported by Mićović and Stephanović (1961). They found that the chemical composition of the ash of the lichens *Ramalina farinacea*, *Usnea hirta* and *Evernia prunastri* differed widely from that of the bark of *Quercus* on which they grew. They noted accumulations of silica, phosphorus, magnesium, iron and aluminium in the lichens.

In addition to the trace elements studied by Lounamaa (1956), lichens have been shown to have a particular affinity for iron; for instance Seaward (1973) found 90 380 ppm of this metal in the terricolous lichen *Peltigera rufescens* near steel smelters at Risby Warren, Scunthorpe, England, and 35 760 ppm in specimens of *Lecanora muralis* collected from asbestos roofs in suburban Leeds. Noeske *et al.* (1970) using spectrographic and chemical analysis and following the studies of Lange and Ziegler (1963) on *Acarospora smaragdula* var. *lesdainii* f. *subochracea*, reported concentrations of 4875 and 14 400 ppm of iron in conjunction with the lichen association *Acarosporetum sinopicae* on mineral-rich mine spoil heaps in the Hartz area, Germany. Such high concentrations of this metal in lichens are often associated with 'oxydated' or ferruginose (i.e rust-red) colouring of the thallus (*see* Gümbel, 1856) which is a permanent feature of some species such as *Lecidea atrata*, *L. silacea*, *Rhizocarpon oederi* and *Acarospora sinopica* and more variable in, for example, *Lecidea lapicida*, *L. lithophila*, *L. macrocarpa*, *L. pantherina*, *L. tumida*, species of *Placopsis* from the southern hemisphere and, occasionally, on the ascocarps of *Rhizocarpon obscuratum*. Many of the colour variants in the latter assemblage have been afforded form or varietal status in taxonomic studies.

Since the work of Lounamaa (1956) the selective affinity of lichens for certain metals, particularly zinc, has been confirmed. Lambinon *et al.* (1964) recorded a zinc content of 93 400 ppm, equivalent to 9.34 per cent of the total dry weight of the thallus, in *Diploschistes scruposus* var. *bryophilus* growing on soil containing 10 900 ppm. *Stereocaulon nanodes* f. *tyroliense*, confined in Belgium to calamine-rich slag, was found by Marquinay *et al.* (1961) to contain 10 900 ppm of zinc on slag containing only 700 ppm. On the basis of the affinity of certain plants to a metalliferous substrate, Lambinon and Auquier (1964) proposed a classification into 'metallophytes', 'pseudometallophytes' and 'indifférants'; *Sterocaulon nanodes* was included in the first category, and *S. dactylophyllum*, *Diploschistes scruposus* var. *bryophilus*, *Baeomyces rufus*, *Lecidea fuscoatra* var. *grisella*, *Cladonia subulata* and *C. cariosa* as 'pseudometallophytes'. The spread of *Stereocaulon nanodes* was attributed, by Lambinon (1964), to the exploitation of zinc and lead.

Significant accumulations in lichens have recently been reported in studies of heavy metal fallout pollution from smelters. Nash (1971, 1972) found a greatly increased uptake of zinc and cadmium by lichens around a zinc smelter in Pennsylvania; for *Micarea trisepta* the values were 23 000 and 320 ppm respectively and for *Verrucaria nigrescens*, 25 000 and 335 ppm. At Risby Warren, Scunthorpe, Seaward (1973) has reported 5000 ppm manganese in his transect material of *Peltigera rufescens*. Nieboer *et al.* (1972) have recorded similar trends and rises in the accumulation of the iron, copper, nickel and zinc content of lichens, especially in species of *Cladonia* and *Umbilicaria*, in the vicinity of the nickel-smelting town of Sudbury, Ontario. These same workers have shown experimentally, using crushed thalli of the same species immersed in 0.1M solutions of metal salts, that the capacity for uptake of iron and copper considerably exceeded that for nickel, cobalt, lead and zinc. In one hour, approximately 60 μmoles of iron or copper per g dry weight of lichen (3600 ppm) were accumulated. In the field studies mentioned the highest concentrations occur in the lichens bordering the totally depleted lichen areas nearest the source of the pollutant.

Of particular interest is the record of 5000 ppm of copper in a new species of lichen, *Lecanora vinetorum*, which was described by Poelt and Huneck (1968) in association with *Acarospora anomala* on decorticated wooden supports used for viticulture and frequently sprayed with Bordeaux mixture ($CuSO_4.5H_2O(4)$: $CaO(4)$:$H_2O(50)$).

A detailed analysis of the lead uptake of lichens, comparable with that of Rühling and Tyler (1968) for mosses, is still urgently needed. They reported considerable uptake of lead by both plants and soil within 50–100 m of large roads. In an analysis of the lead content of mosses from Skåne (southern Sweden) during the period 1860 to 1968, they found that between 1860 and 1875 the lead concentration was 20 ppm, a value which doubled within the period 1875–1900. Between 1900 and 1950 the lead level remained stationary but rose steeply again from 1950 onwards, reaching a peak of 80–90 ppm in 1968. Since, by comparison, the lead concentration in mosses in northern Sweden remained very low during the same period, the authors suggest that regional and historical studies can be valuable in reflecting changes in human activity over a period of time. The affinity of lichens for lead, already noted by Lounamaa (1956), has also been reported for *Stereocaulon nanodes* by Lambinon (1964) and Noeske *et al.* (1970). The latter authors record a significant uptake of this metal by *Cornicularia aculeata.* Seaward (1973) records 3124 ppm of lead in *Lecanora muralis* collected around suburban Leeds, a value which suggests that there already is high background contamination of this metal in the area which is likely to be due to exhaust effluents from vehicles.

From these observations it appears that particular lichens show differing accumulation, tolerance, and selective characteristics towards individual or certain combinations of cations (Noeske *et al.*, 1970). Some species may only be able to thrive on rock rich in a certain metal or in an area polluted by a certain heavy metal fallout. For instance the known affinity of *Stereocaulon nanodes* and perhaps *S. pileatum* for lead may explain why these species are increasing in towns (Kershaw, 1963), especially on walls adjacent to roads polluted by car exhausts but not associated with lead and zinc mining areas. Other lichens show much less dependence on the metal content of their substrate but tend to give high accumulation values when the substrate is rich in certain metals and lower accumulation values when poorer. The observations of Lounamaa (1956) and LeRoy and Koksoy (1962) suggest that the majority of lichens have a marked predisposition for the accumulation of at least some metals (iron, lead, zinc, nickel) from their substrates and the atmosphere. Nieboer *et al.* (*in litt.*) have shown experimentally that species of *Cladonia*, *Stereocaulon* and *Umbilicaria* are selective in their uptake of metal cations from equimolar mixtures in solution. The preference sequence was iron $\gg$ lead $>$ copper $>$ nickel $\equiv$ zinc $>$

cobalt. They noted that this sequence bore some distinct resemblance to the metal contents of the same lichens collected near a nickel smelter in Sudbury, Ontario, providing allowance was made for the relative abundance of the different metals, derived from the smelter, in the area. In their behaviour with certain cations, lichens appear to be unique often accumulating concentrations of certain metals (e.g. copper) which would prove lethal to most other plants. Mosses, although showing some predisposition towards certain metals (e.g. lead), generally resemble higher plants rather than lichens in their behaviour (Lounamaa, 1956).

Studies on the pollution from heavy metal fallout, involving the use of lichens as indicators and monitors, generally presupposes the aerial transport of this type of pollution. However, most research on this aspect has emphasized the role of the immediate substratum in supplying the excess of metals. For instance, Yarilova (1950), on the basis of a survey of the literature and by means of detailed substrate analyses, concluded that the substrate was the main source of macronutrients. Lounamaa (1956) infers that the mineral requirements of lichens are obtained by a frequent wetting and drying process of the rock surface. This relative importance of the substratum has also been emphasized by the apparent affinity of certain corticolous, saxicolous and terricolous species for particular mineral-rich substrata. Critical studies of Bachman (1904, 1911, 1917) and Fry (1924, 1927) have emphasized the closeness of the physical and chemical relationships between substrate and lichens. Detailed chemical interrelationships between lichens and their substrate, particularly concerning weathering processes, have been formulated mostly invoking the process known as chelation (sequestration) in which lichen acids play a vital role (Martel and Calvin, 1952; Schatz *et al.*, 1954, 1956; Schatz, 1962, 1963*a*, 1963*b*). Some support for this hypothesis has recently been given by Jenkins, (1964), Jenkins and Davies (1966), Tuominen (1967), Syers (1969), and Iskander and Syers (1971). Tuominen (1967), however, suggested that it was difficult to separate absorption through chelation from absorption via an ion-exchange mechanism. The hyphae and their associated lichen acids may act as a suitable ion-exchange resin. According to Jackson and Keller

(1970) *Stereocaulon vulcanii* accelerates chemical weathering of basalt lavas in Hawaii.

In a detailed analysis of the pediological implications of trace element relationships in lichens, rock substrates and the atmosphere, Jenkins (1964) and Jenkins and Davies (1966) found cation accumulations within the foliose lichen *Parmelia omphalodes* and the crustose species *Lecanora gangaleoides* growing in the Snowdonia region, Wales, to converge to a significant 'preferred value' dominated by a constant factor which, by comparison with extra British material, was determined to be regional in nature, rather than internal or physiological. From their data there is support for the view that the correlation between accumulation of trace elements in the lichen and their source depends in varying amounts on contributions by both the atmosphere and the substrate. Totally substrate-dependent species would be entirely endolithic or endophloeodal taxa (Hilitzer, 1925); the substrate also appears to predominate in *L. gangaleoides* when growing on ultrabasic rocks, but was found to contribute least in the case of *Parmelia omphalodes* growing on vein quartz. Jenkins and Davies (1966) found a close pattern of correlation between the ash of lichens, as well as organic topsoils, and the ashed particulate material containing minerals derived from the atmosphere. They assessed the major atmosphere particulates source as being, not from volcanic dust, clay fraction of soils or meteorites, but derived from the combustion of coal and oil, the selective volatilization of which results in higher concentrations of copper, iron, molybdenum, tin, lead, etc. (*see* Hartley and Ramage, 1901). The fallout pollutants from smelters, factories and vehicle exhausts should be included in this category. In lichens, generally characterized by very slow growth rates and great longevity (up to 4500 years), the evidence for dominance of atmospheric source of their trace elements is strong. Crustose lichens, in view of their age, could be valuable in assessing changes in the composition of the atmosphere. Such observations are in accord with Stahlecker (1906) on lichen nutrition, but are partially contrary to those of Yarilova (1950), Schatz *et al.* (1954) and Lounamaa (1956).

The very slow growth rates of lichens, their longevity and rapid uptake and accumulation of cations, often far exceeding that required for their normal metabolic processes, presupposes an accumulation of toxic metal ions, especially copper, cadmium and lead, which, in most organisms, would prove lethal even at much lower concentrations. A complete list of the mineral elements found in lichens is cited by Culberson (1969, 1970). Such immunity suggests a process and/or sites of inactivation. The uptake of nutrients in lichens is characteristic of other ecto-hydrates (Buch, 1947), such as mosses, and characteristically occurs freely over the entire surface. Buch (1947) believed that the excess nutrients were accumulated in the thickened walls of the hyphae, whilst Gümbel (1856) noted the external deposition of crystals of ferric oxide on the cortical hyphae of *Rhizocarpon oederi* and *Acarospora sinopica*. Jenkins (1964) found the rhizinae to be the major site of mineral deposit in *Parmelia omphalodes*. The sites of accumulation within the thallus of *Acarospora sinopica* have recently been studied by means of an X-ray micro-probe, by Noeske *et al.* (1970). They found that iron and copper were contained in the crust in and on the upper surface and sides of the areoles and, to a lesser extent, along the juncture between the rock surface and the attachment of the lichen. The surface crust also contains silica, phosphorus, sulphur, and oxygen and it can therefore be assumed that these deposits represent the sulphates, silicates, phosphates and oxides of these metals. Zinc, however, appeared to be distributed throughout the thallus reaching maximum concentration in the lower part of the cortex. According to Nieboer *et al.* (1972) most of the metals accumulated —nickel, copper, zinc, iron—by *Cladonia deformis* in the Sudbury area of Ontario, lie in the cortex of the squamules and there outside the hyphae.

Hypothetical reasons for the enhanced tolerance of lichens to large concentrations of metallic ions have been suggested by Lange and Zeigler (1963). Three tolerance mechanisms are suggested—1) inherent cytoplasmic tolerance; 2) cytoplasmic immobilization and inactivation involving detoxification of cations by means of chemical combination; 3) the deposition of cations in regions external to the inner cell membrane (plasmolemma) or even outside the cell wall. The validity of these theories has been recently tested by Brown and Slingsby (1972) who considered the location of lead and potassium in the thallus of *Cladonia rangiformis*. They found lead to be entirely bound to insoluble anionic sites in an exchangeable form located in the hyphal walls. These observations agree with those of Clymo (1963), Tuominen (1967) and Rühling and Tyler (1970). However, for potassium the problem is certainly more complex, this metal only partly behaving in the same way as lead. The other fraction of this element is concentrated intracellularly or is associated with sites, considered by the authors to be proteinaceous, from which the metal can only be liberated by the total oxidation of the organic matter of the lichen. It is suggested that zinc may behave in a similar fashion which would account for its diffuse distribution in *Acarospora sinopica* (Noeske *et al.*, 1970). In conclusion, Brown and Slingsby are certain that no inherent cytoplasmic tolerance is suggested by their results for *Cladonia rangiformis*. From elution experiments, using 1N hydrochloric acid as an elutant, Nieboer *et al.* (1972) have shown that metals absorbed from solution are in a completely exchangeable form initially, but that the proportion of exchangeable metal falls if the material is air-dried for 24 hr prior to elution. Further, in field material collected near a nickel smelter, the proportion of exchangeable metal was relatively low and varied from metal to metal, being 12.5 per cent for iron, 83 per cent for zinc, 53 per cent for copper, and 20 per cent for nickel. They concluded that changes in the metal-lichen relationship occur after initial uptake, and that binding and/or chelation may be involved besides uptake by a simple ion exchange process as proposed by other workers.

The problems of metal cation uptake and accumulation are discussed further in chapter 12.

Little is known of the maximum tolerance levels of lichens for individual metals. The selective diminution of the number of species and their coverage along transects towards total lichen annihilation which sometimes surround established smelters, has been noted by Nash (1971, 1972), Nieboer *et al.* (1972) and Seaward (1973), and is indicative of the lethal effect of heavy metal pollution. Death of the lichen thallus could result from the final overloading of the system which is normally responsible for the inactivation and detoxification of the accumulated cations. According to the findings of Brown and Slingsby (1972), cell 'poisoning' could affect any one of several inactivation processes in the lichen in relation to the type of metal concerned. Such overloading of the threshold would also interfere with the extra- and intracellular enzyme systems of the lichen (*see* Moiseeva, 1959, 1961). It is not known whether the algal or fungal component is the first affected by excess metal contamination.

Some indication of the processes involved has been suggested by Baddeley, Ferry and Finegan (*in litt.*) who, in a preliminary series of experiments using an oxygen electrode, have shown that copper markedly depresses the respiration of *Cladonia impexa*, *Usnea fragilescens* and *Ramalina fastigiata* within 3 to 4 hours (Table 2). Other metals tested (iron, nickel, cobalt, zinc and lead)

*Table 2 The effect of metallic cations in solution on the respiration rates of* Cladonia impexa, Usnea fragilescens *and* Ramalina fastigiata *(see text for details). Respiration rates are expressed as relative rates (control = 100)*

| | Preincubation period (hr) | | | | |
|---|---|---|---|---|---|
| | 0.25 | 3 | 4 | 15 | 18 |
| *Cladonia impexa* | | | | | |
| $Cu(NO_3)_2$ | 100 | 6 | — | 0 | — |
| $CuCl_2$ | 87 | 21 | — | 0 | — |
| $Fe(NO_3)_3$ | 81 | 50 | — | 22 | — |
| $NiCl_2$ | 56 | 94 | — | 25 | — |
| $Co(NO_3)_2$ | 81 | 62 | — | 25 | — |
| *Usnea fragilescens* | | | | | |
| $CuCl_2$ | 22 | — | 22 | — | 0 |
| $Fe(NO_3)_3$ | 114 | — | 75 | — | 79 |
| $NiCl_2$ | 114 | — | 43 | — | 57 |
| $Co(NO_3)_2$ | 57 | — | 50 | — | 100 |
| $HgNO_3$ | 21 | — | 0 | — | 0 |
| $Pb(NO_3)_2$ | 121 | — | 136 | — | 25 |
| $ZnSO_4$ | 64 | — | 71 | — | 29 |
| *Ramalina fastigiata* | | | | | |
| $CuCl_2$ | 131 | — | 46 | — | 0 |
| $Fe(NO_3)_3$ | 92 | — | 108 | — | 100 |
| $NiCl_2$ | 92 | — | 46 | — | 31 |
| $Co(NO_3)_2$ | 139 | — | 123 | — | 81 |
| $HgNO_3$ | 46 | — | 0 | — | 0 |
| $Pb(NO_3)_2$ | 162 | — | 123 | — | 62 |
| $ZnSO_4$ | 100 | — | 169 | — | 100 |

pH values of solutions: $Cu(NO_3)_2$—5.0; $CuCl_2$—4.0; $Fe(NO_3)_3$—2.5; $NiCl_2$—5.0; $Co(NO_3)_2$—5.0; $HgNO_3$—1.0; $Pb(NO_3)_2$—4.5; $ZnSO_4$—5.0

either had a less severe effect or no effect at all. The massive reduction in respiration rate of *Usnea fragilescens* and *Ramalina fastigiata* caused by mercury is almost certainly attributable, either directly or indirectly, to the very low pH of the solution. The variations in pH values of the other metal salt solutions are considered to be relatively unimportant at least for incubation periods of up to 4 hours. All three lichens respired at not less than 75 per cent of their maximum rates over the range pH 4.2 to pH 5.2. The solution of ferric nitrate, pH 2.5, had little effect on *Usnea fragilescens* and no effect on *Ramalina fastigiata* even after 18 hours' incubation. All solutions were made up at $10^{-2}$M in deionized water and the experiments were carried out at 25°C.

The enhanced uptake and special resistance of lichens to heavy metal cations suggests that certain species could be used for monitoring concentrations of fallout around sources of pollution. In view of the danger to ecosystems of even low concentrations of certain heavy metals, such as copper, cadmium and lead, such information afforded by lichens on the levels of environmental pollution due to heavy metal fallout would be valuable. The work of Nash (1971), Nieboer *et al.* (1972) and Seaward (1973) emphasizes the value of lichens in heavy metal fallout studies and suggests a broad field for further research.

In a study of a transect at the perimeter of a lichen desert around steel smelters at Risby Warren, Scunthorpe, Seaward (1973), using the analytical methods of Goodman and Roberts (1971), was able to show (*see* Table 3) that in the terricolous lichen *Peltigera rufescens* there was a steep fall in the uptake of iron and manganese away from the smelters. The decrease in gradient was smaller for copper and chromium and little variation was noted in the case of lead and nickel. The length of the transect, which was downwind from the smelters, was 780 m. The value for cation uptake from the site on the transect furthest away from the source compared favourably with material of the same species collected in 1907 from East Yorkshire and now in the Thornton Herbarium. The figures cited in Table 3 for the control material can be taken to indicate low levels of heavy metal pollution.

In a detailed analysis of the cadmium and zinc content of certain terricolous and saxicolous lichens around a zinc smelter in Pennsylvania, Nash (1971) has been able to demonstrate an

*Table 3 Accumulation in ppm of heavy metals in* Peltigera rufescens *at sites* (a–f) *along a transect away from steel smelters at Risby Warren, Scunthorpe, Lincolnshire. Station* f *is furthest from the source of pollution* (*Seaward, 1973*)

| | *Sites* (a–b = *100 km; all other sites are 170 m apart. Total distance 780 m*) | | | | | | |
|---|---|---|---|---|---|---|---|
| | a | b | c | d | e | f | control |
| Sulphur | 8 762.00 | 8 074.00 | 8 732.00 | 6 900.00 | 5 876.00 | 6 824.00 | 6 220.00 |
| Iron | 90 380.00 | 77 100.00 | 32 020.00 | 13 760.00 | 26 820.00 | 15 170.00 | 14 150.00 |
| Manganese | 5 000.00 | 3 293.17 | 747.07 | 370.60 | 838.00 | 385.72 | 371.71 |
| Copper | 91.35 | 54.22 | 34.15 | 20.48 | 27.24 | 20.27 | 16.14 |
| Chromium | 127.40 | 64.26 | 61.37 | 32.76 | 41.90 | 24.84 | 25.81 |
| Lead | 454.43 | 138.55 | 125.40 | 46.07 | 120.11 | 58.84 | 78.73 |
| Nickel | 38.46 | 24.10 | 33.35 | 10.85 | 52.38 | 26.15 | 10.33 |

enhanced uptake of both metals, particularly zinc, in areas adjacent to the factory when compared with a non-polluted site. Like Seaward (1973) and Nieboer *et al.* (1972), there the author found that there was a gradual decrease in both the soil content of the mineral coupled with a reduced content of the element in the lichen away from the source. Furthermore, the number of species and their luxuriance and ability to form ascocarps increased further away from the smelter. From his data the limit of influence of sulphur dioxide in the area was considered to be at 5 miles from the source whereas that for zinc was probably between 15 and 25 miles. There was reduced net assimilation rates in two species, *Cladonia uncialis* and *Lasallia papulosa*, when subjected experimentally to cadmium and particularly zinc, at levels lower than those accumulated in the field; respiration was less depressed by both metals (*see* also Baddeley, Ferry and Finegan, *in litt.*, cited above).

**Radionuclides**

As lichens are known to concentrate selectively a wide range of trace metals in significant accumulations within their thalli (Lounamaa, 1956; LeRoy and Koksoy, 1962, and others), it is therefore not surprising that they should show a likewise affinity for almost all radionuclides (Beasley and Palmer, 1966; Hanson *et al.*, 1967; Hill *et al.*, 1965, 1966; Holtzman, 1963, 1966; Jaakkola, 1967; Persson, 1967, 1968, and other workers). Essentially, the mechanical and physiological criteria governing the uptake of radionuclides by lichens and their subsequent concentration and deposition in their thalli are probably in most respects similar to those involving non-radioactive cations. For instance, the uptake of carrier-free $^{137}Cs$ does not appear to be directly linked with metabolism in *Ramalina menziesii* (Handley and Overstreet, 1968) or in *Cladonia stellaris* (=*C. alpestris*) (Tuominen, 1967). However the danger of radionuclides lies in their emitted radiation and the readiness with which they can be accumulated in man, via particular biological pathways. Grodzinski (1959) suggested that the ability of mosses and lichens to accumulate radionuclides in excess is an inherited character, the result of their evolution in an era when natural levels of radioactivity of the earth's crust were appreciably higher. Higher plants, which are of comparatively recent origin, do not show the same ability; lichens may accumulate up to 10 times as much radioactive material as flowering plants; angiosperms with perennial foliage accumulate 2 to 10 times as much as those with annual growth. The radioactivity in mosses and lichens tends to differ from that in flowering plants in that it is associated with heavy metal radioactive elements; potassium only accounts for 2–5 per cent of β-activity in these cryptogams (Gorham, 1959).

Some radionuclides, such as sodium-22 ($^{22}$Na), lead-210 ($^{210}$Pb), polonium and iron-55 ($^{55}$Fe), occur in the natural environment, though seldom in significant concentrations. However, those radionuclides such as $^{90}$Sr ($^{85}$Sr in fresh fission products) and $^{137}$Cs are chiefly derived from widespread fallout from nuclear weapon detonations and to a lesser, though increasing extent, from atomic reactors. $^{137}$Cs appears to be especially important due to its relatively greater half-life in the environment and lichens (Hvinden and Lillegraven, 1961) and particularly enhanced concentration by several species of lichen. The entry and accumulation of pollutant fallout of $^{137}$Cs and $^{90}$Sr in certain ecosystems is important in arctic and subarctic areas which are rich in lichen growth, and where the indigenous human populations depend almost exclusively on local wild-life resources (Watson *et al.*, 1964; Hanson and Palmer, 1965). The assimilation, transport and circulation of $^{137}$Cs and $^{90}$Sr is strikingly portrayed in those food chains which include the ingestion of lichens in bulk by caribou (in Canada and Alaska) or reindeer (in northern Sweden and Russia) which, in turn, form the staple diet of man, chiefly Eskimo and Lapp, respectively (*see* Schulert, 1962; Hanson and Palmer, 1965; Palmer *et al.*, 1963; Miettinen, 1967, 1971; Hanson, 1966*a*, 1966*b*, 1967*b*, 1971; Hanson *et al.*, 1966). The enhanced accumulations in lichens result in greatly increased body burdens of radionuclides in caribou (or reindeer) and subsequently in man. Future radioactivity levels in caribou (or reindeer) and man will depend upon the efficiency of uptake and retention by lichens (Miettinen, 1967).

Poliakov *et al.* (1962), in a detailed study of the role of $^{90}$Sr accumulation in mosses and lichens, stressed the latter's peculiar biochemical and morphological features, including longevity, slow growth rate, and exaggerated metal uptake, and emphasized the role of lichens as indicators or monitors for the intensity and range of radionuclide fallout in any given area where they are abundant. Subsequent work has confirmed this view. Considerable analytical data are now available on the lichen–caribou (or reindeer)–man food chain, perhaps partly stimulated by political, economic and emotive interests, but mainly promoted due to an increasing awareness of any deleterious effect of relatively low but cumulative levels of radiological exposure to man.

Much less, however, is understood of the mechanisms of uptake and subsequent behaviour of radionuclides, either within lichen aggregations or tufts or inside the thallus. Richie *et al.* (1972) examining tufts of *Cladonia* (mainly sect. *Cladina*) in Georgia, USA, noted that $^{137}Cs$ was the dominant fallout radionuclide in their samples, producing concentrations of up to 32–91 pCi/g dry weight (1pCi$=10^{-12}$ Ci). These figures agree with those of Plummer and Helseth (1965). The top 2.5 cm of the tuft contained significantly more than either the central or basal parts of the thallus. This was attributed to the relatively recent increase (since 1945) of atmospheric fallout which is localized only in the perimeter or youngest part of the tuft. There is also a mobilization of $^{137}Cs$ away from the central non-actively growing region of the tufts to the physiologically more active periphery. Despite the presence of holdfast systems and rhizinae in foliose and fruticose lichens, these growth-forms appear to derive little of their radionuclide supply from the soil. Commenting on the efficiency of certain lichens, in particular species of *Umbilicaria*, in accumulating $^{137}Cs$, Svensson and Lidén (1965) noted that 95 per cent of the total airborne compliment of this nuclide brought down by precipitation in northern Sweden is taken up and retained by lichens. Tuominen (1968), studying the translocation of $^{90}Sr$ and $^{137}Cs$ in *Cladonia stellaris* (=*C. alpestris*), found that the rapid translocation of $^{137}Cs$ in this lichen is by a simple diffusion process. He found a difference in the vertical distribution of both radionuclides along the thallus indicating the cation-exchange ability of the thallus. He concluded that the transportation of the two nuclides along the thallus of this species is primarily diffusive, but is also complicated by cationic exchange.

Hanson (1967*a*) outlined the evidence for the greater mobility of

$^{90}$Sr in relation to $^{137}$Cs in lichens. These are: the difference in the $^{137}$Cs/$^{90}$Sr ratio from the upper 7–10 mm (3:2) and the lower part of the thallus (0:34) of *Nephroma arcticum*; the uniform distribution of $^{90}$Sr in the thalli of several Finnish lichens compared with the restriction of $^{137}$Cs to their upper cortices (Salo and Miettinen, 1964; Paakola and Miettinen, 1963); the change in the $^{137}$Cs/$^{90}$Sr ratio from 1.4–2.0 to 3.0–5.0 in most samples of lichens in regions of the Arctic subject to increased radionuclide fallout; and the tracer-labelling experiments by Nevstrueva *et al.* (1967).

The amount of uptake of radionuclides has been studied over a period of years in Alaska (Hanson *et al.*, 1967), Finland (Miettinen and Häsänen, 1967) and northern Sweden (Lidén and Gustafsson, 1967). These studies have confirmed the progressive rise in accumulation of the radionuclide compliment in lichens over a period of several years. For instance, in northern Sweden, 16 to 65 nCi/m$^2$(1nCi$=10^{-9}$Ci) were recorded between 1961 and 1964, and 18 to 48 nCi/m$^2$ in Alaskan material during 1962 and 1965. In common with other cation accumulations in lichens there is considerable variation in radionuclide uptake between different species as well as by the same species in different ecological niches. For example, Burley *et al.* (1962) recorded abnormally high concentrations of $^{137}$Cs in *Umbilicaria mammulata*, and Hanson (1966*a*) noted appreciably higher concentrations of this radionuclide in the thalli of *Cornicularia divergens* on exposed, windswept ridges which are rarely covered by snow, than in stands of *Cetraria delisei* in hollows with late snow patches. Though snow cover appears to shield the lichens, there is evidence that $^{137}$Cs, unlike other radionuclides, is preferentially absorbed from snow melt.

The change in fallout of radionuclides in the atmosphere over a given period compared with their incorporation into natural communities gives a possible estimate of their half-life within lichen communities. This has been estimated as 17 years by Lidén and Gustafsson (1967) and 6 to 10 years by Miettinen and Häsänen (1966). The gradual decline of half-life of radionuclides in lichens, caribou (and reindeer) and man indicates that, in order to maintain the radioactive compliment in the food chain, there is a continued need for an external source of radionuclides, derived, for instance, from nuclear detonations. Since the cessation of nuclear testing, the $^{90}Sr$ and $^{137}Cs$ content in the lichen–caribou–man food chain has appreciably declined. In a study of the body burdens of Anaktuvuk Pass residents, Hanson (1966*b*) noted lower counts for $^{137}Cs$ in 1964 than in 1963. This decline was mirrored in estimates of the amounts of this nuclide in the flesh of caribou which forms their staple diet. Salo and Miettinen (1964), in a similar study of the uptake of $^{90}Sr$ in Lapland, also drew attention to this phenomenon and emphasized the urgent need to obtain information of environmental radioactivity while the environmental levels were still high. The half-life of $^{137}Cs$ in man and reindeer appears to be even shorter, probably due to rapid excretion; Lidén and Gustafsson (1967) and Ekman and Greitz (1967) have both found the values to be as low as 10 to 25 days in reindeer.

The maximum accumulation of radionuclides occurs in reindeer and caribou during the winter months (Scotter, 1966). Scotter (1967) found that terrestrial lichens are the most abundant plants in the winter food regime of barren-ground caribou, comprising more than 50 per cent of their total food intake during this period. There is, however, a rapid decline in $^{137}Cs$ concentration in reindeer and caribou flesh during the summer months, reflecting a change in the feeding habits and short half-life of 10–30 days in those animals (Hanson *et al.*, 1967; Miettinen, 1964; Naversten and Lidén, 1964). According to Schulert (1962), in the spring the caribou from the tundra contain 10–20 times as much $^{90}Sr$ as domestic cattle in the area. From the analysis of urine samples, Schulert (1961) found that Eskimos who consumed caribou contained over four times as much $^{90}Sr$ as the average populations of the northern temperate zone. $^{137}Cs$ is predominantly confined to the flesh, fat and muscles (Ekman and Greitz, 1967; Hanson and Palmer, 1965; Nevstrueva *et al.*, 1967), whereas $^{90}Sr$ is incorporated in bone tissue (Salo *et al.*, 1964; US Scient. Comm., 1964; but *see* Watson *et al.*, 1964). The particular predisposition of strontium probably explains its slow metabolic turnover and the abnormally high accumulations in animals, values which can range from 6–15 times above those recorded in lichens. Since bone is not a normal dietary requirement for man, the values for the uptake of this radionuclide are lower than expected. $^{55}Fe$ is generally incorporated into the haemoglobin of the blood and shows little of the seasonal fluctuation typical of $^{137}Cs$ (Persson, 1969).

Most of the known radionuclides are channelled and concentrated in the lichen–caribou (reindeer)–man food chain. Besides the many studies concerning $^{137}Cs$ and $^{90}Sr$ already listed in this paper, data on other nuclides are discussed in the following: $^{22}Na$ (Perkins and Neilsen, 1965), $^{55}Fe$ (Jaakkola, 1967; Persson, 1967, 1969; Palmer and Beasley, 1965), $^{60}Co$ (Hanson *et al.*, 1967), $^{134}Cs$ (Perkins and Neilsen, 1965; Persson, 1968; Lidén and Andersson, 1962), $^{85}Sr$ (Hanson, 1967), $^{210}Pb$ (Kuranen and Miettinen, 1969; Holtzman, 1963, 1966; Blanchard and Moore, 1970), polonium (Kauranen and Miettinen, 1969; Blanchard and Moore, 1970; Hill, 1962, 1967) and $^{226}Ra$ (Holtzman, 1966). No studies, involving lichens, appear to have been made with $^{131}I$, a short-lived (radioactive half-life of 8 days) important product of fission processes in general.

Detailed surveys incorporating data emphasizing the lichen–caribou (reindeer)–man food chain are available for Alaska (Hanson, 1966*a*), Sweden (Svenssen and Lidén, 1965), Finland (Miettinen and Häsänen, 1967) and USSR (Nevstrueva *et al.*, 1967). These surveys confirm the higher body burdens in the regions where reindeer and caribou are eaten.

The great variability in the uptake, accumulation and loss of radionuclides and their potency reflects the many environmental and sociological factors concerned with the vital food chains. These include varying climatic factors, animal behaviour, seasonal food habits, physiological parameters, and human cultural practices. For instance, the maximum radionuclide concentration in Eskimos in Anaktuvuk Pass, Alaska, in 1962–3 was highest in early summer, tailing off towards the following spring. This delay in the uptake of radionuclides follows the local custom of only culling the caribou in spring, a time when their bodies contain maximum concentrations of radionuclides due to their particular dependence on lichens during the winter. Due to ingestion of the flesh of the caribou, the Eskimos of the area accumulate maximum body burdens 1–2 months later. Foxes and wolves in the area have maximum body burdens during the winter. Svensson and Lidén (1965) have reported delays of up to 10 months for the transfer of $^{137}Cs$ to man from lichens.

The body burden of accumulated radionuclides in man, via the environmental food chains, does not appear to have ever exceeded 2000 nCi (1nCi = $10^{-9}$Ci). One of the largest concentrations in man by this pathway, that of 1740 nCi, was recorded by Hanson (1966*b*) in Eskimos. According to the Federal Radiation Council Staff report No. 9, published by the Government Printing Office, Washington, the recommended maximum concentration is 3000 nCi. Therefore the current amounts do not yet constitute an immediate overt health hazard.

However lichens, because of their ability to concentrate radionuclides and their position in the lichen–caribou (reindeer)–man food chains, must assume considerable importance in monitoring systems, where information is needed on the extent and severity of fallout from nuclear detonations, or on the waste discharge from nuclear reactors. The threshold limit of uptake for individual lichens has yet to be studied in detail.

**Radiation effects**

The behaviour of lichens to ionizing radiation has been studied experimentally by Brodo (1964) and Woodwell and Gannutz (1967). Brodo observed the effect of irradiation on the growth and survival of corticolous lichens on oak/pine woodland at periods of 9 and 22 months along a radiation gradient in Brookhaven Irradiated Forest, Long Island. Based on a photographic analysis, he found that lichens were able to survive within 6 to 8 m of the source at radiation levels of 1000 rd/day. At 18 to 34 m, *Parmelia saxatilis*, a foliose lichen, exposed to irradiation levels of 230–62 rd/day, showed stimulated growth when compared with control material outside the experimental area. Minor deleterious effects on some lichens, mainly confined to species of *Cladonia*, were attributed to alterations in the microclimate and to the greater sensitivity of higher plants to irradiation. The effects of continued exposure for a much longer period have not been recorded.

As a pendant, Woodwell and Gannutz (1967) extended the scope of Brodo's study to include the effect of irradiation on the diversity and other aspects of corticolous lichen communities. After irradiation they found that there was a notable direct general effect in both the composition and density of the lichen associations, resulting in not only a reduction in the population of corticolous and terricolous lichens which was approximately proportional to the rate of irradiation, but a differential mortality rate between crustose, foliose and fruticose growth forms (*see* also Woodwell and Whittaker, 1968). After 12 months' exposure to 2700 rd/day, the diversification of the communities was reduced by 50 per cent. Even so, it was suggested that certain species might be able to survive exposures of up to 10 000 to 12 000 rd/day for as long a period as three years. Although not all lichens appear to be resistant to irradiation, some species are substantially more so than most higher plants. The exact nature of this resistance, common to many micro-organisms, may lie in the fact that irradiation affects the genetical complement of the cells rather than their physiological functioning (Lindgren and Rumann, 1939; Pomper and Attwood, 1955; Sparrow and Evans, 1961; Sparrow and Miksche, 1961). Suggestions as to why lower organisms, including lichens, appear to have enhanced resistance to ionizing radiations are discussed by Sparrow and Woodwell (1962) and Brodo (1964).

## Fertilizers

One of the most important impacts of man on his environment in temperate areas of the world is his increasing and inexorable contribution towards its eutrophication. This effect, predominantly a nitrophytic process (Barkman, 1961), may develop in several ways, the most important of which is by the widespread use of natural and artificial fertilizers, particularly those rich in ammoniates, phosphates and nitrates. Outside contributory factors, which include smoke particulates and dust from quarrying of basic rock and cement manufacture, may raise the pH of the substrates thereby encouraging wholesale nitrification, calculated to be optimum at pH 6.8–7.3 and non-existent below 3.7 (Waksman, 1932). James' unpublished data suggest that dosage with certain fertilizers, when applied in a powdered state to certain lichens, may have an alternative lethal effect. In an experiment in which superphosphate was blown onto the thalli of lichens growing on wayside trees with bark of pH 4.7, the effect was not that of direct physiological damage but of the alternative encouragement of alien algal growth (*Pleurococcus*) over the surface of the treated thalli. In fruticose lichens such as *Usnea subfloridana* the apices of thalli are earliest affected and the lichens show features of progressive dieback. In foliose and crustose species older parts of the thalli are first affected and smothered. In such species as *Pertusaria albescens* final stages show only the margin and the soralia visibly free of alien algal growth. The most badly affected lichens appear to be those with a fibrous cortex, and it may be this factor of increased eutrophication associated with farming and orchard husbandry which has resulted in the virtual extinction of these species, e.g. *Tornabenia atlantica* and *Teloschistes chrysophthalmus*, in the British Isles.

The spread of environmental eutrophication is generally reflected in the present abundance and continued extension of the range of the lichen association the *Xanthorion*. This is dominated in Britain by *Caloplaca citrina*, *Candelariella reflexa*, *Physcia adscendens*, *P. orbicularis*, *P. tenella*, *Physconia grisea*, *P. pulverulenta*, *Xanthoria fallax*, and *X. parietina* on acid bark (pH 4–5) and *Acarospora fuscata*, *Caloplaca holocarpa*, *Candelariella vitellina*, *Lecanora caesiocinerea*, *Physica ascendens*, *P. orbicularis*, *Rinodina subexigua*, *Xanthoria aureola*, *X. candelaria*, *X. parietina* on acid rock.

Prior to the impact of man, the *Xanthorion* would have been mainly restricted to coastal areas and to scattered inland sites such as birds' perching rocks and nesting cliffs, clearings and waterholes where larger mammals tended to congregate, and around old sap exudate tracks of tree wounds. A few species of the association would also have occurred on trees with bark of relatively high pH values such as *Acer campestre*, *A. pseudoplatanus*, and *Ulmus* spp. The gradual penetration of the *Xanthorion* inland, replacing the established primeval woodland communities, must have been assisted by wholesale felling and increasingly intensive agriculture in rural areas. Some evidence of this change is afforded by a study of the lichen flora of the New Forest, Hampshire (Rose and James, 1973), where 250 corticolous and lignicolous species have been recorded for the ancient (=primeval) woodlands; 170 of these species frequently occur outside the old woodlands but only seven of these are associated with eutrophication and are very rare in the old Forest sites. Of the 120 wayside species which have so far been recorded outside the Forest area, 62 are found in communities characteristic of at least some degree of eutrophication influenced by the proximity of farming land. Such drastic changes in the lichen flora as construed from the New Forest data focuses attention on the effects of advancing eutrophication on the existing lichen vegetation of a particular site and serves to amplify the environmental implications of this factor in lichenological studies. The development of the *Xanthorion* community resulting from the dispersal of artificial fertilizers can be considered as indicative of a particular type of air pollution. In badly affected sites the existing lichen associations are radically altered or at least modified, and in extreme cases are entirely decimated and their place taken by the *Pleurococcetum vulgaris* (Barkman, 1958) although this association is not essentially allied to excessive eutrophication alone.

In spite of such easily observed changes surprisingly little study has been made on this important aspect; what little is known concerning the factors involved has been summarized by Barkman (1961). It has not yet been reliably established whether phosphates or nitrates are primarily responsible for the process of eutrophication. Plummer and Moncrief (1964) noted that several lichens were stimulated in growth when dosed with solutions of inorganic fertilizers and Piterans (1968) emphasized a selective effect on different lichens when treated with varying concentrations of 'superphosphate'.

Piterans' results suggest that certain lichens have varying tolerance levels according to different degrees of eutrophication and that the pH of the substratum plays a vital role. From his data different groups of species, indicative of the scale of eutrophication, can be formulated. Such a tentative pattern might be: *Pleurococcus vulgaris*+miscellaneous green and blue-green algae and fungal hyphae→*Candelariella reflexa*, *Caloplaca citrina*, *Physica orbicularis*, *P. tenella*→*Physica ascendens*, *Physconia grisea*, *P. pulverulenta*, *Xanthoria parietina*→*Buellia punctata*, *Buellia canescens*, *Anaptychia ciliaris*→*Parmelia sulcata*, *P. acetabulum*, *P. laciniatula*, *P. elegantula*→*Hypogymnia physodes*, *Platismatia glauca*, *Parmeliopsis* spp.

**Smoke**

All early authors considered smoke as equivalent to air pollution (e.g. Almborn, 1943; Fenton, 1960; Jones, 1952). Fenton (1960) suggested that smoke and sulphur dioxide levels appeared to correlate in distribution but he was unable to make the necessary distinction due to the lack of recording stations in his area of study. In chapter 3 Table 2, Hawksworth has demonstrated a correlation between the mean winter sulphur dioxide values, as recorded by volumetric gauges, and the lichen zones according to the scale of Hawksworth and Rose (1970). In Table 4, presented in this chapter, an attempt is made to relate these lichen zones, at the same sites, to mean winter smoke levels. From the Table it is clear that there is poor correlation. It should be noted that the sites were not chosen for smoke values, but as examples of a range of mean winter sulphur dioxide levels. The evidence confirms the separation of smoke into a particulate fraction (soot) distinct from sulphur dioxide. In a detailed survey of the lichen flora of London, Laundon (1967) noted that, after the passing of the Clean Air Act of 1952, there was a calculated 60 per cent reduction in particulate smoke (soot) but an increase in sulphur dioxide of 80 per cent. Between 1955 and 1963 particulate smoke (soot) was reduced by almost 50 per cent, sulphur dioxide levels remaining fairly constant. Deterioration of the lichen flora did not decrease in rate.

Gilbert (1965) reported that in the centre of Newcastle, soot was responsible for an increase in the pH values of the bark of *Fraxinus* and *Acer pseudoplatanus*. Such changes ought to lead to the development of a lichen vegetation characteristic of eutrophiated bark, but the sulphur dioxide levels in the area are so high that this has proved impossible.

Soot is nutrient-rich and is largely responsible for the dispersal of heavy metal fallout and for some eutrophication of substrates by raising the pH. Although not an important factor in the decimation of lichen communities, soot can promote extraneous algal growth of lichen thalli reminiscent of that caused by fertilizers. Heavy soot fallout encourages the development of black necrotic layers on the surfaces of thalli involving the incorporation of soot particles within the interstices of the cortical

*Table 4 Comparison between mean winter smoke readings of volumetric gauges and the adjacent lichen vegetation at sites in England and Wales according to the scale of Hawksworth and Rose (1970)*

| site[1] | smoke ($\mu g/m^3$)[2] 1967–8 | 1968–9 | 1969–70 | mean | lichen zone 1969–70[3] |
|---|---|---|---|---|---|
| Belper 1 | 187 | 176 | 132 | 165 | 2 |
| Farnsfield 1 | 123 | N | N | 123 | 3 |
| Leicester 13 | 117 | 126 | 80 | 107 | 2 |
| Hayfield 2 | 102 | N | N | 102 | 3–4 |
| Plymouth 13 | 103 | 104 | 86 | 97 | 5 |
| Leicester 14 | N | 104 | 75 | 89 | 0–1 |
| Leicester 3 | (69)[4] | 67 | N | 68 | 0 |
| Leicester 10 | 84 | 68 | 48 | 66 | 3 |
| Sheffield 60 | 43 | 52 | 35 | 43 | 3 |
| Kew 1 | 40 | 41 | 35 | 38 | 2–3 |
| Torquay 3 | 34 | 33 | N | 33 | 8 |
| Prestwood 1 | 30 | 35 | N | 32 | 6 |
| Abbots Ripton 1 | 30 | 34 | 26 | 30 | 5 |
| Aspley Heath 1 | 29 | 38 | 24 | 30 | 3 |
| Plymouth 12 | 34 | 30 | 24 | 29 | 7 |
| Llanberis 1 | 35 | (22)[4] | 30 | 29 | 9 |
| Kingsnorth 5 | 29 | N | 27 | 28 | 4 |
| Didcot 9 | 30 | 31 | 24 | 28 | 6 |
| Didcot 4 | 27 | 31 | 22 | 26 | 6 |
| Didcot 14 | 23 | 28 | 19 | 23 | 6–7 |
| Didcot 1 | 21 | 28 | 19 | 22 | 7 |
| Didcot 6 | 23 | 23 | 20 | 22 | 7 |
| Dursley 5 | (20)[4] | 24 | 22 | 22 | 3–4 |
| Sparsholt | 18 | N | N | 18 | 7 |
| Buxton 2 | 19 | 16 | N | 17 | 3 |
| Rogate 1 | N | N | 16 | 16 | 8 |
| Weymouth 1 | 14 | 15 | 10 | 13 | 9 |
| Balcombe 2 | N | N | 12 | 12 | 7 |
| Camborne 1 | 10 | 14 | 7 | 10 | 8 |
| Pembroke 13 | N | 10 | N | 10 | 9–10 |

[1] for site classification and Nat. Grid Ref. *see* chapter 3, Table 2
[2] mean winter smoke values abstracted from Warren Spring Laboratory (1969–1971)
[3] lichen zones from chapter 3, Table 2
[4] value based on mean readings for four months
N: no data available

hyphae. In the most serious cases the effect would be to deprive the phycobiont of sufficient light, a similar effect to that with lichens and mosses caused by dust fallout from cement factories and quarrying. Heavy dust fallout appears to be lethal to most species and outside the decimated zone the first lichens to colonize are generally strongly eutrophic species. Some lichen taxa have developed morphotypes such as *Lecanora dispersa* f. *dissipata*, *Caloplaca holocarpa* var. *pyrithroma*, *Lecania erysibe* and *Sarcogyne regularis*, characterized by a reduced thalline development and a blackening of the surface.

## References*

Ahti, T. (1967). Preliminary studies on woodland caribou range, especially on lichen stands, in Ontario. *Ontario Dept. Lands Forest, Res. Rept* (Wildlife) no. 74, 134 pp.

Almborn, O. (1943). Lavfloran botaniska trädgården i Lund. *Bot. Notiser*, **96,** 167–77.

Bachman, E. (1904). Die Beziehungen der Kieselflechten zu ihrem substrat. *Ber. dt. bot. Ges.* **22,** 101–4.

Bachman, E. (1911–12). Die Beziehungen der Kieselflechten zu ihrer Unterlage. II. Granat und Quartz. *Ber. dt. bot. Ges.* **29,** 261–73.

Bachman, E. (1917–18). Die Beziehungen der Kieselflechten zu ihrer Unterlage. III. Bergkristall und Flint. *Ber. dt. bot. Ges.* **35,** 464–76.

Barkman, J. J. (1958). *Phytosociology and Ecology of Cryptogamic Epiphytes.* Van Gorcum, Assen.

Barkman, J. J. (1961). De verarming van de cryptogamenflora in ons land gedururende de laatste Londerd jaar. *Natura,* **58**(10), 141–51.

Beasley, T. M. & Palmer, H. E. (1966). Lead-210 and polonium-210 in biological samples from Alaska. *Science, N.Y.* **152,** 1062–4.

Blanchard, R. L. & Moore, J. B. (1970). $^{210}$Pb and $^{210}$Po in tissues of some Alaskan residents as related to consumption of caribou and reindeer meat. *Health Phys.* **18,** 127–34.

Brodo, I. M. (1964). Field studies of the effects of ionising radiation in lichens. *Bryologist* **67,** 76–87.

Brown, D. H. & Slingsby, D. R. (1972). The cellular location of lead and potassium in the lichen *Cladonia rangiformis* (L.) Hoffm. *New Phytol.* **71,** 297–305.

Buch, H. (1947). Über die Wasser- und Mineralstoffversorgung der Moose. II. *Annls. Soc. Sci. fenn.* **9**(20), 1–61.

Burley, J. W. A. B., Gilbert, G. E. & Crum, L. C. (1962). Preliminary radiological investigations of the vegetation and soils of Neotoma. *Neotoma Ecol. Biochem. Lab. Ohio State Univ., Ohio Agr. Expt. Stn* Spec. Report, no. 10, 1–39.

Clymo, R. S. (1963). Ion exchange in *Sphagnum* and its relation to bog ecology. *Ann. Bot.*, N.S. **27,** 309–24.

* See also p. 378.

Culberson, C. F. (1969). *Chemical and Botanical Guide to Lichen Products.* University of N. Carolina Press, Chapel Hill.

Culberson, C. F. (1970). Supplement to 'Chemical and botanical guide to lichen products'. *Bryologist* **73,** 177–377.

Ekman, L. & Greitz, U. (1967). Distribution of radiocesium in reindeer. In *Radioecological Concentration Processes,* pp. 655–61. Ed. B. Åberg & P. F. Hungate, Stockholm. Pergamon Press, Oxford.

Fenton, A. F. (1960). Lichens as indicators of atmospheric pollution. *Ir. Nat. J.,* **13,** 153–8.

Fry, E. J. (1924). A suggested explanation of the mechanical action of lithophytic lichen on rock (shale). *Ann. Bot., Lond.* **38,** 175–96.

Fry, E. J. (1927). The mechanical action of crustaceous lichens on substrata of shale, schist, gneiss, limestone, and obsidian. *Ann. Bot., Lond.* **41,** 437–60.

Gilbert, O. L. (1965). Lichens as indicators of air pollution in the Tyne valley. In *Ecology and the Industrial Society.* Ed. T. Goodman *et al.* pp. 35–47. Oxford.

Goodman, G. T. & Roberts, T. M. (1971). Plants and soils as indicators of metals in the air. *Nature, Lond.* **231,** 287–92.

Grodzinskii, D. M. (1959). On the natural radioactivity of mosses and lichens. *Ukr. bot. Zh.* **16**(2), 30–8.

Gümbel, C. W. (1856). Die neue Färberflechte *Lecanora ventosa* Ach. Nebst Beitrag zur entwickelungeschichte der Flechten. *Denkschr. Akad. Wiss. Wien,* **11**(2), 23–40.

Handley, R. & Overstreet, R. (1968). Uptake of carrier-free $^{137}$Cs by *Ramalina reticulata. Pl. Physiol.* **43,** 1401–5.

Hanson, W. C. (1966*a*). Fallout radionuclides in Alaskan food chains. *Am. J. vet. Res.* **27,** 359–66.

Hanson, W. C. (1966*b*). Caesium-137 body burdens in Alaskan eskimos during the summer of 1965. *Science, N.Y.* **153,** 525–6.

Hanson, W. C. (1967*a*). Caesium-137 in Alaskan lichens, caribou, and eskimos. *Health Phys.* **13,** 383–9.

Hanson, W. C. & Palmer, H. E. (1965). Season cycles of $^{137}$Cs in some Alaskan natives and animals. *Health Phys.* **11,** 1401–6.

Hanson, W. C., Watson, D. G. & Perkins, R. W. (1967). Concentration and retention of fallout radionuclides in Alaskan arctic ecosystems. In *Radioecological Concentration Processes,* pp. 233–45. Ed. B. Åberg & F. P. Hungate, Stockholm. Pergamon Press, Oxford.

Hartley, W. N. & Ramage, H. (1901). The mineral constituents of dust and soot from various sources. *Proc. Roy. Soc., Lond.* **68,** 97–109.

Hawksworth, D. L. & Rose, F. (1970). Qualitative scale for estimating sulphur dioxide air pollution in England and Wales using epiphytic lichens. *Nature, Lond.* **227,** 145–8.

Hilitzer, A. (1925). La Végétation Épiphyte de la Bohème. *Spizy vydáv. přír. Fak. Karl. Univ.,* čislo **41,** pp. 1–200.

Hill, C. R. (1965). Polonium-210 in man. *Nature, Lond.* **208,** 423–8.

Hill, C. R. (1966). Polonium-210 content of human tissues in relation to dietary habit. *Science* **152,** 1261–2.

Holtzman, R. B. (1963). The $^{210}$Pb (RaD) concentrations of some biological materials from arctic regions. In *Argonne Nat. Lab. Radiol. Physics Div.*, summary rep., July 1962–3. Pp. 59–65. USAEC Report. ANL-6769.

Holtzman, R. B. (1966). Natural levels of lead-210, polonium-210 and radium-226 in humans and biota of the Arctic. *Nature, Lond.* **210,** 1094–7.

Hvinden, T. & Lillegraven, A. (1961). Caesium-137 and strontium-90 in precipitation, soil and animals in Norway. *Nature, Lond.* **192,** 1144–6.

Iskandar, I. K. & Syers, J. K. (1971). Solubility of lichen compounds in water: pedogen[et]ic implications. *Lichenologist* **5,** 45–50.

Jaakkola, T. (1967). $^{55}$Fe and stable iron in some environmental samples in Finland. In *Radioecological Concentration Processes*, pp. 247–51. Ed. B. Åberg & P. F. Hungate, Stockholm. Pergamon Press, Oxford.

Jackson, T. A. & Keller, W. D. (1970). Evidence for biogenetic synthesis of an unusual ferric oxide mineral during alteration of basalt by a tropical lichen. *Nature, Lond.* **227,** 522–3.

Jenkins, D. A. (1964). *Trace Element Studies and some Snowdonian Rocks, their Minerals and Related Soils.* Ph.D. thesis, University of Wales, Bangor.

Jenkins, D. A. & Davies, R. I. (1966). Trace element content of organic accumulations. *Nature, Lond.* **210,** 1296–7.

Jones, E. W. (1952). Some observations on the lichen flora of tree boles, with special reference to the effect of smoke. *Revue bryol. lichén* **21,** 96–115.

Kauranen, P. & Miettinen, J. K. (1969). $^{210}$Po and $^{210}$Pb in the arctic food chain and the natural radiation exposure of Lapps. *Health Phys.* **16,** 287–95.

Kershaw, K. A. (1963). Lichens. *Endeavour* **22,** 65–9.

Lambinon, J. (1964). *Stereocaulon nanodes* Tuck. en Wallonie et en Rhénanie. *Lejeunea*, N.S. **27** (April), 1–8.

Lambinon, J. & Auquier, P. (1964). La flore et la végétation des terrains calaminaires de la Wallonie septentrionale et de la Rhénanie aixoise. Types chorologiques et groupes écologiques. *Natura Mosana* **16**(4), 113–30.

Lange, O. L. & Ziegler, H. (1963). Der Schwermetalligehalt van Flechten aus dem *Acarosporetum sinopicae* auf Erzschlackenhalden des Harzes. 1. Eisem und Kupfer. *Mitt. flor.-soz. ArbGemein.*, N.F. **10,** 156–83.

Laundon, J. R. (1967). A study of the lichen flora of London. *Lichenologist* **3,** 277–327.

LeRoy, L. W. & Koksoy, M. (1962). The lichen—a possible plant medium for mineral exploration. *Econ. Geol.* **57,** 107–11.

Lidén, K. & Andersson, I. Ö. (1962). Caesium-134 in man. *Nature, Lond.* **195,** 1040–3.

Lidén, K. & Gustafsson, M. (1967). Relationships and seasonal variation of $^{137}Cs$ in lichen, reindeer and man in northern Sweden 1961–1965. In *Radioecological Concentration Processes*, pp. 193–208. Ed. B. Åberg & F. P. Hungate, Stockholm. Pergamon Press, Oxford.

Lindgren, C. C. & Rumann, G. (1939). The chromosomes of *Neurospora crassa*. *J. Genet.* **36,** 395–404.

Lounamaa, J. (1956). Trace elements in plants growing wild on different rocks in Finland. A semi-quantitative spectrographic survey. *Ann. bot. Soc. zool.-bot. fenn. Vanamo* **29**(4), 1–196.

Lounamaa, J. (1965). Studies on the content of iron, manganese and zinc in macrolichens. *Annls. bot. fenn.* **2,** 127–37.

Maquinay, A., Lamb, I. M., Lambinon, J. & Ramaut, J. L. (1961). Dosage du zinc chez un lichen calaminaire belge: *Stereocaulon nanodes* f. *tyroliense* (Nyl.) M. Lamb. *Physiologia Pl.* **14,** 284–9.

Martel, A. E. & Calvin, M. (1952). *Chemistry of the Metal Chelate Compounds*. New York.

Martin, J. J. & Schatz, A. (1961). Chelation as a pedogenic factor in microbiological weathering of rocks and minerals. *Abstract, Vth Int. Cong. Biochem., Moscow*. Pergamon Press, Oxford.

Mićović, V. M. & Stefanović, V. D. (1961). Studies of the chemical composition of Yugoslav lichens. I. Parallel studies on the chemical composition of the ash of some Yugoslav lichens and of the ash of oak bark. *Bull. Acad. serb. Sci. Cl. Sci., math. nat.* **26**(8), 113–17.

Miettinen, J. K. (1964). Caesium-137 in groups of populations in assessment of radioactivity in man. *IAEA, Vienna,* **2,** 115–20.

Miettinen, J. K. (1969). The present situation and recent developments in the accumulation of caesium-137, strontium-90 and iron-55 in arctic food chains. *Acta Anat.* **73,** Suppl. **56,** 145–50.

Miettinen, J. K. (1971). Radioaktiva nuklider i lav, ren och, människa efter Kärnvapenprov. *Kem. Tidsk.* **1971,** 52–4, 57–8.

Miettinen, J. K. & Häsänen, E. (1967). $^{137}Cs$ in Finnish Lapps and other Finns in 1962–5. In *Radioecological Concentration Processes*, pp. 221–31. Ed. B. Åberg & F. P. Hungate, Stockholm. Pergamon Press, Oxford.

Miettinen, J. K., Jokelainen, A., Roine, P., Lidén, K., Naversten, Y., Bengtsson, G., Häsänen, E. & McCall, R. C. (1963). $^{137}Cs$ and potassium in people and diet—a study of Finnish Lapps. *Annls. Acad. Sci. fenn.* A2 (Chem.) **120,** 5–46.

Moiseeva, E. N. (1959). 'New evidence on the fermentative characteristics of lichens' (trans.). *Bot. Zh. SSSR.* **43,** 29–37.

Moiseeva, E. N. (1961). 'Biochemical properties of lichens and their practical importance' (trans.). *Bot. Zh. SSSR.* **44,** 1128–34.

Nash, T. H. (1971). *Effect of Effluents from a Zinc Factory on Lichens*. Doctorate thesis. State University, Rutgers, N. Brunswick, N. Jersey.

Nash, T. H. (1972). Simplification of the Blue Mountain lichen communities near a zinc factory. *Bryologist* **75,** 315–24.

Naversten, Y. & Lidén, K. (1964). Half life studies of radiocaesium in humans. In *Assessment of Radioactivity in Man.* IAEA Vienna **2,** 79–87.

Nevstrueva, M. A., Ramzaev, P. V., Moiseer, A. A., Ibatullin, M. S., & Teplykh, L. A. (1966). The nature of $^{137}Cs$ and $^{90}Sr$ transport over the lichen–reindeer–man food chain. In *Radioecological Concentration Processes*, pp. 209–15. Ed. B. Åberg & F. P. Hungate, Stockholm. Pergamon Press, Oxford.

Nieboer, E., Ahmed, H. M., Puckett, K. J. & Richardson, D. H. S. (1972). Heavy metal content of lichens in relation to distance from a nickel smelter in Sudbury, Ontario. *Lichenologist* **52,** 292–304.

Noeske, O., Lächli, A., Lange, O. L., Vieweg, G. H. & Ziegler, H. (1970). Konzentration und Localisierung von Schwermetallen in Flechten der Erzschlacken halden des Hartzes. *Vort. bot. Ges.* (*Dtsch. bot. Ges.*), N.F. **4,** 67–79.

Paakola, O. & Miettinen, J. K. (1963). Strontium-90 and caesium-137 in plants and animals in Finnish Lapland during 1960. *Annls. Acad. Sci. fenn.* A2 (chemica) **125,** 6–8.

Palmer, H. E. & Beasley, T. M. (1965). Iron-55 in humans and their foods. *Science, N.Y.* **149,** 431–2.

Palmer, H. E., Hanson, W. C., Griffin, B. I., & Roesch, W. C. (1963). Cesium-137 in Alaskan eskimos. *Science, N.Y.* **142,** 64–6.

Perkins, R. W. & Nielsen, J. M. (1965). Sodium-22 and caesium-134 in food, man and air. *Nature, Lond.* **205,** 866–7.

Persson, B. (1967). $^{55}Fe$ fallout in lichen, reindeer and Lapps. In *Radioecological Concentration Processes*, pp. 253–8. Ed. B. Åberg & F. P. Hungate, Stockholm. Pergamon Press, Oxford.

Persson, R. B. R. (1968). $^{134}Cs/^{137}Cs$ activity ratio in the biosphere from 1956 until 1966. *Health Phys.* **14,** 241–50.

Persson, R. B. R. (1969). Iron-55 in northern Sweden; relationships and annual variation from 1956 until 1967 in lichens and reindeer as well as uptake and metabolism in man. *Health Phys.* **16,** 69–78.

Piterans, A. V. (1968). Vliyaniya superfosfatnego zaveda na razvitie lishainikov. In Nakhutsrishviti, I. G. (ed.) *Materialȳ III Zakavkazskoĭ Konferentsii po sporovȳn rasteniyam* 251–3. Tbilis.

Plummer, G. L. (1967). Fallout radioisotopes in Georgia lichens. In *Symposium on Radioecology. 2nd Nat. Symp., Ann Arbor.* Michigan. May 15–17.

Plummer, G. L. & Helseth, F. (1965). Movement and distribution of radionuclides on granite outcrops within the Georgia Piedmont. *Health Phys.* **11,** 1423–8.

Plummer, G. L. & Moncrief, J. B. (1964). Lichen growth on granite flat rocks in Georgia. *Bull. Georgia Acad. Sci.* **22,** 58–63.

Poelt, J. & Huneck, S. (1968). *Lecanora vinetorum* nova spec., ihre Vergesellschaftung, ihre Ökologie und ihre Chemie. *Öst. Bot. Z.* **115,** 411–22.

Poliakov, I. A., Leont′ev, A. M., Mel′nikov, L. K. (1962). Contribution to $^{90}$Sr fallout in the medium latitudes of the U.S.S.R. *Pochvovedenie* **1962**(11), 45–50.

Pomper, S. & Atwood, K. C. (1955). Radiation studies of fungi. In A. Hollaender (ed.). Pp. 431–53. *Radiat. Biol.* **2,** New York.

Richie, C. A., Richie, J. C., Plummer, G. L. (1972). Distribution of fallout caesium-137 in *Cladonia* mounds in Georgia. *Bryologist* **74,** 359–62.

Rickard, W. H., Davis, J. J., Hanson, W. C. & Watson, D. G. (1965). Gamma-emitting radionuclides in Alaskan tundra vegetation 1959, 1960, 1961. *Ecology*, **46,** 352–6.

Rühling, Å. & Tyler, G. (1968). An ecological approach to the lead problem. *Bot. Notiser* **121,** 321–42.

Rühling, Å. & Tyler, G. (1970). Sorption and retention of heavy metals in the woodland moss *Hylocomium splendens* (Hedw.) Br. et Sch. *Oikos* **21,** 92–117.

Rydzak, J. & Stasiak, H. (1971). Badania nad stanem flory porostów w rejonie przemysłu azotowego w Puławach. *Annls Univ. Mariae Curie-Skłodowska*, C, **26,** 229–342.

Salo, A. & Miettinen, J. K. (1964). Strontium-90 and caesium-137 in arctic vegetation during 1961. *Nature, Lond.* **201,** 1177–9.

Salo, K., Uotila, V., Alha, A., Tamminen, V., Linfors, R. and Laiho, K. (1964). $^{90}$Sr content of human bones in Finland, 1960–62. *Ann. Acad. Sci. Fenn. AV* (*Medica*) **110,** 3–12.

Schatz, A. (1962). Pedogenic (soil forming) activity of lichen acids. *Naturwissenschaften* **49**(22), 518–19.

Schatz, A. (1963*a*). Soil microorganisms and soil chelation. The pedogenic action of lichens and lichen acids. *J. agric. Fd. Chem.* **11,** 112–18.

Schatz, A. (1963*b*). The importance of metal binding phenomena in the chemistry and microbiology of the soil. Part 1: The chelating properties of lichens and lichen acids. *Adv. Front. Plant Sci.* (New Delhi) **6,** 113–34.

Schatz, A., Cheronis, N. D., Schatz, V. & Trelawny, G. S. (1954). Chelation (sequestration) as a biological weathering factor in pedogenesis. *Proc. Pa. Acad. Sci.* **28,** 44–51.

Schatz, V., Schatz, A., Trelawny, G. S. & Barth, K. (1956). Significance of lichens as pedogenic (soil forming) agents. *Proc. Pa. Acad. Sci.* **30,** 62–9.

Schulert, A. R. (1961). Assessment of dietary strontium-90 through urine assay. *Nature, Lond.* **189,** 933–4.

Schulert, A. R. (1962). Strontium-90 in Alaska. *Science, N.Y.* **136,** 146–8.

Scotter, G. W. (1966). Reindeer ranching in Fennoscandia. *J. Range Mgmt.* **18,** 301–5.

Scotter, G. W. (1967). The winter diet of barrenground caribou in northern Canada. *Can. Fld. Nat.* **81,** 33–9.

Seaward, M. R. D. (1973). Lichen ecology of the Scunthorpe heathlands I: Mineral accumulation. *Lichenologist* **5,** in press.
Sparrow, A. H. & Evans, H. J. (1961). Nuclear factors affecting radiosensitivity. I. The influence of nuclear size and structure, chromosome complement and DNA content. *Brookhaven Symp. Biol.* **14,** 76–100.
Sparrow, A. H. & Miksche, J. P. (1961). Correlation of nuclear volume and DNA content with higher plant tolerance to chronic radiation. *Science, N.Y.* **134,** 282–3.
Sparrow, A. H. & Woodwell, G. M. (1962). Prediction in sensitivity of plants to chronic gamma irradiation. *Radiat. bot.* **2,** 9–26.
Stahlecker, E. (1906). Untersuchungen über Thallusbildung und Thallusban in ihren Beziehungen zum Substrat bei siliciseden Krustflechten. *Beitr. wiss. Bot.* **5,** 405–51.
Subbotina, E. N. & Tomoféeff-Ressovskii, N. V. (1961). 'The accumulation of some dispersed elements in water solutions by crustose lichens' (trans.). *Bot. Zhurm. Kyyiv* **46,** 212–21.
Svensson, G. K. & Lidén, K. (1965). The transport of $^{137}Cs$ from lichen to animal and man. *Health Phys.* **11,** 1393–400.
Syers, J. K. (1969). Chelating ability of fumarprotocetraric acid and *Parmelia conspersa*. *Plant Soil* **31,** 205–8.
Tuominen, Y. (1967). Studies on the strontium uptake of the *Cladonia alpestris* thallus. *Annls. Bot. Fenn.* **4,** 1–28.
Tuominen, Y. (1968). Studies in the translocation of caesium and strontium ions in the thallus of *Cladonia alpestris*. *Annls. Bot. Fenn.* **5,** 102–11.
Waksman, S. A. (1932). *Principles of Soil Microbiology* (2nd ed.). Ballière, Tindall & Cox, London.
Watson, D. G., Hanson, W. C. & Davis, J. J. (1964). Strontium-90 in plants and animals of arctic Alaska 1959–61. *Science, N.Y.* **144,** 1005–9.
Woodwell, G. M. & Whittaker, R. H. (1968). Effects of chronic gamma irradiation on plant communities. *Q. Rev. Biol.* **43,** 42–55.
Woodwell, G. M. & Gannutz, T. P. (1967). Effects of gamma radiation on lichen communities of a forest. *Am. J. Bot.* **54,** 1210–15.
Yarilova (1950). *Trudy pochv Inst.* **34,** 110. [Not seen.]

# 9: The Effect of Airborne Fluorides

O. L. GILBERT

Fluoride damage to lichens has recently been reported from several parts of the world including Britain, Canada, France, Norway and the USA. The first observations were of a casual nature, made by workers primarily interested in fluorosis of cattle (Mazel, 1958) or by teams investigating the spread of air pollution from industrial complexes (Martin and Jacquard, 1968). The last few years, however, have seen specific lichen studies being made around isolated fluorine-emitting sources and it is from these that most of our information comes. Until 1971, investigators suffered the disadvantage of being largely unaware of each other.

Fluorine (F), used here to denote the occurrence of fluorine as a component of some fluoric combination, is not particularly common as an air pollutant. Burns and Allcroft (1964) list aluminium smelters, potteries, phosphate factories, brickworks, and the glass and steel industries as the chief producers, and point out that in addition large plants burning low-grade coal, such as power stations, release a certain amount. As there are few stations measuring airborne F, this raises the possibility that in coal-burning districts, F levels are higher than is generally realized (for F content of coal and shales *see* Crossley, 1944*a*,*b*). Because much F-emitting industry is located in conurbations, where it is difficult to separate the effect of any single pollutant, most primary studies have been carried out around isolated aluminium factories. The ones referred to in this paper are listed in Table 1.

## Establishing toxicity

Much of the work to date has been concerned simply with establishing that airborne F is toxic to lichens. This has been done in three ways.

Firstly, field-work has shown that the lichen flora in the vicinity

*Table 1 Fluorine sources mentioned*

| |
|---|
| *Aluminium smelters* |
| Arvida, Canada. Commenced production pre-1940 |
| Fort William, north-west Scotland. Annual production 20 000 tons. Commenced *c* 1930, fume treatment progressively improved, especially since 1957 |
| Invergordon, north-east Scotland. Eventual production 100 000 tons. Commenced spring 1971 |
| Husnes, west Norway (65 000 tons). Commenced *c* 1956 |
| Karmøy, west Norway (90 000 tons). Commenced *c* 1968 |
| Øvre Årdal, west Norway (120 000 tons). Commenced *c* 1947 doubling production in 1962/3 |
| *Chemical factory* |
| Pennsylvania, USA. Principal products titanium and selenium. Commenced *c* 1956 |
| *Brickfields* |
| Bedfordshire. Widespread pollution since *c* 1945 |

of isolated point sources is severely impoverished. In Canada, LeBlanc, Rao and Comeau (1972) investigated epiphytes at 42 sites around the aluminium factory at Arvida. The closest trees (1–2 km) were devoid of lichens which, however, gradually reappeared and increased in cover, frequency and diversity with increasing distance from the works. Indices of Atmospheric Purity (ch 3) were determined and a six-zone map constructed showing areas subjected to different levels of F pollution. Gilbert (1971) investigated a small aluminium factory at Fort William in Scotland finding a pattern of deterioration that was concentric around the works and conspicuously elongated downwind, Fig. 1. By observing lichens in a variety of standardized habitats (especially old wooden fence posts) a 'lichen desert', 'transition zone' and 'normal zone' were distinguished, the affected area being *c* 4 km in its longest diameter. The relationship between damage and F was made even more certain by chemical analysis which showed that near their inner limit the lichens contained elevated amounts of F which fell off with increasing distance from the source (Table 2).

The second line of evidence establishing F toxicity comes from field transplant experiments. Nash (1971) transplanted several lichens of wide ecological amplitude to the vicinity (100 m) of an isolated chemical factory in Pennsylvania. Though a known source of ambient F, this was checked by exposing limed filter

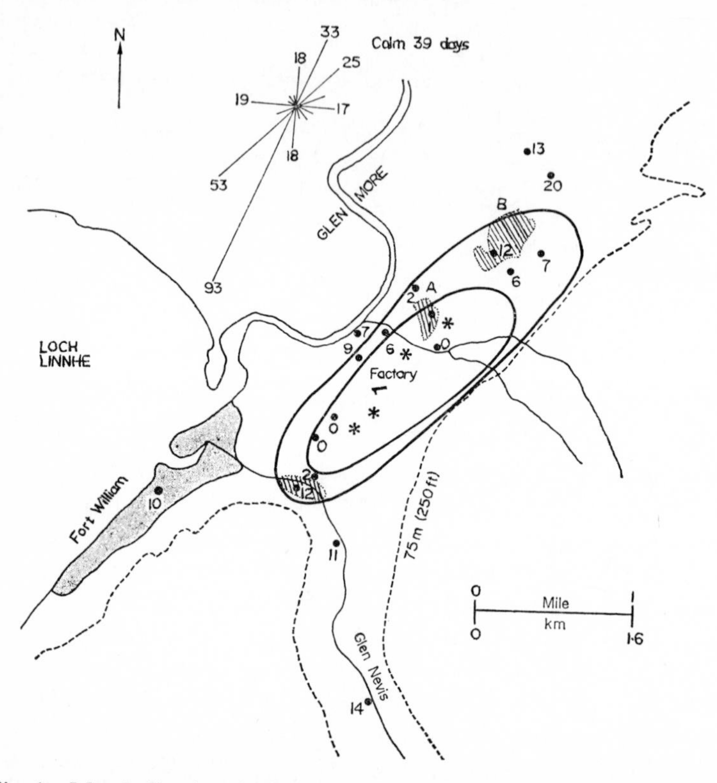


Fig. 1 Map indicating the lichen and bryophyte desert (inner circle) and transitional zone (outer circle) which has developed round the aluminium reduction works near Fort William. Asterisks (*) represent exposed boulders completely devoid of plant growth. Black dots and figures represent 'fence-post sampling sites' with the number of species present. A: Wood killed and felled in 1948; B: Inverlochy Castle Wood. Wind star for 1932–44 and 75 m (250 ft) contour are shown (from Gilbert, 1971)

papers. The transplants were repeatedly injured showing chlorosis, necrosis and finally, disintegration of the thallus. No injury occurred to controls at 6000 m. As in every case, injury was associated with F accumulation, in both the exposed thalli and

*Table 2 Fluoride concentration in lichens (ppm)*

|  |  |
| --- | --- |
| Martin and Jacquard (1968) | |
| *Dermatocarpon miniatum* | Saxicolous collected near Al smelter, 199 |
| *Peltigera rufescens* | Terricolous collected near Al smelter, 184 |
| Nash (1971)[1] | |
| *Cladonia cristatella* | Terricolous. Field transplants to 0.1 km from source for 1 month, 164. Similar, to 6.0 km, 28 |
| *C. polycarpa* | Terricolous. Field transplants to 0.1 km from source for 3 months, >220. Similar, to 6.0 km, 18 |
| *C. cristatella* | Terricolous. Field transplants to 0.1 km from source for 3 months, >220. Similar, to 6.0 km, 21 |
| *Parmelia plittii* | Saxicolous. Field transplants to 0.1 km from source for 3 months, 174. Similar, to 6.0 km, 22 |
| Gilbert (1971)[2] | |
| *Parmelia saxatilis* | Saxicolous, collected downwind of Al smelter, 47(1.6 km), 18(2.1), 17(3), 19(7), 14(11) |
| *Usnea subfloridana* | Lignicolous, collected downwind of Al smelter, 20 —, 7 —, 2 —, 2 —, <1(12) |
| *Ramalina fraxinea, Usnea subfloridana* | Trees, Invergordon (1969). No F detected |
| LeBlanc *et al.* (1971)[3] | |
| *Parmelia sulcata* | Corticolous. Field transplant, E & NE of smelter. (4 months), 990 (1 km), 750(2), 570(4), 475(8), 190(15), 70(40) |
| *Parmelia sulcata* | Corticolous. Field transplant, E & NE of smelter. (12 months), 900 —, 700 —, 516 —, 500 —, 134 — |

[1] Analysis by method of Singer and Armstrong (1959, 1965); [2] Hall (1963); [3] Greenhalgh and Riley (1961)

adjacent limed filter papers, there is good reason to believe that F was responsible. LeBlanc, Comeau and Rao (1971) conducted extensive transplant experiments round the Arvida smelter using lichen-bearing bark discs mounted in groups on wooden boards nailed to trees. Photographic recording of colour changes after 4 and 12 months showed obvious damage occurring at sites up to 10 km away. Analysis of the results produced a reasonable correlation between severity of damage, rate of F accumulation (in *Parmelia sulcata*), and distance from source.

A third approach is through fumigation experiments. Nash used fumigation chambers at the Boyce Thompson Institute, New York, to expose lichens to 4.9 ppb* (4 $\mu g/m^3$) F for nine days. During exposure thalli became chlorotic and subsequent analysis clearly showed injury was associated with the accumulation of F in the lichen tissue. Comeau and LeBlanc (1972) exposed *Hypogymnia physodes* to a range (13–130 ppb) of hydrogen fluoride levels in a laboratory-built chamber and reported that while 13 ppb for 8 hours did not produce definite symptoms, exposure for 36, 72 and 108 hours caused chlorotic spots and made the margins curl up. Sixty-five ppb for 12 hours produced similar symptoms. F accumulation occurred during fumigation whether visible damage was produced or not.

## Floristic and ecological studies

Though no comprehensive account of lichen deterioration round a F source has been prepared, a broad composite picture can be built up from the individual studies.

### *Canada*

While working at Arvida, LeBlanc, Rao and Comeau (1972) examined epiphytes on well-lit roadside trees of the balsam poplar (*Populus balsamifera*), discovering that a small lichen desert of 1–2 km radius was surrounded by an area in which *Bacidia chlorococca*, *Cladonia* squamules, *Lecania cyrtella*, *Lepraria incana*, *Parmelia sulcata* and *Physcia dubia* were sparingly present. The majority of epiphytes came in, between 6–10 km from the aluminium plant, but a few such as *Lecanora impudens* and *Physcia ciliata* were present only beyond 12 km. The cover-abundance of

* ppb: parts per thousand million.

species declined as the pollution source was approached so at their inner limit they were infrequent and of low cover. A resistance factor ($\phi$) was calculated for all species which enabled them to be listed in an approximate order of tolerance, Table 3. This list, especially at the resistant end, is similar to ones prepared for sulphur dioxide sensitivity round Montreal (LeBlanc and DeSloover, 1970) and the iron smelter at Wawa, Ontario (Rao and LeBlanc, 1967). Exact comparison is not possible as different tree species were examined at the three sites, which are up to 1000 km apart.

*Scotland*

At Fort William in Scotland an ecological survey of the total lichen flora enabled the modifying effect of certain environmental features to be assessed. Along the Atlantic seaboard, lichen vegetation is normally very well developed but as the survey progressed it became clear that in the neighbourhood of the smelter lichens are spectacularly depressed in several habitats. The tops of wooden fence posts usually carry a luxuriant 'cap' of lichens but this becomes progressively reduced and in the vicinity of the factory posts are bare. The process of extinction is the same in all species, a general lack of luxuriance, suppression of fruiting and declining cover preceding elimination. Detailed floristics are given in Table 3, where it should be noted that *Usnea subfloridana* is more resistant than might be expected from sulphur dioxide studies. Close to the works, exposed acid rocks are so clean as to appear scrubbed. The first lichen to colonize them is *Stereocaulon pileatum*. Further away three nitrophilous species appear associated with bird droppings and these are soon followed by a diversity of species in no discernible order. The first niches colonized are cracks, horizontal surfaces and sheltered crannies on the boulders.

The detailed effect on epiphytes is hard to determine, as large isolated trees are absent having been killed in the early years of factory operation. On small, exposed birch (*Betula pubescens*), alder (*Alnus glutinosa*) and rowan (*Sorbus aucuparia*), *Lecidea uliginosa*, *Lepraria incana* and *Parmelia sulcata* appear to be the most resistant epiphytes, but this is partly associated with their ability to grow on sheltered areas of the trunk. Recently an

*Table 3 Preliminary indications of lichen sensitivity to airborne fluorides. Lists are divided into groups of approximately similar tolerance; these are numbered for convenience and are not comparable between lists*

| Le Blanc *et al.* (1972) | Gilbert (1971) | Gilbert (Norway) | Gilbert (Invergordon) | Mazel (1958) |
|---|---|---|---|---|
| On *Populus balsamifera* | Lignicolous | Lignicolous | On deciduous trees | Resistant |
| 1 *Cladonia coniocraea* | 1 *Buellia cf punctata* | 1 *Lecidea granulosa* | 1 *Lecanora expallens* | *Solorina saccata* |
| | *Lecidea granulosa* | *L. uliginosa* | *Physconia pulverulenta* | |
| 2 *Bacidia chlorococca* | | | *Xanthoria parietina* | |
| *Lepraria incana* | 2 *Cladonia* squamules | 2 *Parmelia saxatilis* | | More sensitive |
| *Parmelia septentrionalis* | *Lecanora chlarotera* | *P. sulcata* | 2 *Buellia disciformis* | |
| *P. sulcata* | *Lecidea uliginosa* | *Usnea subfloridana* | *Lecanora chlarotera* | *Collema* sp. |
| *Physcia dubia* | *Parmelia saxatilis* | | *Lecidella elaeochroma* | *Xanthoria parietina* |
| | *P. sulcata* | 3 *Parmelia glabratula* | *Usnea subfloridana* | |
| 3 *Buellia punctata* | *Usnea subfloridana* | | | |
| 4 *Lecidea symmicta* | 3 *Cetraria chlorophylla* | Corticolous on conifers | 3 *Alectoria fuscescens* | Very sensitive |
| *Physcia orbicularis* | *Parmelia glabratula* | | *Evernia prunastri* | |
| | *Platismatia glauca* | 1 *Lecidea granulosa* | *P. saxatilis* | *Anaptychia ciliaris* |
| 5 *Candelariella vitellina* | | *L. uliginosa* | *P. sulcata* | *Evernia prunastri* |
| *Hypogymnia physodes* | | | *Ramalina farinacea* | *Parmelia caperata* |
| *Lecania cyrtella* | Corticolous | | *R. fastigiata* | *P. perlata* |
| *Physcia ascendens* | | 2 *Mycoblastus sanguinarius* | *R. fraxinea* | *Usnea* 'barbata' |
| *P. stellaris* | | *Parmeliopsis ambigua* | | *U. hirta* |
| | 1 *Buellia cf punctata* | | | |

6 *Alectoria nidulifera*
*Caloplaca cerina*
*Candelaria concolor*
*Cetraria pinastri*
*Parmelia subaurifera*
*Physconia grisea*
*Ramalina* sp.
*Usnea* sp.
*Xanthoria parietina*
*X. fallax*

7 *Caloplaca aurantiaca*
*Xanthoria polycarpa*

8 *Lecanora dispersa*
*Physcia aipolia*

9 *Lecanora impudens*
*L. chlarotera*
*Physcia ciliata*

2 *Lecidea uliginosa*
*Lepraria incana*
*Parmelia sulcata*

3 *Usnea subfloridana*
*Alectoria fuscescens*
*Cetraria chlorophylla*
*Parmelia glabratula*

Saxicolous, acid

1 *Stereocaulon pileatum*

2 *Candelariella vitellina*
*Lecanora intricata*
*L. polytropa*

3 *Parmelia saxatilis*
*P. sulcata*

4 *Lecidea cyathoides*
*Rhizocarpon geographicum*
*Umbilicaria polyrrhiza*
*Usnea fragilescens*

3 *Lepraria incana*
*P. glabratula*
*P. saxatilis*
*Platismatia glauca*

4 *Cetraria pinastri*
*Haematomma elatinum*
*Pseudevernia furfuracea*

4 *Hypogymnia physodes*
*Parmelia subaurifera*

Martin and Jacquard (1968)

Saxicolous semi-resistant

*Caloplaca holocarpa*
*Candelariella vitellina*
*Lecanora dispersa*
*L. muralis*
*Protoblastenia rupestris*
*Verrucaria nigrescens*

Saxicolous sensitive

*Parmelia conspersa*
*Rhizocarpon geographicum*

Corticolous: semi-resistant

*Lecanora dispersa*
*Physcia ascendens*
*P. ciliata*
*P. orbicularis*
*Xanthoria parietina*

unidentified *Buellia* (*cf B. punctata* but Pd$^+$ orange and strongly sorediate) has been found in the transition zone. Its abundance on conifers and fence posts round the aluminium works is reminiscent of *Lecanora conizaeoides* around towns.

Terricolous lichens appear little affected by F pollution. Stands of *Cladonia* are abundant in heathland surrounding the works, though close to the factory fence, podetia are often scorched and stunted and colonies contain more dead material than is normal. It was observed that stones in long grassland retain a 'skirt' of lichens long after they have disappeared from the more exposed upper parts, so it appears that pollution levels in the sward are considerably reduced and terricolous lichens are not subjected to the regional F concentration.

*The new smelter at Invergordon*: After the first year of operation lichens on exposed trees have been affected at up to 3 km distance, but no damage to saxicolous or terricolous lichens has yet been observed. Epiphyte damage is conspicuous—even to the casual observer—as whole communities often stretching 6 m up a tree bole have taken on a scorched appearance, the only areas of trunk not so affected being the very base, those high up in the canopy and often the side of the trunk facing away from the works, Fig. 2. Fruticose and foliose lichens were the first to be affected (Table 3), quickly turning brownish or whitish from the distal end; later many crustaceous species developed a white marginal halo. Damage is associated with an accumulation of F in the lichen tissue. Healthy *Ramalina farinacea* collected 3 km downwind in 1969 contained only 6 ppm F, scorched samples collected from the same tree in April 1972 contained up to 120 ppm. It was observed that twig communities deteriorate rapidly but that patches of *Xanthorion* developed in association with bark wounds were largely unaffected.

An unexplained feature is that certain individuals in any population appear to show considerably more resistance to F than others. Adjacent, equally exposed thalli of *Hypogymnia physodes*, *Evernia prunastri* or *Ramalina farinacea* can vary in appearance from being completely white, bleached and moribund to completely unaffected. A similar phenomenon occurs when a stand of pine trees (*Pinus sylvestris*) comes under F stress certain individuals die very quickly while others show considerable resistance. These ecotypic differences are thought to be genetically determined.

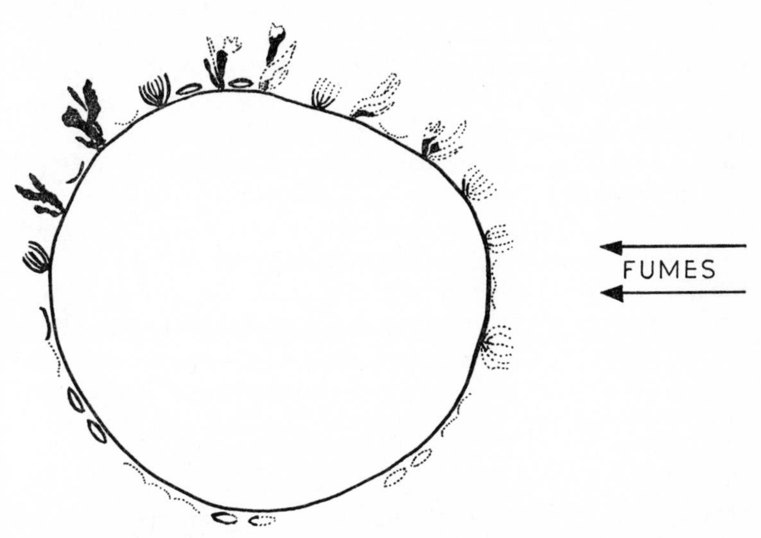


Fig. 2 Pattern of damage to epiphytes on trunk of beech tree (*Fagus sylvatica*) 400 m west of the newly opened smelter at Invergordon, Scotland. Black: living thallus; dotted lines: visibly damaged thallus. *Ramalina farinacea* (tufts), *R. fraxinea* (ribbons), *Hypogymnia physodes* (flattened ellipse), *Parmelia subaurifera* (arcs). Crustaceous lichens not shown

*France*

Martin and Jacquard (1968) also found epiphytes difficult to study due to the lack of suitable trees but decided that most *Parmelia* spp., *Anaptychia ciliaris*, and the larger *Physcia* spp. were among the more sensitive lichens.

*Norway*

Damage to lichen vegetation has been investigated around the large aluminium smelters at Øvre Årdal, Karmøy and Husnes in west Norway. These studies abundantly confirmed the observations made in Scotland and yielded additional information on epiphytes and the effect of calcareous substrates.

In all areas, the outstanding influence shelter can have in controlling the distribution of damage was evident. Near the works all trees are devoid of lichens but further away is a zone in which aspect alone affords considerable protection. Here, the side of trees (and boulders) facing away from the works carry a healthy cryptogamic flora while the side facing towards the works is bare, the bark often being white and flaky. At greater distances the effect is observable as a diversity and luxuriance difference. On a regional scale this phenomenon can be seen affecting entire woods, the marginal trees of which are the first to lose their lichens.

Calcareous substrata have not often been encountered near F sources. Concrete fence posts 1.2 km north-west of the Karmøy smelter carried 12 lichens, the foliose ones showing conspicuous signs of damage. On an adjacent asbestos roof, lichens remained only along the ridge where bird droppings were abundant. At Øvre Årdal asbestos roofs appeared quite bare and concrete in the town yielded only *Lecanora dispersa*.

*Sweden*

Skye (1972), who has investigated the lichen flora round several fluorine sources in Scandinavia, found that the pattern of damage varied, but at one site he recognized the epiphytes *Alectoria cf. capillaris* and *Pseudevernia furfuracea* as sensitive, and corticolous *Hypogymnia physodes* as showing some resistance.

From current studies it is not possible to place lichens in a strict order of F tolerance, nor to discover much about sensitivity in different habitats because the dramatic modifying effect of shelter makes comparison difficult. Preliminary indications of species sensitivity are, however, given in Table 3, where it should be noted that lichens with profuse growth forms are often the most sensitive. The general order of increasing habitat sensitivity may run terricolous, acid saxicolous, corticolous, with several major habitats still to place.

## Patterns of deterioration

Today, with the demand for aluminium doubling every ten years, new smelters are continually being built and old ones increasing production. Though fume treatment continues to improve, it has not been perfected, so round most smelters F pollution is still spreading out over new ground. A consequence of this is that the lichen flora and the pollution are not in equilibrium, and, as a result, the edge of the deserts are characterized by a zone of damaged thalli. At Husnes and Karmøy, extensively damaged thalli were observed in all habitats. They varied from only dead fragments remaining, to moribund, through moderate damage but with regenerating lobes, to slight chlorosis on elevated parts of the thallus.

High-level point source emission can produce fumigation patterns which are capricious, damage occurring where the plume happens to come down to ground level. This can result in a very irregular margin to the desert, the detail of which is determined by local winds and topography. In hilly country pockets of isolated damage can occur far from the works and conversely, oases of unaffected vegetation may survive close to the factory fence. At Husnes an example of topographic screening was observed, a sharp 30 m high ridge 300 m east of the smelter protecting epiphytes in its lee. At Øvre Årdal the pollution cloud frequently drifts up the deep, narrow Utladal valley at a considerable elevation. Sites on the floor, 5 km up this valley, show less damage than sites on high exposed spurs several kilometres further away.

## Effect on morphology and metabolism

A bleaching (chlorosis) followed by necrosis has often been observed affecting lichens which suddenly come under pollution stress from a newly opened smelter. Pinkish colours which develop in *Parmelia saxatilis* and *P. sulcata*, and the elephant grey often assumed by *Xanthoria parietina*, suggest that this is accompanied by the breakdown of lichen acids. Microscopic studies of transplanted material have indicated progressive plasmolysis and loss of green colour from the algal cells.

By extracting pigments from injured field transplants of *Cladonia cristatella* and *Parmelia plittii*, Nash demonstrated that chlorophylls *a* and *b* are initially broken down to their respective phaeophytins and that with continued exposure all the pigments including β-carotene and the xanthophylls are degraded. He noted that this was in agreement with Newman (1961) who demonstrated that F inactivates the whole pigment system in higher plants. LeBlanc, Comeau and Rao (1971) have reported a slightly different pattern of pigment breakdown. Nash has produced evidence that transplanted thalli accumulate more F and are more liable to damage when fumigated under conditions of high (87 per cent) relative humidity (Table 4).

*Table 4 Accumulation of fluoride by lichens exposed to four days of uniform ambient fluoride levels (5 μgF/m³) but under varying relative humidity regimes. Data are in μgF/g dry wt (from Nash, 1971)*

| Species | Relative humidity 40% | 63% | 87% |
|---|---|---|---|
| *Cladonia cristatella* | 10 | 32 | 82 |
| *Parmelia caperata* | 11 | 26 | 89 |

## Fluoride accumulation

Atmospheric sampling has shown that aluminium smelters release F as gaseous hydrogen fluroride and as volatile fluorides ($Na_3AlF_6$, $SiF_4$, $CaF_2$, $AlF_3$), the particulate fraction predominating. The pollution cloud, which is visible, frequently has two sources originating from tall chimneys and seeping out of the factory at ground level through doors, windows and ventilators (Agate *et al.*, 1949).

In a careful piece of work, Nash (1971) suggested that the critical level of F within the lichen thallus may lie between 30–80 ppm. Gilbert (1971) found that near their inner limit, washed thalli of *Usnea subfloridana* and *Parmelia saxatilis* contained 20 and 47 ppm soluble F respectively which largely bears this out. In contrast LeBlanc, Comeau and Rao (1971) have consistently recorded higher values. Their control *Parmelia sulcata* contained 70 ppm F and when transplanted could accumulate up to 700 ppm F in four months without showing visible damage. Current measurements of F content in lichens is summarized in Table 4. A partial explanation of the widely divergent values may be found in the work of Comeau and LeBlanc (1972) who observed that after three weeks' recuperation, fumigated *Hypogymnia physodes* transplants lost between 36 and 47 per cent of the accumulated fluoride. It has also been reported from several sources that rain can wash particulate F off plant material.

## Discussion

It must be understood that research into the lichen/F pollution problem is still in its infancy; no major studies have yet been undertaken and in no aspect does knowledge approach the sophistication evident in recent lichen/sulphur dioxide work, which has just celebrated its centenary. Though profiting considerably from previous sulphur dioxide research, F investigations must at present stand apart for the following reasons. F deserts are chiefly new or expanding rapidly so the affected lichen flora is not in equilibrium with the pollution; they are a result of point source emission from high stacks which produce a pattern of intensive, but intermittent fumigations; the pollutant is predominantly in a particulate, not gaseous form. For these reasons precise comparison between F and most sulphur dioxide deserts is not possible.

These preliminary studies are unanimous in finding F toxic to lichens, but as yet there is not much agreement on the order of sensitivity. It appears, however, that there will be some differences from the accepted pattern of sensitivity to sulphur dioxide. Ecological observations have not been included in all surveys, but it already seems clear that degree of shelter can have a major effect on the distribution of damage. The reason for this has not been investigated, but it could be a general feature either of point source emission from high stacks or a result of the pollution being largely in a particulate form. There is evidence that species are better able to tolerate the pollution when growing in eutrophicated conditions.

Synergistic effects between F and sulphur dioxide have been looked for in the Bedfordshire brickfields (mean annual sulphur dioxide *c* 110 $\mu g/m^3$; fluorosis to cattle) but the area over which lichen vegetation is depressed is apparently no larger than would be expected from sulphur dioxide alone (Gilbert, 1968).

Lichens are already proving useful indicators of the spread of F pollution from aluminium smelters. Such areas are also characterized by heavy damage to conifers and certain deciduous trees (*see* ch 10). Injury to epiphytic lichens appears less spectacular if the tree they are growing on is also dying and it will be interesting to discover whether *Pinus sylvestris*, *Abies* and *Picea* are more, or less, sensitive to F than most lichens. Whatever the finding, lichens can always provide valuable confirmatory evidence of F pollution as, compared to a tree crop, they are hardy, less prone to lethal disease, devastating insect attacks, or the vagrancies of weather, only to air pollution. It is necessary to check however that F is being accumulated. It is now clear that this element can be concentrated more rapidly than was once thought.

## Acknowledgements

Part of this work was carried out while in receipt of a grant from the Sheffield University Research Fund. Thanks are due to A. W. Davison for determining the F content of certain lichen samples.

## References

Agate, J. N. *et al.* (1949). Industrial Fluorosis. *Medical Research Council Memo.* **22.**

Burns, K. N. and Allcroft, R. (1964). Fluorosis in cattle. *Animal disease surveys. Report* **2**(1). London: HMSO.

Comeau, G. and LeBlanc, F. (1972). Influence du fluor sur le *Funaria hygrometrica* et l'*Hypogymnia physodes*. *Can. J. Bot.* **50,** 847–56.

Crossley, H. E. (1944*a*). Fluorine in coal III. The manner of occurrence of fluorine in coal. *J. Soc. Chem. Ind., Lond.* **63,** 289–92.

Crossley, H. E. (1944*b*). Fluorine in coal IV. The industrial significance of fluorine in coal. *J. Soc. Chem. Ind., Lond.* **63,** 342–7.

Gilbert, O. L. (1968). *Biological indicators of air pollution.* Ph.D. thesis, University of Newcastle upon Tyne.

Gilbert, O. L. (1971). The effect of airborne fluorides on lichens. *Lichenologist* **5,** 26–32.

Greenhalgh, R. and Riley, J. P. (1961). The determination of fluoride in natural waters, with particular reference to seawater. *Anal. Chim. Acta* **25,** 179–88.

Hall, R. J. (1963). The Spectrophotometric determination of sub-microgram amounts of fluorine in biological specimens. *Analyst, Lond.* **88,** 76–83.

LeBlanc, F., Comeau, G. and Rao, D. N. (1971). Fluoride injury symptoms in epiphytic lichens and mosses. *Can. J. Bot.* **49,** 1691–8.

LeBlanc, F. and DeSloover, J. (1970). Relation between industrialization and the distribution and growth of epiphytic lichens and mosses in Montreal. *Can. J. Bot.* **48,** 1485–96.

LeBlanc, F., Rao, D. N. and Comeau, G. (1972). Indices of atmospheric purity and fluoride pollution pattern in Arvida, Quebec. *Can. J. Bot.* **50,** 991–8.

Martin, J.-F. and Jacquard, F. (1968). Influence des fumées d'usines sur la distribution des lichens dans la vallée de la Romanche (Isère). *Pollution Atmospherique* **10,** 95–9.

Mazel, A. (1964). *Fluoruroses industrielles.* Thesis, University of Toulouse.

Nash, T. H. (1971). Lichen sensitivity to hydrogen fluoride. *Bull. Torrey bot. Club* **98,** 103–6.

Newman, D. W. (1961). *A study of the mechanism of fluoride induced chlorosis.* Ph.D. thesis, University of Utah. [Not seen.]

Rao, D. N. and LeBlanc, F. (1967). Influence of an iron-sintering plant on corticolous epiphytes in Wawa, Ontario. *Bryologist* **70,** 141–57.

Singer, L. and Armstrong, W. D. (1959). Determination of fluoride in blood serum. *Anal. Chem.* **31,** 105–9.

Singer, L. and Armstrong, W. D. (1965). Determination of fluorine: Procedure based on diffusion of hydrogen fluoride. *Anal. Biochem.* **10,** 495–500.

Skye, E. (1972). *Lichens as indicators of fluorine compounds.* Abstract of a talk at Symposium of the Fluoride Problem in the Primary Aluminium Smelting Industry. Trondheim.

# 10: The Effect of Air Pollution on other Plants, Particularly Vascular Plants

T. H. NASH III

The term 'air pollution' generally refers to airborne gases or particulates which, when accumulated to levels in excess of those readily removed by normal atmospheric cleansing processes, become detrimental to organisms and deleterious to inorganic materials. Sulphur oxides, hydrogen fluoride, ozone, nitrogen oxides, and peroxyacetyl nitrate (PAN) are the most important phytotoxic, gaseous pollutants (Treshow, 1970*a*). Ethylene, chlorine, hydrogen chloride, and ammonia are of secondary importance. The phytotoxicity of particulate pollutants has also been recognized, arsenic, cadmium, copper, fluoride, iron, lead, nickel and zinc compounds being among the more important components of particulates (Vandergrift, 1981). Industrial activities, motor vehicles, and heating facilities are major sources of these pollutants.

Most air pollution problems have arisen since the advent of the Industrial Revolution. The rapid acceleration in industrialization and mechanization of society since the advent of World War II has resulted in such a dramatic, regional increase in problems related to air pollution that such pollution is now generally recognized to have a significant financial impact on society. Today in California alone, air pollution is believed to be responsible for US $500 million damage to agricultural crops each year (Heggestad, 1968). Crops dependent on their appearance for their salability may be completely ruined by the incidence of chlorotic or necrotic markings. Productivity is also severely affected, as in the Sudbury area of Ontario, Canada, where Linzon (1958, 1970) has demonstrated that *Pinus strobus* has had a negative growth rate.

Robinson (1970) has classified the effects of air pollution on plants into three general categories: (1) acute effects due to relatively short-term exposures (hours or days) to high levels of pollutants, (2) chronic effects due to exposure to relatively low levels of pollutants for more extended periods of time (weeks), and (3) long-term effects due to the impact of pollutants over decades. Chronic and acute effects are presumably due to the direct action of a gas(es) or particulates on plants. Long-term effects may be caused indirectly by air pollutants; for instance, by by-products of the gas, rather than from the gas itself (e.g. the effect of nitrate in the case of oxides of nitrogen). Accumulation of heavy metals in the soils and vegetation over a period of years may most properly be classified as a long-term effect.

## Vascular plants

The effects of air pollution on vascular plants, as determined by field observations and experimental fumigations, have been documented extensively in the literature. Some of the more comprehensive reviews include the following: Katz (1949), Thomas (1951), Zimmerman (1955), Thomas and Hendricks (1956), Thomas (1961), Darley *et al.* (1963), Garber (1960 and 1962), Darley, E. F. and Middleton, J. T. (1966), Brandt and Heck (1968), Hindawi (1970), Treshow (1970*a*), Agricultural Research Council (1967), and Jacobson and Hill (1970). Much of the Russian literature is now available in English translation by M. Y. Nuttlonson, Silver Springs, Maryland (American Institute of Crop Ecology).

### *Sulphur dioxide*

Sulphur dioxide was the first gas to be widely recognized as an air pollutant. Burning of fuels, especially coal and petroleum products, is a major source of sulphur dioxide. Thus in temperate climates where dense human populations exist, there are many small sources of sulphur dioxide in urban areas. Industrial operations, particularly the smelting of sulphide ores, and the production of electricity from oil and coal are also major sources of sulphur dioxide. Ambient sulphur dioxide does not result solely from man's activities; volcanism contributes large quantities as well. Natural background concentrations of sulphur dioxide generally range between 0.28 and 2.8 $\mu g/m^3$ (0.0001–0.001

ppm). Whenever mean annual local concentrations of sulphur dioxide exceed about 27–224 μg/m³ (0.01–0.08 ppm), extensive phytotoxic effects begin to appear in a number of species, although some are affected at lower concentrations.

Historically, the effects of sulphur dioxide on plants have been recorded in a voluminous literature over the past eight decades. Recent summaries have been presented by the Agricultural Research Council (1967), Daines (1968) and Barrett and Benedict (1970). Classically acute and chronic damage has been described, based on field and fumigation studies. Symptomatology varies considerably among different plant groups. In dicotyledonous plants acute damage is expressed in the form of marginal or intercostal necrotic areas. Damaged areas at first appear dull dark green, but subsequently they become bleached to an ivory colour, or less commonly they become a red or brown colour. The necrotic tissue is visible from both sides of the leaf, and eventually this dead tissue may disintegrate leaving a ragged leaf. Leaves which become severely marked will be shed. Chronic injury is expressed as chlorosis, which frequently appears as a yellowing in intercostal areas. In monocotyledonous plants and grasses acute damage takes the form of necrotic tissue, usually appearing as streaking, beginning at the leaf tip and spreading to the leaf base; chronic damage may only appear as a bleaching of the leaf tips. In conifers, damage initially appears as banding around the needles and later the terminal portion turns reddish brown.

The precise mechanism by which sulphur dioxide damage is induced is not fully understood. According to the currently accepted dogma proposed by Thomas and Hendricks (1956), the expression of necrotic damage is a function of the sulphite concentration in the plant tissues. When sulphur dioxide becomes dissolved in the mesophyll tissue, it reacts with water to form the highly toxic sulphite ion. Given time, sulphite ions will slowly oxidize to sulphate ions, which are 30 times less toxic because of their lower reducing potential. If the formation of sulphite occurs at a faster rate than the cell can convert the sulphite to sulphate, acute necrotic damage in the form of necrosis will appear. However, if there is a constant low concentration of sulphur dioxide, sulphate concentration in the cell may become sufficiently high to cause chronic symptoms.

The role of stomata in the occurrence of injury has been controversial. Zimmerman and Hitchcock (1956) found that there was no relation between the number of stomata and the degree of injury. Although Katz (1949) stated that sulphur dioxide has no effect on stomata, Majernik and Mansfield (1970) and Unsworth *et al.* (1972) have shown that stomata open wider and remain open longer when exposed to sulphur dioxide.

The concentration of sulphur dioxide during fumigation and the duration of the fumigation strongly affect the amount of damage incurred. Under ideal environmental conditions, the most sensitive non-coniferous plant species will exhibit chronic symptoms at concentrations of 0.1–0.3 ppm (280–840 $\mu g/m^3$) and acute symptoms at concentrations of 0.3–0.5 ppm (840–1400 $\mu g/m^3$) (Treshow, 1970*a*). The threshold point of susceptibility varies tremendously between species. For instance, Thomas and Hendricks (1956) considered privet to be 16 times more resistant to sulphur dioxide than barley or lucerne. Darley *et al.* (1966) found that plants exposed to levels of sulphur dioxide just below the threshold for acute injury for short-time periods, and ones exposed to lower levels of sulphur dioxide for longer periods of time are injured in the same way.

Coniferous trees are among the more sensitive vascular plants to sulphur dioxide. In fumigation studies Douglas fir (*Pseudotsuga menziesii*) seedlings were injured by 0.29 ppm (812 $\mu g/m^3$) after 44 hours (Treshow, 1970*a*) and eastern white pine (*Pinus strobus*) by 0.1 ppm (280 $\mu g/m^3$) after 8 hours (Berry *in* Treshow, 1970*a*). In the field, Lines (*in* Gilbert, 1970*b*) reported that sulphur dioxide was responsible for the reduced productivity and virtual failure of many plots planted in the southern Pennines of England since 1951. Knabe (1971) found that in the Ruhr area, pine trees could not survive if the mean annual values of sulphur dioxide exceed 0.07–0.08 ppm (196–224 $\mu g/m^3$) and that slight damage appeared at only 0.01 ppm (28 $\mu g/m^3$). Studies at Kvarntorp in Sweden showed that mean annual sulphur dioxide concentrations of 0.02 ppm (56 $\mu g/m^3$) led to a drop in the growth rate of the forest. The Swedish Royal Ministry for Foreign Affairs and the Royal Ministry of Agriculture (1971) consider that maximum sulphur dioxide concentrations of only 0.02 ppm (56 $\mu g/m^3$) should be permitted to avoid damage to sensitive coniferous trees.

Short-duration, high-concentration fumigations have been shown to induce more damage than long-duration, low-concentration fumigations even if the total amount of sulphur dioxide is the same (Haut, 1961). The effects of extremely short fumigations (30 min) may be ameliorated if the fumigations are separated by periods when no sulphur dioxide is present (Zahn, 1961). However, doubling the sulphur dioxide concentration will not be compensated for by simply doubling the duration of the recovery period. Guderian, Haut and Stratmann (1960) and Zahn (1963) have presented concentration-time equations for predicting the effect of sulphur dioxide fumigations. Recently Zahn (1970) has demonstrated that preconditioning plants at sublethal concentrations to sulphur dioxide will induce greater resistance in the plants to subsequent exposures to lethal concentrations of sulphur dioxide.

Whether or not any damage occurs at concentrations below which visible symptoms appear has been an area of active controversy. Katz (1949) reported that there was no reduction in yield, photosynthesis, respiration, and no alteration of stomata, plant structure, or plant composition when alfalfa was exposed to 0.1–0.2 ppm (280–560 $\mu g/m^3$) sulphur dioxide. Furthermore, satisfactory formulae which estimate the percentage yield reduction as a direct function of the amount of visibly injured tissue have been widely used (Barrett and Benedicut, 1970). However, Thomas and Hendricks (1956) did find a slight reduction in photosynthesis in alfalfa when it was exposed continuously to 0.13 ppm (364 $\mu g/m^3$) sulphur dioxide for six weeks. Matushima and Harada (1964) have also reported reduced yield in *Citrus* at sublethal concentrations. Thus, although some injury may occur at sulphur dioxide concentrations below which visible damage is induced, the bulk of the evidence suggests that this 'invisible' injury is slight or negligible.

Plant tissues are susceptible to sulphur dioxide and plant processes are altered by sulphur dioxide fumigations. In several species photosynthesis is depressed during the period of fumigation at a rate proportional to the concentration, but the photosynthetic rate recovers to normal levels after cessation of the fumigation (Thomas and Hill, 1937; Vogl, 1964; Thompson *et al.*, 1967). In severely affected tissue, chlorophylls and carotene are destroyed and violaxanthin and lutein are partially destroyed (Mamaev and Nikolaevskiy, 1968). Katz (1939) observed plasmolysis initially in affected tissue and Solberg and Adams (1956) observed that chloroplasts disintegrated first and that the vascular tissue was the most resistant. Haut (1961) found that plants were most sensitive shortly before flowering. In severely affected pine forests Hedgcock (1912) found that reproductive organs aborted before maturing. Later Katz (1939) found that there was no effect on pine pollination at 10 ppm (28 000 $\mu g/m^3$) sulphur dioxide, but Matsuoka, Udagawa and Ono (1969) have reported that pear pollination was affected at 1.0 ppm (2800 $\mu g/m^3$). Growth in a variety of species is severely affected (Bleasdale, 1959; Guderian and Stratmann, 1962). In the Sudbury area of Canada, Linzon (1958, 1970) has demonstrated that white pine has a negative growth rate. In Japan Matsushima and Harada (1964) have demonstrated that leaf fall increases and fruit set decreases in *Citrus*.

Susceptibility of tissue to damage from sulphur dioxide is dependent on the tissue's age. In dicotyledons the younger, fully expanded leaves are frequently the most sensitive, but expanding leaves are the last ones to show injury (Stratmann, 1963). Observations on cereal crops have indicated that seedlings are much more resistant to sulphur dioxide than are more mature plants (Holmes *et al.*, 1915; Brisley and Jones, 1950; Thomas, 1958; Haut, 1961). On the other hand, conifers are much more susceptible in the seedling stage (Katz, 1949). In mature conifers older needles are shed prematurely, but middle-aged needles show the most necrosis (Scheffer and Hedgcock, 1955).

Environmental factors strongly affect the susceptibility of plants to sulphur dioxide. In general, conditions of high light intensity, moist soil, high relative humidity and moderate temperatures are conditions under which plants are most susceptible (Katz, 1949; Thomas and Hendricks, 1956; Thomas, 1961; Stratmann, 1963). Plants are more resistant at night than during the day (Thomas, 1958; Haut, 1961). Conditions which cause moisture stress also induce resistance (Oertli, 1959). Seasonal variability in sensitivity has been observed: the most sensitive period being spring or early summer (Katz and McCallum, 1952; Leone, Brennan, and Daines, 1965). The nutrient status of the soil is also very important and Berry (in Treshow, 1970) has demonstrated that nitrogen-deficient plants are much more susceptible than normal plants. Furthermore, the addition of fertilizers apparently reduces susceptibility (Cotrufo and Berry, 1970; Materna, 1960; Miyazaki, Okinaga and Harata, 1954). Topography and soil substrate are also important. Pfeffer (1965) found that plants growing on hillsides at 2 to 5 times chimney height were much more severely injured than plants at equivalent distances on horizontal surfaces and he also found that plants growing on limestone and basalt were less severely affected than those growing on sandy soils. Jordan and Reisenhauer (1957) have suggested that sulphur dioxide may act by interfering with calcium uptake.

*Fluorides*

Although fluorides occur widely in soils, rocks and minerals, they generally become phytotoxic only when fluoride-containing materials are treated industrially by heating or by application of acid, such that fluoride is released into the atmosphere. Fluoride injury to vegetation has been recognized since the latter part of the nineteenth century (Haselhoff, Bredemann and Haseloff, 1932). However, the magnitude of the fluoride problem has greatly increased since the advent of World War II, which accelerated industrial expansion. Aluminium, rare earth metals, steel, phosphorus, chemical, and fertilizer factories, ceramic, brick and glass works are sources of fluorides. The gas, hydrogen fluoride, is the principal agent which causes fluoride damage, although silicon tetrafluoride and cryolite are of secondary importance.

The phytotoxic effects of fluorides have been summarized by various authors, including Cristiani and Gautier (1925), Hitchcock, Zimmerman and Coe (1962), Garber (1966), Bossavy (1966) and Treshow and Pack (1970). Symptoms vary tremendously between plant groups. In broad leaf dicotyledons, if accumulation of fluoride by the leaf is relatively slow, the fluoride is translocated to the margins of the leaf where a marginal necrosis develops. A distinct reddish-brown band typically separates the necrotic tissue from healthy tissue. If the ambient concentration of fluoride is extremely high, accumulation of fluoride may occur at several points in the leaf. This results in a scattered distribution of necrotic and chlorotic tissue. In monocotyledons the tips of the leaves are the first area to become necrotic with a red-brown margin. In cereals the necrotic tissue may appear almost white. Corn typically exhibits chlorotic flecking concentrated along the leaf margin and apex. In conifers injury begins at the needle tip and spreads to the base. Initially chlorotic, the tissue turns reddish brown with age.

Plants vary tremendously in their susceptibility to fluorides. Certain varieties of *Gladiolus* develop necrosis when fumigated with concentrations as low as 0.1 ppb,* but other varieties are resistant at concentrations ten times higher (Hitchcock, Zimmerman and Coe, 1962). Variation within varieties of a species has also been demonstrated for roses (Brewer, Sutherland and Guillemet, 1967). Resistant species are not injured by hydrogen fluoride fumigations at concentrations of 10 ppb (Thomas and Hendricks, 1956).

Accumulation of fluoride in leaves above background concentrations may be used to establish definitively fluoride as the cause of injury. Around fluoride sources, sampling along transects will disclose gradients of fluoride concentration in soils or plants (Reinhard, 1959; Hluchan, Mayer and Abel, 1964; Treshow and Pack, 1970). Background concentrations of fluoride in plants generally vary between 0.5 and 25.0 ppm by weight (Garber, 1966; Treshow, 1970*a*). The range of 25–105 ppm fluoride is the critical range for sensitive species (Bolay and Bovay, 1965). Resistant species, however, may accumulate several hundred ppm before chlorosis or necrosis appears (Treshow, 1970*a*). Accumulation of fluoride by plants exposed to hydrogen fluoride has been shown to be approximately a linear function of concentration and duration (Hitchcock, Zimmerman and Coe, 1962; McCune and Hitchcock, 1970). Several caveats, however, must be considered in evaluating fluoride accumulation data. Concentrations may be diluted by plant growth, by the leaching effect of rain, or by volatilization (Treshow and Pack, 1970). Sampling must be done in a uniform manner. Zimmerman and Hitchcock (1956) found that concentrations in the tip of *Gladiolus* leaves may be 25–100 times higher than at the leaf base. Older leaves will have

* ppb: parts per thousand million.

higher concentrations than younger leaves (Benedict, Ross and Wade, 1964). If the fluoride source is particulate rather than gaseous, considerably higher fluoride concentrations may occur before injury is observed (McCune *et al.*, 1965).

Fluorides affect metabolic pathways in a variety of ways. Within the plant tissue, fluorides are thought to remain soluble with all the physical properties of inorganic fluoride (Jacobson *et al.*, 1966). Inorganic fluoride has commonly been used as a protein inhibitor, and as such, fluorides may interfere with such plant processes as respiration, photosynthesis, carbohydrate metabolism, protein synthesis, cell wall formation, energy balance, and nucleotide and nucleic acid synthesis (Treshow, 1970*a*). In respiration, Ross *et al.* (1968) have suggested that fluoride inhibits enolase and that resistant varieties are somewhat more dependent on the pentose phosphate pathway than on the glycolytic pathway. Givan and Torrey (1968) found that fluoride interfered with the aerobic oxidation processes *per se*, rather than simply glycolytic inhibition. Initially fluoride fumigations may increase respiration, but after damage appears respiration decreases (McNulty and Newman, 1957; Yu and Miller, 1967). Lords and McNulty (1965) have suggested that stimulation of respiration, which was measured as oxygen consumption, may result from a blockage of ADP-ATP interconversion. Photosynthesis is apparently unaffected until damage appears (Thomas and Hendricks, 1956). While studying chlorotic damage, McNulty and Newman (1961) demonstrated that the early stages of pigment synthesis were affected. Radioactive fluoride studies have shown that short-term accumulation of fluoride was associated with soluble proteins, chloroplast, cell walls, and mitochondria in decreasing order (Ledbetter, Mavrodineanu and Weiss, 1960). Chromosomal aberrations, which suggest blockage of DNA synthesis, have been observed at concentrations below which visible damage appears (Mohamed, 1969, 1970; Hart, 1969). Chang (1968) has shown that RNA structure is affected by fluoride treatment because of a reduction in cytosine content.

Fluorides are strongly detrimental to plant growth and development. In the field, growth may be severely reduced and some species may be entirely eliminated from areas near fluoride sources (Adams *et al.*, 1952; Anderson, 1966). *Citrus* fumigated with 1 to 5 ppb fluoride for 26 months, had 25 per cent to 35 per cent smaller leaves and reduced linear shoot growth compared with controls (Brewer, 1960). Leonard and Graves (1966) have demonstrated that orange trees suffered a 27 per cent decrease in yield for each 50 ppm fluoride accumulated in the spring leaves. In *Gladiolus* Brewer, Guillemet and Sutherland (1966) have shown that flower weight, size and number of florets, and corm size and weight were reduced. Fruits, such as plums (Kotte, 1929) and peaches (Benson, 1959), are frequently injured by fluorides. Pack (1969) has shown that fluoride-fumigated bean plants are slow to mature and that their seeds are shrivelled and low in starch. Later Pack (1971) showed that the growth of the $F_1$ progeny was much less vigorous. Poovaiah and Wiebe (1969) have shown that tyloses are formed in *Geranium* leaves when they are exposed to fluorides.

The influence of environmental variables on plant response to fluoride fumigations has not been adequately explored. Greenhouse experiments have indicated that turgid cells are most susceptible to injury (Zimmerman and Hitchcock, 1956), but field observations have shown that plants under moisture stress are frequently the most severely affected (Treshow and Pack, 1970). Daines *et al.* (1952) have shown that higher relative humidity increases susceptibility and that plants fumigated in darkness suffer less damage than plants fumigated in daylight. Reports of the effects of nutrient status are contradictory. Adams and Sulzbach (1961) reported that nitrogen deficiency increases susceptibility, whereas McCune *et al.* (1966) reported that nitrogen and calcium status have little effect on susceptibility, but that potassium or phosphorus deficiency increases susceptibility.

### *Ozone*

Ozone is the principal phytotoxic component of photochemical smog. Although ozone damage was initially described by Middleton, Kendrick, and Schwalm in 1944, ozone was not identified as the causal agent of the damage until Richard, Middleton and Newitt's work of 1958. Today it is considered by many to be the most important air pollutant in the world (Treshow, 1970*a*). Although ozone is an important constituent of the upper atmosphere, Berry (1964) has found that the background concentration in the lower portion of the atmosphere usually ranges between 1 and 2 pphm. Today in our cities the concentration of ozone ranges up to 100 pphm, which is well above the phytotoxic level (Treshow, 1970*a*). The primary source of ozone in urban atmospheres is from the photolysis of nitrogen dioxide and the concomitant removal of nitric oxide, which react with hydrocarbons, leaving an oxygen radical which combines with an oxygen molecule to form ozone (Hill, Heggestad and Linzon, 1970). Unlike fluorides (and to a lesser extent sulphur dioxide), which primarily affect relatively local areas, ozone may be transported tens, or even hundreds of miles from its point of origin in phytotoxic concentrations. Damage which was initially simply classified as oxidant injury in the Los Angeles area is now divided into ozone, peroxyacetyl nitrate (PAN), and nitrogen dioxide damage. The latter two pollutants are discussed in separate sections.

Ozone-induced symptoms in plants have been summarized by Hill *et al.* (1961), Treshow (1970*b*), and Hill, Heggestad and Linzon (1970). In most species, ozone characteristically causes a necrotic stipple or flecking of tissue on the upper surface of the leaf adjacent to small veins. Internally the palisade tissue is the most sensitive to ozone. Its cells frequently become nonfunctional and disintegrate before the lower portion of the mesophyll becomes injured. The space formed by the disintegrating cells initially appears bleached from the upper surface. After a few days the colour may change to tan or pale yellow. A darker colour will appear if new pigments are produced. At higher concentrations ozone damage will extend to other leaf tissues, and consequently the necrotic areas will expand and coalesce making damage visible from both surfaces. Recently matured leaves are usually the most susceptible to ozone. In conifers the stipple initially appears at the tips of new needles, but at the base of old needles. The most sensitive species are injured by ozone fumigations between 5 and 12 pphm for 2–4 hours, while resistant species tolerate concentrations as high as 100 pphm. Not only does susceptibility vary between species (Davies and Wood, 1972), but also among varieties of a species (Brennan, Leone and Daines, 1964).

Ozone has definite detrimental effects on growth and reproduction, but these areas need to be studied in greater detail. Loss of leaves, smaller fruit, and poor growth in *Citrus* has been blamed on ozone (Richards and Taylor, 1965). Ozone may inhibit growth at concentrations below which visible injury is induced, since Miller *et al.* (1969) have shown that carbon dioxide assimilation is reduced at these concentrations. Feder and Campbell (1968) found that exposure of carnations to 7.5 pphm for 10 days inhibited flower bud formation.

Ozone affects the internal structure of cells in a variety of ways. The chloroplast is apparently the first organelle to be disrupted (Hill *et al.*, 1961). Further studies by Thomson, Dugger and Palmer (1966) have shown that the stroma of chloroplasts are granulated before disintegration, that nuclei are shrunken to an irregular shape, that the plasmalemma separates from the wall, and that the vacuole collapses. Lee (1968) has shown that ozone exposures cause mitochondria to swell rapidly which increases the permeability of their membranes.

Several metabolic processes are affected by ozone (Dugger and Ting, 1970). Although ozone may initially inhibit respiration, the preponderant effect is to stimulate respiration (Macdowall, 1965). Tomlinson and Rich (1969) demonstrated in tobacco leaves that 60 per cent of the saturated fatty acids and 10 per cent of the unsaturated fatty acids are removed after ozone exposure. Mudd, McManus and Ongun (1970) showed that lipid metabolism is inhibited in chloroplasts by ozone, possibly due to inhibition of sulphydryl-requiring enzymes. Sulphydryl groups are needed by chloroplasts to produce the long-chain fatty acids required to repair damaged cell membranes. The sulphydryl content of leaves was shown to decrease after ozonation (Tomlinson and Rich, 1968). Dass and Weaver (1968) found that ozone increases peroxidase activity and decreases lactic dehydrogenase activity. MacKnight (1968) demonstrated that 20–40 pphm ozone severely reduced transpiration because of stomatal closure.

The factors which affect susceptibility to ozone are only partially elucidated. Hanson, Thorne and Jativa (1970) found greater resistance to ozone in petunias with greater ascorbic acid content. Because high relative humidity stimulates stomatal apertures to increase, greater ozone damage was found at higher humidities than at lower relative humidities (Otto and Daines, 1969). Shoemyen (1967) found that well-watered plants were more susceptible to ozone damage. High nitrogen levels apparently increase susceptibility (Menser and Hodges, 1967). In experiments where the temperatures were set at 5°C, 17°C, and 30°C, the greatest ozone injury was found at the highest temperature (Koritz and Went, 1953).

### *Nitrogen oxides*

Nitric oxide and nitrogen dioxide, the principal oxides of nitrogen, are primarily produced by high temperatures in combustion reactions, such as the burning of coal or in the running of automobiles. Nitrogen oxides are one of the important groups of chemicals found in photochemical smog. Nitric acid factories are secondary sources of nitrogen oxides. Historically, fumigations with nitrogen oxides have been primarily limited to the past ten years.

Phytotoxic effects of nitrogen oxides have been summarized by Haut and Stratmann (1967) and by Taylor and MacLean (1970). Acute injury in dicotyledons is typified by irregular-shaped necrotic markings, which are intercostal and usually occur near the margins of the leaf. Necrotic tissue is white, tan, or brown, and it may closely resemble sulphur dioxide injury. Benedict and Breen (1955) observed a dark waxy coating on the leaf surface after exposing Kentucky bluegrass, mustard, pigweed and cheeseweed. No visual chronic symptoms have yet been ascribed to nitrogen oxides.

Although higher concentrations of nitrogen oxides than sulphur dioxide are required to produce necrotic markings, plants respond physiologically to subacute dosages of nitrogen oxides. Heck (1964) found definite necrotic markings on cotton, pinto beans, and endives after 48-hour exposures to 1.0 ppm. Using oats and alfalfa, Hill and Bennett (1970) found definite inhibition of photosynthesis at 0.6 ppm nitric oxide or nitrogen dioxide but no visible markings were observed. Experimenting with oranges, Thompson *et al.* (1970) found severe defoliation and leaf chlorosis at 0.5 and 1.0 ppm nitrogen dioxide, and increased leaf drop, reduced fruit yield, but otherwise no visible damage at 0.25 ppm. The experimental concentrations which have been used are generally higher than those which have been observed naturally, although a concentration as high as 3.0 ppm total nitrogen oxides has been observed in Los Angeles (Tebbins, 1968). Thompson, Kats and Hensel (1971) found no discernible effect on oranges which had been exposed to ambient levels of nitrogen oxides (from 0 to 0.20 ppm) for 8 months in the Los Angeles basin. Decreases in dry weight have been reported for pinto bean and tomato plants fumigated at 0.3 ppm for 10 days (Taylor and Eaton, 1966).

Experimental conditions which affect susceptibility have not been extensively investigated. Benedict and Breen (1955) reported that moist soil conditions caused greater sensitivity than dry conditions. Taylor and MacLean (1970) found that plants were more sensitive at low light intensities. Haut and Stratmann (1967) found that night fumigations were possibly more detrimental than day fumigations. MacLean *et al.* (1968) have noted variation in susceptibility among different orange tree varieties, and they have noted that older leaves are more susceptible than young leaves.

*Peroxyacetyl nitrate* (*PAN*)

Peroxyacetyl nitrate is one of the photochemical reaction products of the interaction between nitrogen oxides and unsaturated hydrocarbons. Initially identified as compound 'X' (Stephens *et al.*, 1956), it was later identified (Stephens *et al.*, 1961). Although PAN is perhaps most important as a component of the Los Angeles smog, damage ascribed to PAN has been found in the eastern half of the United States and in Europe. Several compounds homologous to PAN may also be formed, including peroxypropionyl nitrate (PPN), peroxybutyryl nitrate (PBN), and peroxyisobutyryl nitrate ($P_{iso}BN$). Although the latter compounds are more phytotoxic than PAN (Taylor, 1968, 1969), they also occur at considerably lower concentrations than PAN. Consequently, the subsequent discussion focuses on PAN.

The phytotoxic effects of PAN have been summarized by Taylor (1969), Taylor and MacLean (1970) and Treshow (1970*a*). In broad-leafed dicotyledons, acute PAN injury is characterized by under-surface glazing or bronzing of the leaves. Typically PAN attacks the spongy leaf parenchyma, whereas ozone attacks the palisade parenchyma. Fumigations at concentrations below 0.1 ppm, which are realistic concentrations, frequently produce a chlorotic stipple. On monocotyledons PAN causes distinct transverse bands to develop; glazing and bronzing seldom occur. Young leaves are usually the most susceptible ones to PAN, and species vary widely in their sensitivity to PAN (from 15 to 100 ppb).

The chloroplasts are particularly sensitive to PAN, and Thomson, Dugger and Palmer (1965) demonstrated that small, electron-dense granules appear in the chloroplast stroma soon after fumigation. The granules appear to fuse into rods and eventually the chloroplast disintegrates. Consequently, it is not surprising that PAN inhibits photosynthesis (Dugger, Mudd and Koukol, 1965), which may be due to inhibition of certain enzyme activity (Mudd, 1963). Optimum conditions for PAN injury include full light intensity, which implies an active photosynthetic mechanism.

Growth is apparently inhibited by the action of PAN on indoleacetic acid (Ordin, Garber and Kindinger, 1970). PAN also has the ability to oxidize sulphydryl groups of enzymes, such as phosphoglucomutase (Mudd, 1963). Dugger, Koukol and Palmer (1966) have shown that a correlation exists between the sulphydryl content of bean plants and their susceptibility to PAN.

*Other gaseous pollutants*

Ethylene damage to plants has been recognized since the nineteenth century when ethylene was an important constituent of illuminating gases (Crocker and Knight, 1908). Today the primary source of ethylene is the internal combustion engine, and concentrations as high as 3.0 ppm have been measured (Treshow, 1970*a*). Because of the high concentrations of ethylene in urban areas, floral industries have frequently been forced to move out beyond the suburbs. Heck and Pires (1962) and Heck, Daines and Hindawi (1970) have summarized our knowledge of the phytotoxic effects of ethylene. The limits of susceptibility range between 1 ppb and 1 ppm. Injury from ethylene usually develops over long periods of time and may include interveinal chlorosis, epinasty of leaves, or necrosis. Injury appears on older tissue first. Ethylene is believed to affect growth hormones since vertical growth is inhibited and lateral growth is stimulated.

Chlorine damage to plants is generally confined to local areas where chlorine is used, such as in water purification plants, chlorox manufacturers, refineries, or glass makers (Heck, Daines and Hindawi, 1970). No good data on ambient concentrations are available. In experimental fumigations Brennan, Leone and Daines (1965) found the most sensitive species to be injured at 0.1 ppm after 2-hr exposures. Symptoms induced by chlorine are highly variable, including interveinal chlorosis (Zimmerman, 1955) and marginal or interveinal necrosis (Brennan, Leone and Daines, 1965, 1969). Barton (1940) has reported inhibition of seed germination, and both Zimmerman (1955) and Schmidt (1951) have recorded leaf drop.

However, hydrogen chloride has only been reported in phytotoxic concentrations near a few industrial factories, such as those producing plastics, and in vicinities of dumps burning large quantities of chloride-containing materials (Hasselhoff and Lindau, 1903). These authors have reported that *Viburnum* and *Larix* seedlings were killed after exposure to 5–20 ppm hydrogen chloride. Shriner and Lacasse (1969) found interveinal bronzing followed by necrosis in tomatoes. Godish and Lacasse (1969) exposed tomatoes to 8–10 ppm hydrogen chloride for 2 hr and then found 25–50 per cent reduction in photosynthesis, 20–32 per cent stimulation in respiration, and up to 41 per cent reduction in transpiration.

Ammonia is infrequently emitted by fertilizer factories and it is present in urban air as a by-product of various combustion processes (Treshow, 1970*a*). Damage in the field has largely resulted from accidental industrial spills. High levels may cause tissue collapse with or without chlorophyll loss. Benedict and Breen (1955) reported necrotic spotting along the leaf margin in weed species, the most sensitive of which was injured at 3 ppm. After exposure at 200–400 ppm Brennan, Leone and Daines (1962) found that peach and apple fruit developed black markings. Bredemann and Radeloff (1932) reported that trees were just as sensitive to night fumigations as to day fumigations.

### *Interactions*

Measurements of ambient levels of pollutants show that individual pollutants are rarely present alone. In particular, the smog complex over urban areas is a mixture of ozone, nitrogen oxides,

PAN, sulphur oxides, hydrocarbons, and many other pollutants. Experimental fumigations in the future should therefore be conducted with multiple pollutants to examine the interactions between pollutants. Synergism occurs when combinations of pollutants produce symptoms at lower concentrations than the pollutants do individually. Damage from this synergism frequently is unlike damage from either pollutant alone. Synergism between ozone and sulphur dioxide has been demonstrated for peanuts (Applegate and Durrant, 1969), white pine (Dochinger *et al.*, 1970) and Ponderosa pine (Karpen, 1970).

*Particulates*

Classically, heavy metal pollution has been associated with ore-smelting operations and mining. However, heavy metal pollution also results from many other sources, such as electrical power generation, various manufacturing enterprises, additives in gasoline, fertilizers, and various fungicides and insecticides (Vandegrift *et al.*, 1981). In the United States particulate matter in urban areas has averaged approximately three times (100 $\mu g/m^3$) higher over a ten-year period than that in non-urban areas (Spirtas and Levin, 1971). In New York City lead, vanadium, cadmium, chromium, copper, magnesium, nickel, and zinc have been found in particularly high concentration (Kneip *et al.*, 1970). Roadside contamination with cadmium, nickel, lead and zinc has been documented by Lagerwerff and Specht (1970), and Martinez *et al.* (1971) found that *Tillandsia usneoides* growing near roads served as a sensor for lead. Soil contamination with heavy metals has been discussed extensively by Bear (1957).

Frequently these heavy metals are present in sufficient concentration to cause severe damage to vegetation. Haywood (1910) has discussed the effects of arsenic and copper in the vicinity of a copper smelter; Lundegardh (1927), the effects of lead and zinc in the vicinity of a lead smelter; Pelz, Beyer, and Bleyer (1963), the interaction of arsenic and sulphur dioxide around a lead smelter; and Buchauer (1971), the effects of cadmium and zinc in the vicinity of a zinc smelter. Buchauer has presented strong experimental evidence that zinc and cadmium are more important phytotoxic agents than sulphur dioxide in the Palmerton, Pennsylvania, area. Perhaps the largest area devastated by heavy metals is Copper Hill, Tennessee, where 17 000 acres were completely denuded and another 30 000 acres severely affected (Hedgcock, 1912). Although the primary cause of vegetation injury in this area was probably sulphur dioxide, the area has remained barren years after the smelter ceased operations, principally due to the residual copper in the soil (Hursh, 1948). The problem of revegetating the lower Swansea valley area of England where slag wastes are responsible for high concentrations of copper, zinc, lead, silver, iron, nickel, cobalt, and arsenic has been discussed extensively by Weston *et al.* (1965).

The effects of heavy metals on plants are summarized by Treshow (1970*a*). Chlorotic symptoms induced by heavy metals frequently resemble nutrient deficiency symptoms of essential elements. The specific mechanism by which injury is induced is unknown for most of the heavy metals although competition among various ions is frequently proposed. Copper, nickel and beryllium are phytotoxic at particularly low concentrations. A few papers dealing specifically with phytotoxic concentrations of heavy metals include the following: Dilling (1926); Hewitt (1952); Hunter and Vergnano (1953); Berge (1952); Chapman (1960); and Venkatasubramanyam *et al.* (1962). Sensitivity of different plants to heavy metals varies widely. Mechanisms by which tolerant plants survive are discussed by Turner (1969) and Bradshaw (1970).

In addition to the chemical effect of heavy metals, physical effects may also be important. Dust from cement kilns in the presence of water vapour will form crusts on leaves (Peirce, 1910). Peirce further demonstrated that the encrustation interfered with light required for photosynthesis and reduced the starch content of orange tree leaves. Similar results were found by Czaja (1962) and Bohne (1963) for a variety of plants. Dzaja (1966) presented histological evidence that dust may clog stomata.

## Mosses

Mosses are approximately as sensitive to air pollution as lichens. City centres in Stockholm (Skye, 1968), Newcastle (Gilbert, 1968) and Montreal (LeBlanc, 1961; LeBlanc and DeSloover, 1970) are practically devoid of epiphytic mosses. Areas with relatively unaffected populations of mosses are only found many miles from the urban centre. While studying corticolous, saxicolous, and terricolous mosses around a zinc factory, Nash (1972) found only five species growing in the vicinity of the factory in contrast to over 60 species in a control area 35 miles away. Other studies, which were restricted to corticolous mosses, found similar reductions in species diversity around an iron sintering factory in Wawa, Ontario (Rao and LeBlanc, 1967), and in the Sudbury, Ontario, area where several nickel factories are present (LeBlanc and Rao, 1966; LeBlanc, 1969). With the exception of a few tolerant species, such as *Pottia truncata* (Nash, 1972) and *Pohlia nutans* (LeBlanc, 1969; Nash, 1972), the abundance of most moss species is reduced in the polluted areas. DeSloover and LeBlanc (1970) have also shown that fertility of mosses is decreased in polluted areas. Gilbert (1968, 1970*a*) demonstrated that shelter, pH and buffering capacity of the substratum and nutrient flushing were important variables in determining moss survival in polluted areas.

Results of experimental work indicate that mosses are sensitive to sulphur dioxide, ozone, fluorides, and some heavy metals. While experimenting with the relatively high concentration of 5 ppm sulphur dioxide, Coker (1967) observed degradation of chlorophyll and plasmolysis of cells after a 24-hour sulphur dioxide fumigation. Nash (1972) found that some moss species were sensitive to 0.5 ppm sulphur dioxide when their mature gametophytes were fumigated for 12 hours; other species were tolerant of 4 ppm. *Polytrichum ohioense*, a tolerant species, was killed (protonema or gametophore) at 0.5 ppm sulphur dioxide when it was grown in culture. In liquid cultures Gilbert (1968) found that moss protonema were more sensitive to sulphur dioxide than mature moss gametophytes. Comeau and LeBlanc (1971), experimenting with ozone at 0.25, 0.5, 1.0 and 2.0 ppm, found a stimulatory effect at the lower concentrations and inhibition at the higher concentrations. In transplant experiments LeBlanc, Comeau and Rao (1971) found that corticolous mosses were killed in the vicinity of an aluminium factory emitting fluorides. The ability of mosses to accumulate heavy metals has been used by Shackette (1965) in geochemical prospecting and by Ruhling and Tyler (1968, 1969, 1971) to study regional deposition of heavy metals. In extensive culture work Nash (1972) found that mosses were extremely sensitive to cadmium (down to $10^{-8}$M) and fairly sensitive to zinc (down to $10^{-6}$M).

## Fungi

On the basis of field studies a few non-lichenized fungi have been observed to be absent from polluted areas. One of the earliest field observations is that of Jones (1944) who noted that *Rhytisma acerinum* (tar-spot) on *Acer pseudoplatanus* '. . . is almost invariably present on sycamore, but is absent in the smoky neighbourhood of Manchester (T. G. Tutin), Newcastle (G. L. Drury), Birmingham, etc.' Jones uses 'smoke' here in a broad sense to cover all air pollutants (*see* chapter 8, p. 167). Köch (1955) found that the oak mildew (*Microsphaera alphitoides*) was absent from areas with sulphur dioxide pollution. Saunders (1966), in his detailed study of *Diplocarpon rosae* (black spot of roses), found a relationship between ambient sulphur dioxide and the intensity of infection; this fungus is limited by mean annual sulphur dioxide levels of *c* 100 $\mu g/m^3$. Other species known to be absent from polluted areas include *Melampsorella cerastii*, *Peridermium coloradense*, *Melampsora* spp., *Gymnosporangium* spp. and *Phragmidium* spp. (Scheffer and Hedgcock, 1955), *Puccinia graminis* (Johansson in Skye, 1958) and *Hysterium pulicare* (Skye, 1968). Little work has been done on the distribution of fungi in relation to air pollutants when compared with that on the lichenized fungi (*see* ch 3) but the study of Ing (1969) on the fungal flora of Stanmore Common in north London yielded 270 species in an area where the mean winter sulphur dioxide levels are about 120 $\mu g/m^3$.

Some fungi have been shown to be relatively sensitive to sulphur dioxide in laboratory experiments and consequently food chemists have used fumigation techniques with this pollutant to prevent fungal growth. Critical summaries of the experimental work in this field have been provided by Saunders (1970, 1971). McCallan and Weedon (1940) studied the effects of sulphur dioxide, chlorine, hydrogen sulphide, ammonia and hydrogen cyanide on eight species of fungi. These workers found a reciprocal relation between the duration of exposure to sulphur dioxide and concentration of sulphur dioxide. Exposures at 96 per cent relative humidity were found by Couey and Uota (1961) to be twenty times more inhibitory than exposures at 75 per cent relative humidity in *Botrytis cinerea.* Couey and Uota also discovered that the toxicity of sulphur dioxide to this fungus increased 1.5 times with each rise of 10°C. In aqueous solution, fungal spore germination may be inhibited by sulphur dioxide concentrations as low as 15 ppm.

Webster (Agricultural Research Council, 1967) notes that although some plant pathogenic fungi are more susceptible to sulphur dioxide than their hosts, in general they are inhibited only by concentrations at which the host is also adversely affected (Guderian and Stratmann, 1962).

Fungi also appear to be sensitive to ozone. Price (1968), who fumigated *Helminthosporium sativum* at 35 pphm ozone for 144 hours, found that growth and lipid content were reduced. Treshow *et al.* (1969) exposed *Colletotrichum lindemuthianum* to 10 pphm ozone for 4 hours each day for four days, and they found decreased growth, inhibition of sporulation, loss of pigmentation, and a 28 per cent decrease in lipid content. Hibben and Stotzky (1969), while experimenting with several fungal species, found that spore germination was inhibited by exposure to 25 pphm for 6 hours in the more sensitive species.

## References*

Adams, D. F., Mayhew, R. M., Gnagy, R. M., Richey, E. P., Koppe, R. K. and Allen, I. W. (1952). Atmospheric pollution in the Ponderosa 'pine' blight area, Spokane County, Washington. *J. Eng. Chem.* **44,** 1356–65.

Adams, D. F. and Sulzbach, C. W. (1961). Nitrogen deficiency and fluoride susceptibility of bean seedlings. *Science, N.Y.* **133,** 1245–6.

Agricultural Research Council (1967). *The effects of air pollution on plants and soil.* London: Agricultural Research Council.

Anderson, F. K. (1966). *Air pollution damage to vegetation in Georgetown Canyon, Idaho.* M.Sc. thesis, University of Utah.

Applegate, H. G. and Durrant, L. C. (1969). Synergistic action of ozone-sulfur dioxide on peanuts. *Environ. Sci. Technol.* **3,** 759–60.

Barrett, T. W. and Benedict, H. M. (1970). Sulfur dioxide. In: Jacobson, J. S. and Hill, A. C. (ed.) *Recognition of air pollution injury to vegetation: A pictorial atlas,* C1–C17. Pittsburgh: Air Pollution Control Association.

* See also p. 378.

Barton, L. V. (1940). Toxicity of ammonia, chlorine, hydrogen cyanide, hydrogen sulphide, and sulphur dioxide gases. IV. Seeds. *Contr. Boyce Thompson Inst. Pl. Res.* **11,** 357–63.

Bear, F. E. (1957). Toxic elements in soils. In: U.S. Department of Agriculture, *Soil. The year book of agriculture:* 165–71. Washington, D.C.: U.S. Department of Agriculture.

Benedict, H. M. and Breen, W. H. (1955). The use of weeds as a means of evaluating vegetation damage caused by air pollution. *Proceedings 3rd National Air Pollution Symposium,* 177–90.

Benedict, H. M., Ross, J. M. and Wade, R. W. (1964). The disposition of atmospheric fluorides by vegetation. *Int. J. Air Wat. Pollut.* **8,** 279–89.

Benson, N. R. (1959). Fluoride injury or soft suture and splitting of peaches. *Proc. Am. Soc. Hort. Sci.* **74,** 184–98.

Berge, H. (1952). Zinc as plant nutrient and plant toxin II. *Kgl. Norske Videnskabers Selskabs Skr.* **4,** 5–33.

Berry, C. R. (1964). Differences in concentrations of surface oxidant between valley and mountaintop conditions in the southern Appalachians. *J. Air Pollut. Contr. Ass.* **14,** 238–9.

Bleasdale, J. K. A. (1959). The effect of air pollution on plant growth. *Symp. Inst. Biol.* **8,** 81–7.

Bohne, H. (1963). Schadlichkeit von Staub aus Zimentwerken für Waldbestande. *Allgem. Forstz.* **18,** 107–11.

Bolay, A. and Bovay, E. (1965). Observations sur la sensibilité aux gaz fluorés de quelques espèces végétales du Valais. *Phytopathol. Z.* **53,** 289–98.

Bossavy, M. J. (1966). Les necroses due au fluor. *Pollut. Atmos.* **8,** 176–84.

Bradshaw, A. D. (1970). Plants and industrial waste. *Trans. Proc. bot. Soc. Edinb.* **41,** 71–84.

Brandt, C. S. and Heck, W. W. (1968). Effects of air pollutants on vegetation. In: Stern, A. C. (ed.) *Air Polution* **1,** 401–43. Ed. 2. New York: Academic Press.

Bredemann, G. and Radeloff, H. (1932). Ueber Schädigung von Pflanzen durch Ammoniakgase und ihren Nachweis. *Z. Pflanzenkrankh. Pflanzenschultz* **42,** 457–65.

Brennan, E., Leone, I. and Daines, R. H. (1962). Ammonia injury to apples and peaches in storage. *Pl. Dis. Reptr* **46,** 792–5.

Brennan, E., Leone, I. A. and Daines, R. H. (1964). The importance of variety in ozone plant damage. *Pl. Dis. Reptr* **48,** 923–4.

Brennan, E., Leone, I. and Daines, R. H. (1965). Chlorine as a phytotoxic air pollutant. *Int. J. Air Wat. Pollut.* **9,** 791–7.

Brewer, R. F., Creveling, R. K., Guillemet, F. B. and Sutherland, F. H. The effects of hydrogen fluoride gas on seven *Citrus* varieties. *Proc. Am. Soc. Hort. Sci.* **75,** 236–43.

Brewer, R. F., Guillemet, F. B. and Sutherland, F. H. (1966). The effects of atmospheric fluoride on gladiolus growth, flowering, and corm production. *Proc. Am. Soc. Hort. Sci.* **88,** 631–4.

Brewer, R. F., Sutherland, F. H. and Guillemet, F. B. (1967). The relative susceptibility of some popular varieties of roses to fluoride air pollution. *Proc. Am. Soc. Hort. Sci.* **91,** 771–6.

Brisley, H. H. and Jones, W. W. (1950). Sulphur dioxide fumigation of wheat with special reference to its effect on yield. *Plant Physiol.* **25,** 666–81.

Chang, C. W. (1968). Effect of fluoride on nucleotides and ribonucleic acid in germinating corn seedling roots. *Plant Physiol.* **43,** 669–74.

Chapman, H. D. (1960). The diagnosis and control of zinc deficiency and excess. *Bull. Res. C. Israel, Bot.* **8,** 105–30.

Coker, P. D. (1967). The effects of sulphur dioxide pollution on bark epiphytes. *Trans. Br. bryol. Soc.* **5,** 341–7.

Comeau, G. and LeBlanc, F. (1971). Influence de l'ozone et l'andydride sulfureux sur la régénération des feuilles de *Funaria hygrometrica* Hedw. *Nat. Can.* **98,** 347–58.

Cotrufo, C. and Berry, C. R. (1970). Some effects of a soluble NPK fertilizer on sensitivity of eastern white pine to injury from $SO_2$ air pollution. *Forest Sci.* **16,** 72–3.

Couey, H. M. and Uota, M. (1961). Effects of concentration, exposure time, temperature, and relative humidity on the toxicity of sulfur dioxide to the spores of *Botrytis cinerea*. *Phytopathology* **51,** 815–19.

Cristiani, H. and Gautier, R. (1925). Emanations fluorées des usines: étude experimentale de l'action du fluor sur les vegetaux. *Ann. Hygiene Publ.* **3,** 49–64.

Crocker, W. and Knight, L. I. (1908). Effect of illuminating gas and ethylene upon flowering carnations. *Bot. Gaz.* **46,** 259–76.

Czaja, A. T. (1962). Über das Problem der Zementstaubwirkungen auf Pflanzen. *Staub* **22,** 228–32.

Czaja, A. T. (1966). Über die Einwirkung von Stäuben, speziell von Zementofenstaub auf Pflanzen. *Angew. Bot.* **40,** 106–20.

Daines, R. H. (1968). Sulfur dioxide and plant response. *J. Occup. Med.* **10,** 516–24.

Daines, R. H., Leone, I. A. and Brennan, E. (1952). The effect of fluorine on plants as determined by soil nutrition and fumigation studies. In: McCabe, L. C. (ed.) *Air Pollution*, 97–105. New York: McGraw-Hill.

Darley, E. F., Dugger, W. M., Mudd, J. B., Ordin, L., Taylor, O. C. and Stephens, E. R. (1963). Plant damage by pollution derived from automobiles. *Arch. Environ. Health* **6,** 761–70.

Darley, E. F. and Middleton, J. T. (1966). Problems of air pollution in plant pathology. *Ann. Rev. Phytopath.* **4,** 103–18.

Darley, E. F., Nichols, C. W. and Middleton, J. T. (1966). Identification of air pollution damage to agricultural crops. *Bull. Agr. Calif.* **55,** 11–19.

Dass, H. C. and Weaver, G. M. (1968). Modification of ozone damage to *Phaseolus vulgaris* by antioxidants, thiols and sulfhydryl reagents. *Can. J. Pl. Sci.* **48,** 569–74.

Davis, D. D. and Wood, F. A. (1972). The relative susceptibility of eighteen coniferous species to ozone. *Phytopathology* **62,** 14–19.

DeSloover, J. and LeBlanc, F. (1970). Pollutions atmosphériques et fertilité chez les mousses et chez les lichens épiphytiques. *Bull. Acad. Soc. lorr. Sci.* **9,** 82–90.

Dilling, W. J. (1926). Influence of lead and the metallic ions of copper, zinc, thorium, beryllium and thallium on the germination of seeds. *Ann. appl. Biol.* **13,** 160–7.

Dochinger, L. S., Bender, F. W., Fox, F. L. and Heck, W. W. (1970). Chlorotic dwarf of eastern white pine caused by an ozone and sulphur dioxide interaction. *Nature, Lond.* **225,** 476.

Dugger, W. M., Koukol, J. and Palmer, R. L. (1966). Physiological and biochemical effects of atmospheric oxidants on plants. *J. Air Pollut. Contr. Assoc.* **16,** 467–71.

Dugger, W. M., Mudd, J. B. and Koukol, J. (1965). Effect of PAN on certain photosynthetic reactions. *Arch. Environ. Health* **10,** 195–200.

Dugger, W. M. and Ting, I. P. (1970). Air pollution oxidants—their effects on metabolic processes in plants. *Ann. Rev. Pl. physiol.* **21,** 215–34.

Feder, W. A. and Campbell, F. J. (1968). Influence of low levels of ozone on flowering of carnations. *Phytopathology* **58,** 1038–9.

Garber, K. (1960). Neuere Literatur über Rauch-, Staub- und Abgasschäden. *Angew. Bot.* **34,** 65–103.

Garber, K. (1962). Neuere Literatur über Rauch-, Staub- und Abgasschäden II. *Angew. Bot.* **36,** 127–84.

Garber, K. (1966). Die Beeinflussung der Pflanzenwelt durch fluorhaltige Immissionen. *Angew. Bot.* **40,** 12–21.

Gilbert, O. L. (1968). Bryophytes as indicators of air pollution in the Tyne Valley. *New Phytol.* **67,** 15–30.

Gilbert, O. L. (1970*a*). Further studies on the effect of sulphur dioxide on lichens and bryophytes. *New Phytol.* **69,** 605–27.

Gilbert, O. L. (1970*b*). A biological scale for the estimation of sulphur dioxide pollution. *New Phytol.* **69,** 629–34.

Givan, C. V. and Torrey, J. G. (1968). Fluoride inhibition of respiration and fermentation in cultured cells of *Acer pseudoplatanus. Physiologia Pl.* **21,** 1010–19.

Godish, T. J. and Lacasse, N. L. (1969). Effect of acute exposure to hydrogen chloride gas on photosynthesis, respiration and transpiration of tomato var. Bonny Best. National Air Pollution Control Association, 69–138.

Guderian, R., van Haut, H. and Stratmann, H. (1960). Problems of measurement and evaluation of the effect of gaseous impurities on vegetation. *Zeits. Pflanzenkrank L* **67,** 257–64.

Guderian, R. and Stratmann, H. (1962). Field trials for the determination of $SO_2$ effects on vegetation. I. Review of experimental techniques and experimental evaluation. *Forschungsberichte des Landes NRW*, no. 1118.

Hanson, G. P., Thorne, L. and Jativa, C. D. (1970). *Ozone tolerance of petunia leaves as related to their ascorbic acid concentration.* Arcadia: Los Angeles State and County Arboretum. [Preprint.]

Hart, G. E. (1969). *Cytogenic effects of fluoride: Technical progress report.* Texas Agricultural and Mechanical Univ., College Station, Research Grant AP 00447.

Haselhoff, E., Bredemann, G. and Haseloff, W. (1932). *Entstehung und Beurteilung von Rauchschäden.* Berlin: Verlagsbuchhandlung Gebrüder Bornträger.

Haselhoff, E. and Lindau, G. (1903). *Die Beschädigung der Vegetation durch Rauch.* Leipzig: Bornträger.

Haut, H. van (1961). The effect of sulphur dioxide on plants in laboratory experiments. *Staub* **21,** 52–6.

Haut, H. van and Stratmann, H. (1967). Experimentelle untersuchungen uber die Winkunge von Stuckstoffdioxide auf Pflanzen. *Schriftenreihe der Landesanstalt für Immission- und Bodennutzungs schutz des landes Nordrhein-Westfalen, Essen* **7,** 50–70.

Haywood, J. K. (1910). Injury to vegetation and animal life by smelter waste. *U.S. Department of Agric., Chem., Bull.* **113** (revised), 1–63.

Heck, W. W. (1964). Plant injury induced by photochemical reaction products of propylene-nitrogen dioxide mixtures. *J. Air Pollut. Contr. Ass.* **14,** 255–61.

Heck, W. W., Daines, R. H. and Hindawi, I. J. (1970). Other phytotoxic pollutants. In: Jacobsen, J. S. and Hill, A. C. (ed.) *Recognition of air pollution injury to vegetation: A pictorial atlas,* F1–F24. Pittsburgh: Air Pollution Control Association.

Heck, W. W. and Pires, E. G. (1962). Growth of plants fumigated with saturated and unsaturated hydrocarbon gases and their derivatives. *Texas Agr. Expt. Sta. Rept.* **MP-603.**

Hedgcock, G. G. (1912). Winter-killing and smelter-injury in the forests of Montana. *Torreya* **12,** 25–30.

Heggestad, H. E. (1968). Diseases of crops and ornamental plants incited by air pollutants. *Phytopathology* **58,** 1089–97.

Hewitt, E. J. (1952). Metal interrelationships in plant nutrition. I. Effect of some metal toxicities on sugar beet, tomato, oat, potato, and narrow stem kale grown in sand culture. *J. exp. Bot.* **4,** 59–64.

Hibben, C. R. and G. Stotzky (1969). Effects of ozone on the germination of fungus spores. *Can. J. Microbiol.* **15,** 1187–96.

Hill, A. C. and Bennett (1970). Inhibition of apparent photosynthesis by nitrogen oxides. *Atmos. Environ.* **4,** 341–8.

Hill, A. C., Heggestad, H. E. and Linzon, S. N. (1970). Ozone. In: Jacobsen, J. S. and Hill, A. C. (ed.) *Recognition of air pollution injury to vegetation: A pictorial atlas,* B1–B22. Pittsburgh: Air Pollution Control Association.

Hill, A. C., Pack, M. R., Treshow, M., Downs, R. J. and Transtrum, L. G. (1961). Plant injury induced by ozone. *Phytopathology* **51,** 356–63.

Hindawi, I. J. (1970). *Air pollution injury to vegetation.* Raleigh: National Air Pollution Control Administration.

Hitchcock, A. E., Zimmerman, P. W. and Coe, R. R. (1962). Results of ten years' work (1951–60) on the effect of fluorides on gladiolus. *Contr. Boyce Thompson Inst. Pl. Res.* **21,** 303–44.

Hluchan, E., Mayer, J. and Abel, E. (1964). The influence of aluminium-works exhalations on the content of fluorides in soil and grass. *Pol'-nohospodarstvo* **10,** 257–62. [Slovak.]

Holmes, J. A., Franklin, E. C. and Gould, R. A. (1915). Selby Report. *U.S. Bureau of Mines, Bull.* **98.**

Hunter, J. G. and Vergnano, O. (1953). Trace-element toxicities in oat plants. *Ann. appl. Biol.* **40,** 761–77.

Hursh, C. R. (1948). Local climate in the Copper Basin of Tennessee as modified by the removal of vegetation. *U.S. Department of Agric. Circ.* **774.**

Ing, B. (1969). Fungi at Stanmore. *J. Ruislip Dist. nat. Hist. Soc.* **18,** 23–9.

Jacobson, J. S. and Hill, A. C. (1970). *Recognition of air pollution injury to vegetation: A pictorial atlas.* Pittsburgh: Air Pollution Control Association.

Jacobson, J. S., Weinstein, L. H., McCune, D. C. and Hitchcock, A. E. (1966). The accumulation of fluorine by plants. *J. Air Pollut. Contr. Ass.* **16,** 412–17.

Jones, E. W. (1944). Biological flora of the British Isles, *Acer* L. *J. Ecol.* **32,** 215–52.

Jordan, H. V. and Reisenhauer, H. M. (1957). Sulphur and soil fertility. In: *U.S. Department of Agriculture Yearbook of Agriculture, Soils,* 107–11.

Karpen, D. N. (1970). Ozone and sulfur dioxide synergism: Foliar injury to a Ponderosa Pine geographic race plantation in the Puget Sound region. *Pl. Dis. Reptr* **54,** 945–8.

Katz, M. (1939). Effect of sulfur dioxide on vegetation. *Nat. Res. Counc. (Canada) Publ.* no. **815.**

Katz, M. (1949). Sulfur dioxide in the atmosphere and its relation to plant life. *Ind. Engng. Chem.* **41,** 2450–65.

Katz, M. and McCallum, A. W. (1952). The effect of sulfur dioxide on conifers. In: McCabe, L. C. (ed.) *Air Pollution,* 84–96. New York: McGraw-Hill.

Knabe, W. (1971). Air quality criteria and their importance for forests. *Mitt. forstl. BundVersAnst. Wien* **92,** 129–50.

Kneip, T. J., Eisenbud, M., Strehlow, C. D. and Freudenthal, P. C. (1970). Airborne particulates in New York City. *J. Air Pollut. Contr. Ass.* **20,** 144–9.

Köch, G. (1955). Eichenmehltau und Rauchgasschäden. *Z. PflKrankh. PflPath. PflSchutz* **45,** 44–5.

Koritz, H. G. and Went, F. W. (1953). The physiological action of smog on plants. I. Initial growth and transpiration studies. *Plant Physiol.* **28,** 50–62.

Kotte, W. (1929). Rauchschaden an Steinobst-Früchten. *Nachrbl. Deut. PflSchutzdienst (Berlin)* **9,** 91–2.

Lagerwerff, J. V. and Specht, A. W. (1970). Contamination of roadside soil and vegetation with cadmium, nickel, and zinc. *Environ. Sci. Technol.* **4,** 583–6.

LeBlanc, F. (1961). Influence de l'atmosphère polluée des grandes agglomérations urbaines sur les épiphytes corticoles. *Rev. can. Biol.* **20,** 823–7.

LeBlanc, F. (1969). Epiphytes and air pollution. In: *Air Pollution, Proceedings of the first European Congress on the influence of air pollution on plants and animals, Wageningen 1968,* 211–21. Wageningen: Centre for Agricultural Publishing and Documentation.

LeBlanc, F., Comeau, G. and Rao, D. N. (1971). Fluoride injury symptoms in epiphytic lichens and mosses. *Can. J. Bot.* **49,** 1691–8.

LeBlanc, F. and DeSloover, J. (1970). Relation between industrialization and the distribution and growth of epiphytic lichens and mosses in Montreal. *Can. J. Bot.* **48,** 1485–96.

LeBlanc, F. and Rao, D. N. (1966). Réaction de quelques lichens et mousses épiphytiques à l'anhydride sulfreux dans la région de Sudbury, Ontario. *Bryologist* **69,** 338–46.

Ledbetter, M. C., Mavrodineanu, R. and Weiss, A. J. (1960). Distribution studies of radioactive fluorine-18 and stable fluorine-19 in tomato plants. *Contr. Boyce Thompson Inst. Pl. Res.* **20,** 331–48.

Lee, T. T. (1968). Effect of ozone on swelling of tobacco mitochondria. *Plant. Physiol.* **43,** 133–9.

Leonard, C. D. and Graves, H. B. (1966). Effect of airborne fluoride on Valencia orange yields. *Proc. Fla. State Hort. Soc.* **79,** 79–86.

Leone, I. A., Brennan, E., and Daines, R. H. (1965). Factors influencing $SO_2$ phytotoxicity in New Jersey. *Pl. Dis. Reptr* **49,** 911–15.

Linzon, S. N. (1958). The influence of smelter fumes on the growth of white pine in the Sudbury region. *Can. Dept. Agr. Forest. Biol. Div. Sci. Ser.* (*Toronto*).

Linzon, S. N. (1970). Economic effects of sulphur dioxide on forest growth. *63rd annual meeting of the Air Pollut. Control Association.* St Louis.

Lords, J. L. and McNulty, I. B. (1965). Estimation of ATP in leaf tissue employing the firefly luminescent reactions. *Utah Acad. Sci. Arts Lett.* **42,** 163–4.

Lundegardh, H. (1927). The influence upon the growth of plants of zinc and lead, precipitated from factory fumes into the soil. *Kgl. Landtbruks-Akad. Handl. Tid.* **66,** 626.

McCallan, S. E. A. and Weedon, F. R. (1940). Toxicity of ammonia, chlorine, hydrogen cyanide, hydrogen sulphide, and sulphur dioxide gases. II. Fungi and bacteria. *Contr. Boyce Thomson Inst. Pl. Res.* **11,** 331–42.

McCune, D. C. and Hitchcock, A. E. (1970). Fluoride in forage: factors determining its accumulation from the atmosphere and concentration in the plant. *International Clean Air Congress,* paper **MB-40B.**

McCune, D. C., Hitchcock, A. E., Jacobson, J. S. and Weinstein, L. H. (1965). Fluoride accumulation and growth of plants exposed to particulate cryolite in the atmosphere. *Contr. Boyce Thompson Inst. Pl. Res.* **23,** 1–12.

McCune, D. C., Hitchcock, A. E. and Weinstein, L. H. (1967). Effect of mineral nutrition on the growth and sensitivity of gladiolus to hydrogen fluoride. *Contr. Boyce Thompson Inst. Pl. Res.* **23,** 295–9.

MacDowall, F. D. H. (1965). Predisposition of tobacco to ozone damage. *Can. J. Pl. Sci.* **45,** 1–12.

MacKnight, M. (1968). *Effects of ozone on stomatal activity of pinto bean.* M.Sc. thesis, University of Utah.

MacLean, D. C., Weinstein, L. H., McCune, D. C., Mandl, R. H., Hitchcock, A. E. and Woodruff, G. N. (1968). Effects of acute hydrogen fluoride and nitrogen dioxide exposures on citrus and ornamental plants of central Florida. *Environ. Sci. Tech.* **2,** 444–9.

McNulty, I. B. and Newman, D. W. (1957). Effects of atmospheric fluoride on the respiration rate of bush bean and gladiolus leaves. *Pl. Physiol., Lancaster* **32,** 121–4.

McNulty, I. B. and Newman, D. W. (1961). Mechanism(s) of fluoride-induced chlorosis. *Pl. Physiol., Lancaster* **36,** 385–8.

Majernik, O. and Mansfield, T. A. (1970). Direct effect of $SO_2$ pollution on the degree of opening of stomata. *Nature, Lond.* **227,** 377–8.

Mamaev, S. A. and Nikolaevskiy, V. S. (1968). Some peculiarities of the susceptibility of scotch pine to sulfur dioxide injury. *Tr. Inst. Ekol. Rast. Zhivotn., Ural. Filial, Akad. Nauk. SSSR* **2,** 203–7.

Martinez, J. D., Nathany, M. and Dharmarajan, V. (1971). Spanish moss, a sensor for lead. *Nature, Lond.* **233,** 564–5.

Materna, J. (1960). Forstliche Massnahmen zur Erfassung und Verhuetung von Waldrauchschaeden im tschechischen Teil des Erzgebirges. *Forst. Holzwirtschaft* **15,** 1–10.

Matsuoka, Y., Udagawa, O. and Ono, T. (1969). Effects of sulfur dioxide on pear pollination. *J. Japan Soc. Air Pollut.* **4,** 130.

Matushima, J. and Harada, M. (1964). Sulphur dioxide injury to fruit trees. I. Comparisons of resistance of fruit trees and effects on leaf fall and growth of citrus species. *Bull. Fac. Agric. Mil. Univ.* **30,** 11–32.

Menser, H. A. and Hodges, G. H. (1967). Nitrogen nutrition and susceptibility of tobacco leaves to ozone. *Tobacco* **165,** 30–3.

Miller, P. R., Parmeter, J. R., Flick, B. H. and Martinez, C. W. (1969). Ozone dosage response of Ponderosa pine seedlings. *J. Air Pollut. Contr. Ass.* **19,** 435–8.

Miyazaki, S., Okinaga, T. and Harata, M. (1954). The effect of fertilizer on the growth of black locust (*Robinia pseudo acacia*, L.) seedlings transplanted in Kosaka bare lands injured by the strong sulphate smoke. [Kosaka kozan no engaichi ni okeru niseakashiya no shihi shokusai shiken.] *Ringyo Shikenja Aomori Shijo Gyomu Kokoku* **1,** 1–10.

Mohamed, A. H. (1969). Cytogenetic effects of hydrogen fluoride on plants. *Fluoride Quart. Repts* **2,** 76–84.

Mohamed, A. H. (1970). Chromosomal changes in maize induced by hydrogen fluoride gas. *Can. J. Genet. Cytol.* **12,** 614–20.

Mudd, J. B. (1963). Enzyme inactivation by peroxyacetyl nitrate. *Archs Biochem. Biophys.* **102,** 59–65.

Mudd, J. B., McManus, T. T. and Ongun, A. (1970). Inhibition of lipid metabolism in chloroplasts by ozone. *International Clean Air Congress,* paper **MB-33B.**

Nash, E. (1972). *The effects of effluents from a zinc smelter on mosses.* Ph.D. thesis, Rutgers State University.

Oertli, J. J. (1959). Effects of salinity on susceptibility of sunflower plants to smog. *Soil Sci.* **87,** 249–51.

Ordin, L., Garber, M. J. and Kindinger, J. I. (1970). Effect of 2,4-D on cell wall metabolism of peroxyacetyl nitrate pretreated *Avena* coleoptil sections. *Physiologia Pl.* **23,** 117–23.

Otto, H. W. and Daines, R. H. (1969). Plant injury by air pollutants; influence on stomatal apertures to plant response on ozone. *Science, N.Y.* **160,** 1209–10.

Pack, M. R. (1969). *Effects of hydrogen fluoride on production and food reserve content of bean seed* [Paper presented at Pacific Northwest International Section Meeting of the Air Pollution Control Association].

Pack, M. R. (1971). Effects of hydrogen fluoride on bean reproduction. *J. Air Pollut. Contr. Ass.* **21,** 133–7.

Peirce, G. J. (1910). An effect of cement dust on orange trees. *Plant World* **13,** 283–8.

Pelz, E., Beyer, H. and Bleyer, G. (1963). Untersuchungen zur Diagnose und Wirkung von Rauchschadden in der Umgebung einer Bleihuette. *Wiss. Z. Tech. Univ. Dresden* **12,** 209–16.

Pfeffer, A. (1965). The effect of air polluted with sulphur dioxide on the countryside. In: *Preprints of the Czechoslovak Reports, International Symposium on the control and utilization of sulphur dioxide and fly-ash from the flue gases of large thermal power plants.* Liblice House of Scientific Workers.

Poovaiah, B. W. and Wiebe, H. H. (1969). Tylosis formation in response to fluoride fumigation of leaves. *Phytopathology* **59,** 518–19.

Price, H. E. (1968). *The effect of ozone on lipid production in the fungus* Helminthosporium sativum. M.Sc. thesis, Utah University, Salt Lake City.

Rao, D. N. and LeBlanc, F. (1967). Influence of an iron-sintering plant on corticolous epiphytes in Wawa, Ontario. *Bryologist* **70,** 141–57.

Reinhard, H. (1959). Die Fluorschaden im unteren Frichtal. *Schweiz. Arch. Tierheilk.* **101,** 1–4.

Richards, B. L., Middleton, J. T. and Hewitt, W. B. (1958). Air pollution with relation to agronomic crops: V. oxidant stipple to grape. *Agron. J.* **50,** 559–61.

Richards, B. L. and Taylor, O. C. (1965). Significance of atmospheric ozone as a phytotoxicant. *J. Air. Pollut. Contr. Ass.* **15,** 191–3.

Robinson, G. D. (1970). *Long term effects of air pollution, a survey.* Bethesda, Maryland: National Air Pollution Administration.

Ross, C. W., Wiebe, H. H., Miller, G. W. and Hurst, R. L. (1968). Respiratory pathway, flower color, and leaf area of gladiolus as factors in the resistance to fluoride injury. *Bot. Gaz.* **129,** 49–52.

Rühling, Å. and Tyler, G. (1968). An ecological approach to the lead problem. *Bot. Notiser* **121,** 321–42.

Rühling, Å. and Tyler, G. (1969). Ecology of heavy metals—a regional and historical study. *Bot. Notiser* **122,** 248–59.

Rühling, Å. and Tyler, G. (1971). Regional differences in the deposition of heavy metals over Scandinavia. *J. appl. Ecol.* **8,** 497–507.

Saunders, P. J. W. (1966). The toxicity of sulphur dioxide to *Diplocarpon rosae* Wolf causing blackspot of roses. *Ann. appl. Biol.* **58,** 103–14.

Saunders, P. J. W. (1970). Air pollution in relation to lichens and fungi. *Lichenologist* **4,** 337–49.

Saunders, P. J. W. (1971). Modification of the leaf surface and its environment by pollution. In: Preece, T. F. and Dickinson, C. H. (ed.) *Ecology of leaf surface micro-organisms*, 81–101. London and New York: Academic Press.

Scheffer, T. C. and Hedgcock, G. G. (1955). Injury to northwestern forest trees by sulfur dioxide from smelters. *U.S. Department of Agric. Tech. Bull.* **1117.**

Schmidt, H. (1951). Beobachtung uber Gasschaden an Obstbaumen. *Deut. Baumsch* **3,** 10–12.

Schriner, D. S. and Lacasse, N. L. (1969). Distribution of chlorides in tomato following exposure to hydrogen chloride gas. *Phytopathology* **59,** 402.

Shacklette, H. T. (1965). Bryophytes associated with mineral deposits and solutions in Alaska. *U.S. Geol. Surv. Bull.* **1198-C.**

Shoemyen, J. (1967). Ozone, soil moisture, maturity level: interaction causes weather fleck on shade tobacco. *Sunshine State Agr. Res. Rept.* **1967,** 8–9.

Skye, E. (1958). Luftföroreningars inverkan på busk- och bladlavfloran kring skifferoljeverket i Närkes Kvarntorp. *Svensk bot. Tidskr.* **52,** 133–90.

Skye, E. (1968). Lichens and air pollution. *Acta phytogeogr. suec.* **52,** 1–123.

Solberg, R. A. and Adams, D. F. (1956). Histological responses of some plant leaves to hydrogen fluoride and sulfur dioxide. *Am. J. Bot.* **43,** 755–60.

Spirtas, R. and Levin, H. J. (1971). Patterns and trends in levels of suspended particulate matter. *J. Air Pollut. Contr. Ass.* **21,** 329–333.

Stephens, E. R., Darley, E. C., Taylor, O. C. and Scott, W. E. (1961). Photochemical reaction products in air pollution. *Int. J. Air Wat Pollut.* **4,** 79–100.

Stephens, E. R., Hanst, P. L., Doerr, R. C. and Scott, W. E. (1956).

Reactions of $NO_2$ and organic compounds in air. *Ind. Engng. Chem. int. Edn* **48,** 1498–504.
Stratmann, H. (1963). Determination of sulphur dioxide emissions into the atmosphere which endanger vegetation. *Stand und Leistung, agriculturchemischer und agrarbiologisucher Forschung,* **10,** 13–16.
Swedish Royal Ministry for Foreign Affairs and Swedish Royal Ministry of Agriculture (1971). *Air pollution across national boundaries. The impact on the environment of sulfur in air and precipitation, Sweden's case study for the United Nations conference on the human environment.* Stockholm: Swedish Preparatory Committee for the United Nations Conference on the Human Environment.
Taylor, O. C. (1968). Effects of oxidant air pollutants. *J. Occup. Med.* **10,** 53–60.
Taylor, O. C. (1969). Importance of peroxyacetyl nitrate (PAN) as a phytotoxic air pollutant. *J. Air Pollut. Contr. Ass.* **19,** 347–51.
Taylor, O. C. and Eaton, F. M. (1966). Suppression of plant growth by nitrogen dioxide. *Pl. Physiol., Lancaster* **41,** 132–5.
Taylor, O. C. and MacLean, D. C. (1970). Nitrogen oxides and peroxyacetyl nitrates. In: Jacobson, J. S. and Hill, A. C. (ed.)) *Recognition of air pollution injury to vegetation: a pictorial atlas,* E1–E14. Pittsburgh: Air Pollution Control Association.
Tebbens, B. D. (1968). Gaseous pollutants in the air. In: Stern, A. C. (ed.) *Air Pollution* **1,** 23–46. Ed. 2. New York: Academic Press.
Thomas, M. D. (1951). Gas damage to plants. *A. Rev. Pl. Physiol.* **2,** 293–322.
Thomas, M. D. (1958). Air pollution with relation to agronomic crops. I. General status of research on the effects of air pollution on plants. *Agron. J.* **50,** 545–50.
Thomas, M. D. (1961). Effects of air pollution on plants. In: *Air Pollution.* Geneva: World Health Organization.
Thomas, M. D. and Hendricks, R. H. (1956). Effect of air pollution on plants. In: Magill, P. L., Holder, H. R. and Ackley, C. (ed.) *Air Pollution Handbook:* New York: McGraw-Hill.
Thomas, M. D. and Hill, G. M. (1937). Relation of sulphur dioxide in the atmosphere to photosynthesis and respiration of alfalfa. *Pl. Physiol., Lancaster* **12,** 309–83.
Thompson, C. R., Hensel, E. G., Kats, G. and Taylor, O. C. (1970). Effects of continuous exposure of navel oranges to nitrogen dioxide. *Atm. Environ.* **4,** 349–55.
Thompson, C. R., Kats, G. and Hensel, E. G. (1971). Effects of ambient levels of $NO_2$ on navel oranges. *Envir. Sci. Tech.* **5,** 1017–19.
Thompson, C. R., Taylor, O. C., Thomas, M. D. and Ivie, J. O. (1967). Effects of air pollutants on apparent photosynthesis and water use by citrus trees. *Envir. Sci. Tech.* **1,** 644–50.
Thomson, W. W., Dugger, W. M. and Palmer, R. L. (1965). Effects of peroxyacetyl nitrate on ultrastructure of chloroplasts. *Bot. Gaz.* **126,** 66–72.

Thomson, W. W., Dugger, W. M. and Palmer, R. L. (1966). Effects of ozone on the fine structure of the palisade parenchyma cells of bean leaves. *Can. J. Bot.* **44,** 1677–82.

Tomlinson, H. and Rich, S. (1968). The ozone resistance of leaves as related to their sulfhydryl and adenosine triphosphate content. *Phytopathology* **58,** 808–10.

Tomlinson, H. and Rich, S. (1969). Relating lipid content and fatty acid synthesis to ozone injury of tobacco leaves. *Phytopathology* **59,** 1284–6.

Treshow, M. (1970*a*). *Environment and plant response.* New York: McGraw-Hill.

Treshow, M. (1970*b*). Ozone damage to plants. *Environ. Pollut.* **1,** 155–61.

Treshow, M., Harner, F. M., Price, H. E. and Kormelink, J. R. (1969). Effects of ozone on growth, lipid metabolism, and sporulation of fungi. *Phytopathology* **59,** 1223–5.

Treshow, M. and Pack, M. R. (1970). Fluoride. In: Jacobson, J. S. and Hill, A. C. (ed.) *Recognition of air pollution injury to vegetation: a pictorial atlas,* D1–D17. Pittsburgh: Air Pollution Control Association.

Turner, R. (1969). Heavy metal tolerance in plants. In: Rorison, I. H. (ed.) *Ecological aspects of the mineral nutrition of plants.* Oxford: Blackwell.

Vandergrift, A. E., Shannon, L. J., Salkee, E. E., Gorman, P. G. and Park, W. R. (1971). Particulate air pollution in the United States. *J. Air Pollut. Contr. Ass.* **21,** 321–8.

Venkatasubramanyam, V., Adiga, P. R., Sivarama Sastry, K. and Sarma, P. S. (1962). The influence of iron and magnesium on cobalt and zinc toxicities in germinating seedlings of *Phaseolus radiatus. J. Sci. Industr. Res.* **21,** 167–70.

Vogl, M. (1964). Physiologische und Biochemische Beitrage zur Rauchschadenforschung. *Biol. Abl.* **5,** 587–94.

Weston, R., Gadgil, P., Salter, B. and Goodman, G. (1965). Problems of revegetation in the lower Swansea Valley, an area of extensive industrial dereliction. In: Goodman, G. T., Edwards, R. W. and Lambert, J. M. (ed.) *Ecology and the Industrial Society,* 297–326. Oxford: Blackwell.

Yu, M.-H. and Miller, G. W. (1967). Effect of fluoride on the respiration of leaves from higher plants. *Plant Cell Physiol.* (*Tokyo*) **8,** 483–93.

Zahn, R. (1961). Effects of sulphur dioxide on vegetation: Results of experimental exposure to gas. *Staub* **21,** 56–60.

Zahn, R. (1963). The significance of continuous and intermittent sulphur dioxide action for plant reaction. *Staub* **23,** 343–52.

Zahn, R. (1970). The effect on plants of a combination of subacute and toxic sulfur dioxide doses. *Staub* **30,** 20–3.

Zimmerman, P. W. (1955). Chemicals involved in air pollution and their effects upon vegetation. *Prof. Papers Boyce Thompson Inst. Pl. Res.* **2,** 124–45.

Zimmerman, P. W. and Hitchcock, A. E. (1956). Susceptibility of plants to hydrofluoric acid and sulfur dioxide gases. *Contr. Boyce Thompson Inst. Pl. Res.* **18,** 263–79.

# 11: Air Pollution and Lichen Physiology: Progress and Problems

L. C. PEARSON

The absence of lichens in cities is generally attributed to air pollution; over a century ago, the 'air pollution hypothesis' was developed by Nylander (1866) based on observations of the cryptogamic vegetation in the Luxembourg Gardens of Paris. Three decades later, Arnold (*see* Barkman, 1958) transplanted healthy bits of lichen thalli into the industry-polluted atmosphere of Munich where they soon died, and about the same time, Sernander began his classical studies of the lichen vegetation of Stockholm. Sernander (1912, 1926) described the central part of the city as a 'lichen desert', completely devoid of lichen life, surrounded by a 'struggle zone' in which some kinds of lichens could survive although the thalli were often different in form and colour from healthy specimens. Several other investigators (e.g. Mrose, 1941; Skye, 1958, 1968; Brodo, 1961, 1967; Fenton, 1960; and Gilbert, 1965, 1970) have contributed data demonstrating conclusively that a highly significant negative correlation exists between the degree of air pollution in or near a city or near other industrial sites and the abundance of lichens. This work is comprehensively reviewed in earlier chapters of this volume.

Rydzak (1956, 1969), however, has rightly pointed out that high correlation does not necessarily indicate a cause and effect relationship and that the abundance of lichens is also, to an extent, correlated with other characteristics of the city environment, *viz.* changes in air temperature and humidity, and overall vegetative cover. Granted that many kinds of lichens may be absent from the city environment because it is too dry for them, the 'Drought Hypothesis' fails to account for the very abundant growth of lichens in the desert areas of Asia, Africa, and North America, and for the absence of lichens in rural and forested areas near smelters and other industrial plants outside of cities. Nor does it account for the gradual rather than sharp decline in lichen vegetation at the edges of and in rural areas surrounding cities, and for the repeated observations of lichens remaining alive in the dry air of laboratories for long periods of time. It must be concluded, therefore, that the 'Drought Hypothesis' is inadequate to explain the absence of or the poor growth of most kinds of lichens in cities. The field data and views on the 'Drought Hypothesis', supported principally by Rydzak, are critically reviewed by Coppins in chapter 7. It is time that more attention was paid to the physiological effects of air pollution on lichens.

The few physiological studies that have been made thus far with lichens involving experimental manipulation of the atmospheric environment have mostly made use of highly unnatural levels of pollutants. For this reason, they have been severely criticized. Nevertheless, they have been very significant for two reasons: (1) they have demonstrated that experimental studies of this type are practical, and (2) they have suggested some ways in which pollutants may act physiologically. What are needed most now are studies involving more 'realistic' levels of air pollution and studies on the mode of action of sulphur dioxide and other pollutants on the physiological mechanisms of the lichen. However, until we know more about the physiological responses of lichens to 'normal' environmental factors, it will be difficult to assess the significance of studies involving lichens grown in polluted air. In chapter 12 Farrar comments briefly on some aspects of lichen physiology which are considered relevant to experimental studies on lichens involving air pollutants. Recent advances made in growing lichens under laboratory conditions should help in this regard.

**The pollutants**

Fluorides, ozone, peroxyacyl nitrates (PANs), carbon monoxide, sulphur dioxide, oxides of nitrogen, and dust are among the best-known pollutants of city air. Because sulphur dioxide is often the most abundant flue gas discharged by factories and power stations, and is also a major constituent of effluent from domestic heating plants, it has received the most attention in studies of air pollution effects on lichens. Lundström (1968), for example, reported that in Stockholm, sulphur dioxide, nitric oxide, and dust are the principal air pollutants, and that on cold days the sulphur dioxide content of the air frequently rises above the maximum allowable limit designated by the National Institute for Health and Hygiene as being safe for humans (25 pphm or *c* 700 $\mu g/m^3$ for any half-hour period or 5 pphm or *c* 140 $\mu g/m^3$ for any 30-day average). Skye (1968) reported that while dust was highly correlated with traffic, sulphur dioxide was highly correlated with temperature, increasing about 3 pphm or 84 $\mu g/m^3$ for every 10° drop in temperature during the winter months.

In Stockholm, the almost complete absence of lichens from the city centre, even in park-like areas on the various islands where trees are abundant, is largely attributable to sulphur dioxide in the air (Lundström, 1968; Skye, 1968). In some areas other atmospheric pollutants are probably more damaging. In California, the principal toxicants, in order of importance, are PANs, ethylene, and fluorides, with sulphur dioxide locally important. These four account for most of the $8 000 000 annual damage to crops from air pollution in that state (Darley *et al.*, 1966). Nitrogen dioxide and ozone are also important in California. In cities in Idaho, the pollutants arising from photochemical conversions of automobile exhausts likewise appear to be the most common pollutants. An Idaho Falls school teacher has collected data revealing a pattern of lichen distribution very similar to that in Stockholm with a 'lichen desert' in the area dominated by slow-moving automobile traffic and the railroad yards and with increased lichen cover observable as one travels from the city centre to the outlying rural areas (G. Kimbro, unpublished data).

That these pollutants are harmful to humans and to other animals and crop plants is now well established. Lave and Seskin (1970) conservatively estimate the financial cost of air pollution from the point of view of health at over $2 000 000 000 a year. This does not include brain damage from carbon monoxide or other pollutants, nor the costs of psychological illness, but only those costs resulting directly from medical expenses or loss of earning ability. They then suggest that despite this great cost, remarkably little is known about the physiological effects of air pollution. Likewise, air pollution-induced plant disease is very expensive, and yet little is known about the physiological effects of air pollution on plants. Recent reviews of the known physiological effects of air pollutants on crop plants have been prepared by Dugger and Ting (1970) and others cited by them. In chapter 10 of this volume Nash includes comment on the effects of various gaseous and particulate air pollutants on physiological processes in higher plants, including crop species.

## Experimental studies in the field

Although much valuable information has been gained from the many purely correlative studies comparing the frequency of lichens and the proximity to the city centre, the maximum gain in knowledge is achieved when laboratory and field-work are co-ordinated (Pringsheim, 1967), or when experimental studies are conducted in the field. Often, the establishment of a new source of pollution, such as a factory, has been the source of the experimental manipulation needed for a comparative study.

Skye (1958) studied the distribution of lichens downwind from a shale-oil plant that had been established during World War II in a rural area in central Sweden. Sulphur dioxide was the most abundant of the pollutants. Within a few years of its establishment, the lichen vegetation had completely deteriorated for some distance downwind while remaining pretty much unchanged upwind. From his observations, he was able to suggest certain species of lichens as promising indicators of air pollution conditions. As a follow-up study, a 50 kg cylinder of sulphur dioxide was placed near a lichen-covered oak tree in a rural area near Uppsala and the valve opened just enough to allow slow leakage of the gas. In about a month, noticeable morphological changes were evident: *Parmelia sulcata*, which was the most abundant lichen on the experimental tree, acquired a reddish-violet colour visible for some distance, and the thallus lobes or apical tips of other lichens, especially *Hypogymnia physodes*, *Evernia prunastri*, and *Ramalina farinacea*, became darkened. By spring, some six to eight months later, the lichens on the side of the tree nearest the source of pollution had fallen from the tree. Four years later, no colonization of the trees had yet taken place. Spectrophotometric observations revealed that the chlorophyll content in the fumigated *P. sulcata* was appreciably lower than in fresh specimens collected nearby. With the exception of grass leaves upon which the sulphur dioxide from the cylinder had directly discharged, there was no apparent damage to any vascular vegetation in this study (Skye, 1968).

It was hypothesized from this study that the reduced concentration of chlorophyll in the sulphur dioxide-damaged tissues would be accompanied by reduced photosynthesis. Therefore, Pearson and Skye (1965) collected lichens from four locations in and near Uppsala and observed their physiological behaviour in the laboratory. Photosynthesis was reduced in all cases in lichens collected near the city centre compared with those collected in a rural area. Respiration appeared to have been slightly increased in the lichens from the city centre although the difference was not statistically significant. The shape of the photosynthetic curves suggests that photo-respiration was stimulated by the pollution (Fig. 1). There was a tendency for the photosynthetic mechanism to become fatigued upon prolonged exposure to light in the lichens from the city centre but not in those collected in the rural areas. Since sulphur dioxide was the most abundant air pollutant in Uppsala, it was assumed that it was responsible for the physiological differences observed.

The transplant method has been effectively used in recent studies of air pollution effects. Brodo (1961) transplanted lichens from rural Long Island onto trees near the centre of New York City. These transplants died whereas lichens transplanted to trees near the place of origin or further from the city survived. LeBlanc and Rao (1966) transplanted lichens onto trees in the vicinity of smelters emitting sulphur dioxide (*see* ch 3). In a little over a year, these lichens were dead. Few observations of actual anatomical or physiological changes were reported in these two papers. Skye (personal communication) has examined material from the centre of Uppsala and from nearby rural areas and has observed brown cells in the algal layer of the former specimens.

Many lichens produce antibiotics (*see* Capriotti, 1959; Malicki, 1968; Pyatt, 1967). When the fresh thalli of *Peltigera canina* are macerated in a Waring blender and used as an extract for germinating seeds of various grasses, *Festuca ovina*, *F. rubra*, *Lolium perenne*, or *Poa pratensis*, germination is retarded (Pyatt, 1967). Pyatt (1968) used an extract from lichens growing near the steelworks in Wales, where the air was heavily polluted with

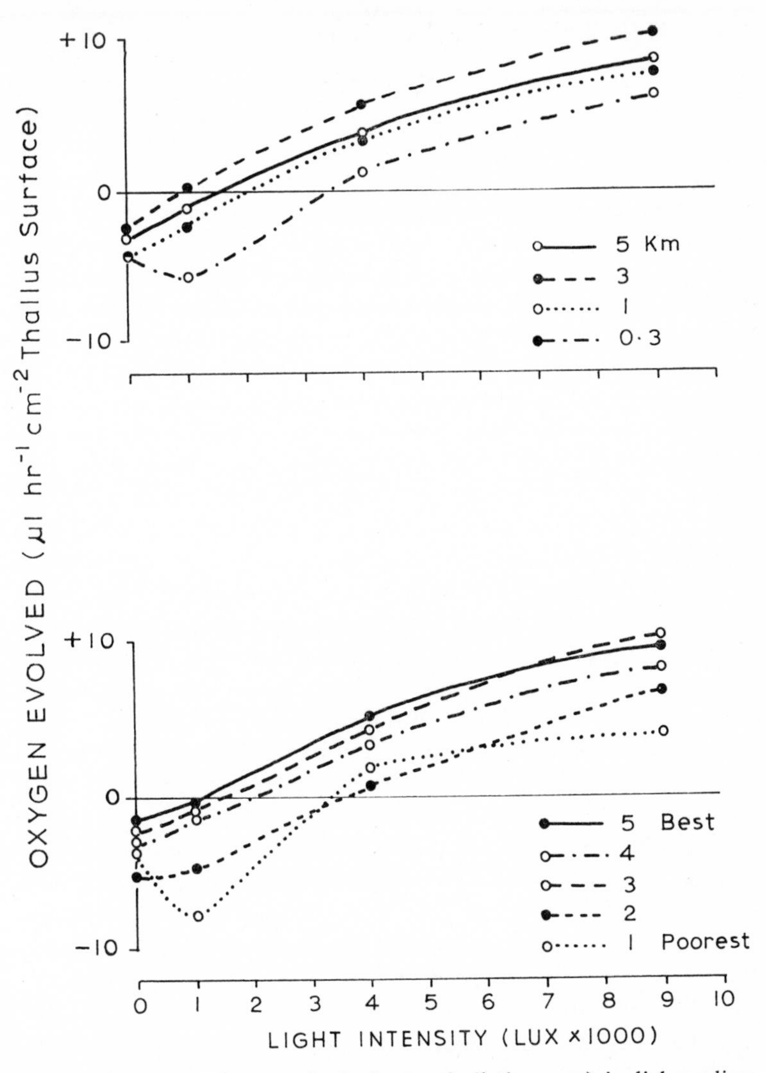


Fig. 1 Apparent photosynthesis (net assimilation rate) in lichen discs measured by the Warburg apparatus. (Top) Oxygen evolution by discs of *Parmelia sulcata* collected at four sites in or near Uppsala, Sweden. Collection sites were Ultuna, 5 km from the city centre; Ulleråker, 3 km from the city centre; Polackbacken, 1 km from the city centre; and Slottsbacken, 0.3 km from the city centre. Three discs were collected at each site; each point on the graph is the average for the three discs at that light intensity. (Bottom) Same data as above but rearranged to give average oxygen evolution for each of five subjective scores: the healthiest appearing discs were assigned a score of 5 and the unhealthiest appearing were assigned a score of 1

sulphur dioxide, for germination and observed no retarding effect. He then treated *P. canina* thalli from an unpolluted area with 2 ppm and 10 ppm of sulphur dioxide in the laboratory. The extract from lichens treated at 10 ppm had completely lost its inhibitory power; that from the lichens treated at 2 ppm had partially lost this power.

Two students at Ricks College have recently studied the effects of sulphur dioxide on desert lichens. Choosing a site where there was no disturbance by cultivation or urbanization for at least four or five km in all directions, M. Hansen built a small furnace with a smokestack one metre high in which he daily burned two or three kilograms of sulphur, providing the wind was from the south or south-west, the prevailing wind direction here. After a few days of this procedure, he removed bits of *Lecanora melanophthalma* and *L. rubina* from the rocks at various distances downwind as well as from some locations upwind and compared respiration rates in a home-made Warburg-type respirometer. The rate of respiration seemed to have been increased by exposure to the sulphur dioxide fumes; however, there was considerable variation among samples and so the differences were not statistically significant. S. Pearson studied the amino acid composition of the proteins of *L. melanophthalma* using paper chromatography and observed the fact that the $R_F$ values of both cysteine and cystine decreased in direct proportion to the degree of pollution. This was noticeable after two days, and had become very pronounced at the end of ten days when the experiment was terminated. The correlation between air pollution, as determined by the distance from the furnace, and change in the amino acids was high and statistically significant. The $R_F$ value of methionine was also slightly lower in the fumigated specimens; none of the other amino acids, asparagine plus three unidentified acids, were at all affected.

Future field-work, concerned with the effect of air pollution on lichens, will hopefully pay more attention to the following factors: (1) genetic variability among lichen populations of the same species, (2) development of models to enable us to estimate both microclimatic variability and pollution effects and (3) greater use of cover and biomass in comparing different lichen communities.

It is already known that different populations of the same species of lichen, or at least very similar species of lichens, differ physiologically in light compensation point (Pearson, 1967). It is not known whether the differences are due to (*a*) different ecotypes or even species of the phycobiont, (*b*) different ecotypes of the mycobiont, or (*c*) simply a difference in proportion of algal tissue to fungal tissue in the lichen. Brodo (1967) has discussed the use of models to assist in differentiating microclimatic effects from pollution effects. Models encourage the paying of greater attention to the individual components of the environment as has been urged by Gilbert (1970). Concerning the use of cover as a measure of lichen abundance, most lichenologists have apparently felt that it is too time-consuming to measure anything but frequency. Frequency is convenient to use, and it is also more objectively measured; however, the measurement of cover is not difficult, especially when long narrow quadrats, rather than square or circular quadrats, are used as recommended many years ago by Christidis (1931) and others. Oosting (1950) has written, 'The use of frequency as a single determination in analytical procedure has proven unsatisfactory, although numerous attempts have been made to show its adequacy.' G. Kimbro in her unpublished report of lichens in the Idaho Falls area found that although the percentage cover consistently decreased towards the centre of the city, the percentage frequency (with 50 plots) fluctuated somewhat erratically and in some cases was higher near the city centre than in the surrounding rural areas. The additional time spent in obtaining measures of either cover or biomass should pay well in additional information available; furthermore, it is possible to measure variation and to estimate a confidence value, such as the standard error, when cover or biomass data are available.

### Laboratory studies

In recent years, an increasing number of studies of a purely physiological nature have been conducted with lichens. In most of the studies (e.g. Lange, 1962; Ried, 1960; Atanasiu, 1970), it has simply been assumed that lichens collected in the field continue to function normally when brought into the laboratory. Pearson and Skye (1965) reported no evidence of physiological abnormalities in lichens that had been stored in the laboratory for several months. A moderate degree of success has been attained, however, in growing lichens in the laboratory, in growth chambers (Pearson, 1970; Harris and Kershaw, 1971), and in synthesizing lichens from the isolated mycobiont and phycobiont partners (Ahmadjian, 1966, 1967). As these methods are improved, more and more laboratory studies will be possible utilizing genetically controlled plant material. As we learn more about the physiological behaviour of 'normal' lichens, laboratory studies with lichens exposed to atmospheric pollutants will take on added meaning (*see* ch 12).

Pearson and Skye (1965) exposed lichens to high levels of sulphur dioxide in flasks kept in growth chambers (Fig. 2). No attempt was made to duplicate conditions occurring in nature; in fact, we suspected that if more natural levels were used, the lichen discs would disintegrate before enough time had lapsed for measurable results to be obtained. The curves suggest a gradual increase in respiration rate and a gradual decrease in photosynthetic rate as either the concentration of the gas is increased or the length of exposure time is increased until at rather high concentrations or long exposures both respiration and photosynthesis rapidly drop. Photosynthesis seems to cease before respiration does. The actual concentrations of sulphur dioxide employed are not known; the values indicated in Fig. 2 were calculated as though sulphur dioxide were not soluble in water whereas the gas is actually very soluble and the values indicated are thus much too high. Nevertheless, they serve to indicate relative concentrations. The measurements plotted in Fig. 2 represent separate, individual discs; it is suspected that part of the deviations from the smooth curve suggested was due to genetic factors.

Rao and LeBlanc (1966) exposed thalli of four species of lichens to concentrations of 5 ppm sulphur dioxide in flasks in the laboratory under varying conditions of humidity. They observed permanent plasmolysis, bleaching of chlorophyll, and the appearance of black spots in the algal layer of the fumigated lichen thalli. Sulphurous acid and magnesium ions were detected in the acetone-water extracts of the fumigated thalli, and phaeophytin *a* was detected in the ether-soluble fraction. They hypothesized that hydrogen ions from the sulphurous acid had

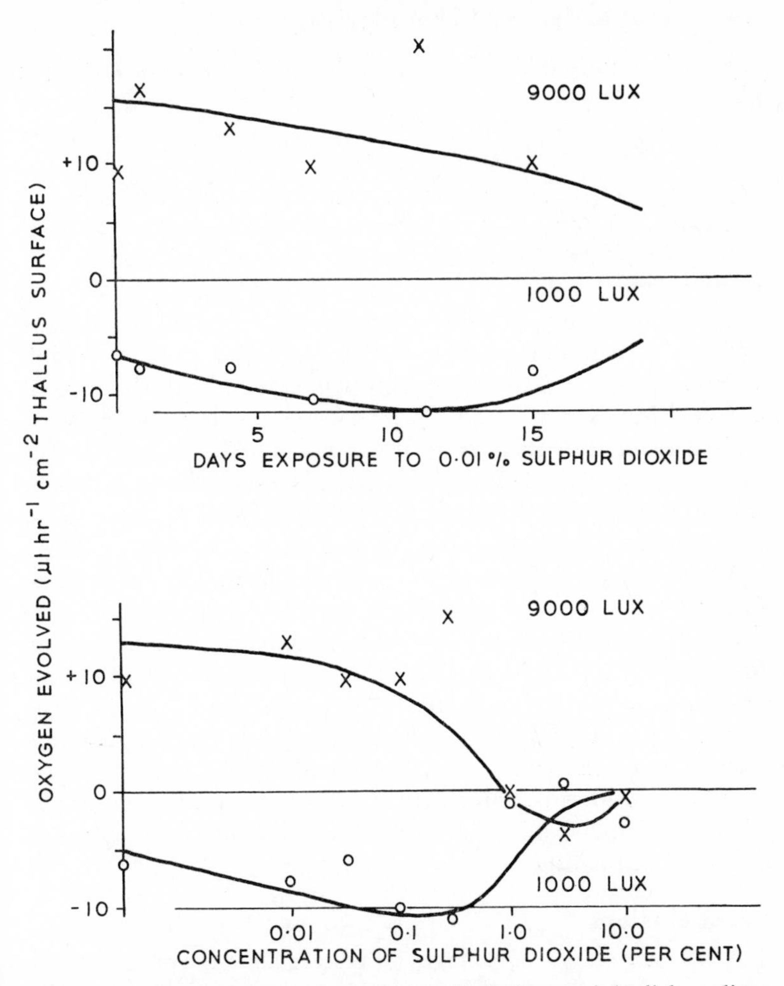


Fig. 2 Apparent photosynthesis (net assimilation rate) in lichen discs exposed to varying concentrations of sulphur dioxide. (Top) As the lichens are exposed to sulphur dioxide for longer periods of time, respiration gradually increases and photosynthesis gradually decreases up to a point when both sharply decrease. (Bottom) As the lichens are exposed to increasing concentrations of sulphur dioxide, respiration gradually increases and photosynthesis gradually decreases to a point where both begin to decrease sharply. The figures on the x-axis represent concentrations that would result if sulphur dioxide were not soluble in water; since sulphur dioxide is soluble, the indicated values should be regarded as relative values only

replaced magnesium ions in the chlorophyll thus converting it to phaeophytin:

$$2H^+ + \text{chlorophyll } a \rightarrow Mg^{2+} + \text{phaeophytin } a$$

It was suspected that the brown spots on the plastids of 'gonidial' cells in the fumigated thalli were due to phaeophytin. Sulphate accumulation and phaeophytin accumulation increased as the moisture increased.

Chromatography of *Peltigera polydactyla* and *P. praetextata* extracts made from herbarium material indicated a relatively high correlation between age and quantity of pigment with chlorophyll *a* decreasing to zero in the specimens approaching 100 years old and phaeophytin *a* increasing (Pearson, unpublished data). All of the chlorophylls yield phaeophytins when treated with acid (Strain, 1958); thus, phaeophytin *b* is produced from chlorophyll *b*, phaeophytin *c* from chlorophyll *c*, and so on.

While much of the damage to lichens from sulphur dioxide fumigation is due to degradation of the chlorophyll, this is undoubtedly not the only way in which damage occurs. Sulphur fumigation has long been recognized as a control method of rust in cereal crops, although the expense involved has made it impractical; the rust fungi are more sensitive to the sulphur dioxide than the host plant. Apparently there have been no laboratory studies conducted to ascertain the relative sensitivity of the isolated mycobionts and phycobionts to sulphur fumigation or to any of the other known air pollutants.

## Conclusions

Lichens have several advantages for research into the physiological effects of air pollutants in plants: (1) their sensitivity, (2) their variability in sensitivity, not all lichens being equally sensitive, (3) their anatomy which is different from that of crop plants and other plants subject to air pollution injury, and (4) the possibility of studying the effects of pollution not only on the whole plant but on its autotrophic and heterotrophic parts separately. There are some real problems facing lichenologists who are interested in this type of research, however: (1) lichens are not prestigious organisms with which to work and hence the workers are few; (2) it is difficult to grow lichens under laboratory conditions;

(3) there is a need for more information about normal physiological processes in lichens, and until this problem is solved it will be difficult to get full meaning out of studies on the physiological behaviour of fumigated lichens; (4) for many of the pollutants that may be of special significance in lichen physiology, there are not available good measures of the degree of pollution in the air; in vascular plants this is also a problem but not as serious a problem since the economic value of crop plants makes it possible to use tests that would be too expensive for a lichenologist to use.

Some observations made by Lave and Seskin (1970) are of special interest. Air pollution, according to them, costs us billions of dollars every year in medical bills and lost earning power; yet of even greater concern, perhaps, is the widespread unhappiness today over the deteriorating environment and dissatisfaction with the urban way of life—and it is the sudden awareness of air pollution that is in part responsible for this, they say.

## References

Ahmadjian, V. (1966). The artificial re-establishment of the lichen *Cladonia cristatella*. *Science, N.Y.* **151,** 199–201.

Ahmadjian, V. (1967). *The lichen symbiosis*. Waltham, Mass.: Blaisdell.

Atanasiu, L. (1970). The respiratory quotient in lichens and mosses. *Lucr. Grăd. bot. Buc.* **1968,** 81–4.

Barkman, J. J. (1958). *Phytosociology and ecology of cryptogamic epiphytes*. Assen, Netherlands: Van Gorcum.

Brodo, I. M. (1961). Transplant experiments with corticolous lichens using a new technique. *Ecology* **42,** 838–41.

Brodo, I. M. (1967). Lichen growth and cities: A study on Long Island, New York. *Bryologist* **69,** 427–49.

Capriotti, A. (1959). The effects of 'usno' on yeasts. *G. Microbiol.* **7,** 187–206.

Christidis, B. G. (1931). The importance of the shape of plots in field experimentation. *J. Agr. Sci.* **21,** 14–37.

Darley, E. F., Nichols, C. W. and Middleton, J. T. (1966). Identification of air pollution damage to agricultural crops. *Bull. Calif. Dep. Agric.* **55,** 11–19.

Dugger, W. M. and Ting, I. P. (1970). Air pollution oxidants—their effects on metabolic processes in plants. *Ann. Rev. Pl. Physiol.* **21,** 215–234.

Fenton, A. F. (1960). Lichens as indicators of atmospheric pollution. *Ir. Nat. J.* **13,** 153–9.

Gilbert, O. L. (1965). Lichens as indicators of air pollution in the Tyne Valley. In: Goodman, G. T., Edwards, R. W. and Lambert, J. M. (ed.) *Ecology and the industrial society*, 35–47. Oxford: Blackwell.

Gilbert, O. L. (1970). Further studies on the effect of sulphur dioxide on lichens and bryophytes. *New Phytol.* **69,** 605–27.

Harris, G. P. and Kershaw, K. A. (1971). Thallus growth and the distribution of stored metabolites in the phycobionts of the lichens *Parmelia sulcata* and *P. physodes*. *Can. J. Bot.* **49,** 1367–72.

Lange, O. L. (1962). Die Photosynthese der Flechten bei tiefen Temperaturen und nach Frostperioden. *Ber. dt. bot. Ges.* **75,** 351–2.

Lave, L. B. and Seskin, E. P. (1970). Air pollution and human health. *Science, N.Y.* **169,** 723–33.

LeBlanc, F. and Rao, D. N. (1966). Réaction de quelques lichens et mousses épiphytiques à l'anhydride sulfreux dans la région de Sudbury, Ontario. *Bryologist* **69,** 338–46.

Lundström, H. (1968). Luftföroreningars inverkan på epifytfloran hos barrträd i Stockholmsområdet. *Stud. Forest suec.* **56,** 1–55.

Malicki, J. (1968). Wpływ kwasów porostowych na mikroorganizmy glebowe. Cźęść II. Wpływ wyciągów wodnych z gatunków *Cladonia* an bakterie glebowe. *Annls Univ. Mariae Curie-Skłodowska,* C,**22,** 159–163.

Mrose, H. (1941). Die Verbreitung baumbewohnender Flechten in Abhängigkeit vom Sulfatgehalt der Niederschlagwässer. *Bioklim. Beibl.* **8,** 58–60.

Nylander, W. (1866). Les lichens du Jardin du Luxembourg. *Bull. Soc. bot. Fr.* **13,** 364–72.

Oosting, H. J. (1950). *The study of plant communities*. San Francisco: Freeman.

Pearson, L. C. (1967). Light compensation point measurements in four populations of saxicolous lichens. *J. Idaho Acad. Sci.* **6,** 1–4.

Pearson, L. C. (1970). Varying environmental factors in order to grow intact lichens under laboratory conditions. *Am. J. Bot.* **75,** 659–664.

Pearson, L. C. and Skye, E. (1965). Air pollution affects pattern of photosynthesis in *Parmelia sulcata,* a corticolous lichen. *Science, N.Y.* **148,** 1600–2.

Pringsheim, E. G. (1967). Phycology in the field and in the laboratory. *J. Phycol.* **3,** 93–5.

Pyatt, F. B. (1967). The inhibitory influence of *Peltigera canina* on the germination of graminaceous seed and subsequent growth of the seedlings. *Bryologist* **70,** 326–9.

Pyatt, F. B. (1968). The effect of sulfur dioxide on the inhibitory influence of *Peltigera canina* on the germination and growth of grasses. *Bryologist* **71,** 97–101.

Rao, D. N. and LeBlanc, F. (1966). Effects of sulfur dioxide on the lichen algae with special reference to chlorophyll. *Bryologist* **69,** 69–75.

Ried, A. (1960). Nachwirkungen der Entquellung auf den Gaswechsel von Krustenflechten. *Biol. Zbl.* **79,** 657–78.

Rydzak, J. (1956). Wpływ małych miast na floıę porostów. Cźęšé I. Dolny Slask. *Annls Univ. Mariae Curie-Skłodowska*, C, **10,** 1-32.

Rydzak, J. (1959). Influence of small towns on the lichen vegetation. Part VII. Discussion and general conclusions. *Annls Univ. Mariae Curie-Skłodowska*, C, **13,** 275–323.

Rydzak, J. (1969). Lichens as indicators of the ecological conditions of the habitat. *Annls Univ. Mariae Curie-Skłodowska*, C, **23,** 131–64.

Sernander, R. (1912). Studier öfvar lafvarnes biologi I. Nitrofila lafvar. *Svensk bot. Tidskr.* **6,** 803–83.

Sernander, R. (1926) *Stockholms natur*. Uppsala: Almqvist and Wiksells.

Skye, E. (1958). Luftföroreningars inverkan på busk- och bladlavfloran kring skifferoljeverket i Närkes Kvarntorp. *Svensk bot. Tidskr.* **52,** 133–90.

Skye, E. (1968). Lichens and air pollution. *Acta phytogeogr. suec.* **52,** 1–123.

Strain, H. H. (1958). *Chloroplast pigments and chromatographic analysis.* University Park, Penna.: Phi Lambda Upsilon.

*Note added in proof:*

Since this paper went to press, S. Pearson has confirmed her field findings with laboratory observations of the effects of sulphur dioxide and carbon monoxide on lichens. Both pollutants caused similar morphological symptoms. The $R_F$ values of sulphur-containing amino acids decreased in the laboratory study in the same manner as in the field studies; there were no changes in the amino acids as a result of carbon monoxide fumigation, however.

# 12: Lichen Physiology: Progress and Pitfalls

J. F. FARRAR

The use of laboratory experiments is a crucial step in establishing the role of any environmental variable in affecting lichen growth and distribution. Only when it has been shown that known and controlled changes in that variable, applied under realistic conditions, have measurable effects on lichen physiology, can it be assumed that it may be of importance in the field. However, relating the results of laboratory work to field conditions is at best difficult, and if all possible care is not taken in designing and interpreting experiments, it may be completely unjustified. The purpose of the present paper is briefly to review the current knowledge of lichen physiology, with special reference to the design and interpretation of experiments. It is not intended to be an exhaustive review; the older literature in particular is covered in the excellent reviews of Smith (1962), Hale (1967), and Ahmadjian (1967), and emphasis here will be placed on recent findings. Only whole thalli are dealt with: the symbionts in pure culture behave so distinctly that work on them is of little relevance. 'Lichen substances' are also omitted: they are reviewed widely elsewhere, notably by Culberson (1969). Experimental procedures are further reviewed by Richardson (1971). As for the work concerning sulphur dioxide, air pollution, and lichens, the reader is left to integrate the contents of this chapter with the rest of this book.

The material falls into three sections: some overlap and repetition is unavoidable, and some work has been split up into various sections. The first deals with the fundamental pathways and processes of lichen metabolism, and the second with the interplay between these and the environment. The short concluding section aims to give a rather personal synthesis of the available data, and its implications for further research.

## Pathways and processes

### *Respiration*

Respiration is a complex phenomenon, and any respiration rate represents the sum of several distinct metabolic processes. Lichen respiration has an algal and a fungal component, and in each symbiont, respiration from glycolysis, the pentose phosphate pathway, and a variety of catabolic processes, are presumably included. No critical work on the biochemistry of respiration has been reported from lichens. Basal respiration (i.e. dark respiration by the intact thallus when no active uptake is proceeding) is insensitive to cyanide in *Peltigera polydactyla* (Smith, in press) and *Hypogymnia physodes* (Farrar, unpublished). Fungal respiration is commonly cyanide-insensitive, and whilst blue-green algae such as *Anabaena* and *Nostoc* are very cyanide-sensitive, basal respiration in *Chlorella* is only affected by cyanide at high concentrations (Gibbs, 1962). Thus in lichens containing blue-green algae it may be possible to differentiate between the symbionts by using cyanide. As algae in lichens are believed to occupy only 5–10 per cent of the thallus by weight (Drew and Smith, 1967; Kershaw and Millbank, 1970; Millbank, 1972) most of the measured respiration is probably fungal in origin. A second type of respiration obtains during active uptake of organic and inorganic nutrients. This is characteristically highly sensitive to inhibitors and has a rather higher RQ than basal respiration (Harley and Smith, 1956; Smith, 1960*b*), and, as it is superimposed on basal respiration, higher rates are observed as uptake proceeds.

Respiratory quotients (RQ's) typically fall between 0.7–0.9 (Quispel, 1960) for basal respiration. These cannot be used as indicators of the respiratory substrate, as departure from the theoretically expected RQ can, and usually does, occur (Beevers, 1961). There is good reason for believing the main respiratory substrates in lichens to be polyols, as suggested by Smith (1962) and Lewis and Smith (1967). Drew (1966) found evidence that mannitol was the main substrate in *Peltigera polydactyla*, and Farrar (unpublished) found that in *Hypogymnia physodes*, arabitol losses in the dark correspond to calculated loss by respiration. The theoretical value of the RQ for polyols is 0.92, but if oxidation of the polyol is incomplete the RQ will fall. In *Hypogymnia physodes* Farrar (unpublished) has observed that arabitol levels fall in the dark but mannitol levels rise slightly, and so this might explain the low RQ's observed. Prolonged maintenance of respiration during dark starvation (Drew, 1966; Farrar, unpublished) makes it unlikely that lichen respiration will be substrate limited under normal conditions.

*Methods of measurement.* Techniques used to measure respiration in lichens include manometry, infra-red gas analysis, and the oxygen electrode. Each of these techniques has its limitations. Manometry can involve exposing the lichens to unnatural gas concentrations, is comparatively insensitive and the lichens are used saturated and in a saturated atmosphere. It has the advantage of enabling both oxygen and carbon dioxide to be measured. Both infra-red gas analysis and the oxygen electrode each measure only one gas—carbon dioxide and oxygen respectively—and so significant changes in RQ may be overlooked. The oxygen electrode involves vacuum infiltration of the material, which may profoundly affect exchangeability of the gases; however, it is extremely sensitive. Infra-red gas analysis has the advantage that the lichen is supplied with a stream of air of variable and measurable humidity, and the conditions are thus as natural as is practicable. However, large amounts of material are needed to obtain reliable results.

### *Photosynthesis*

It is important to distinguish between true photosynthesis, which is the amount of carbon fixed by the alga, and net assimilation rate (net carbon assimilation rate, net photosynthesis), which is the net gain in carbon to the lichen. Measurement of gas exchange, by any technique, results in a net assimilation rate which can only be converted into a true photosynthesis rate by assuming that dark respiration rates obtain in the light. Photorespiration, a distinct form of respiration found in the light, is recognized for some plants, but is still an area of controversy (Jackson and Volk, 1970); hence the term is best forgotten until critical work has been done on lichens. A depression in net assimilation rate (NAR) may be due to either a drop in photosynthesis, or to a rise in respiration. True photosynthesis can only be measured using radioactive isotope techniques, which have problems of their own when absolute quantification is required, rather than comparative work (e.g. Hill, 1971) for which they are eminently suitable. All reports on photosynthetic rates in lichens are based on gas-exchange measurements, and most have been concerned with the effects of environmental variables; these will be discussed below. Two points are of relevance here: Smyth (1934) showed that carbon dioxide concentration affected NAR in *Peltigera polydactyla*, indicating the need for caution in manometric experiments, and Ried (1960*a*) found variation of NAR with age in *Umbilicaria pustulata*; hence uniform sampling of material is desirable.

The mode of expression of photosynthetic rates merits consideration. As mentioned above, the algae occupy only 5–10 per cent of the thallus by weight, and yet NAR's, along with most other lichen parameters, are usually expressed relative to fresh or dry weight. It is clear that changes in the amount of fungal material present will result in changes in NAR per unit weight, although there may be no change in photosynthesis per unit alga. In comparing thalli of different ages, or from different habitats, this must be borne in mind. For example Harris (1971*b*) has found a linear relationship between NAR per mg, and number of algal cells per sq. cm, in *Parmelia caperata*. Expression on an algal cell number basis is probably best, but is tedious; expression against chlorophyll is unsatisfactory as chlorophyll levels can vary widely under certain conditions (see below). The use of area as an index, as in the disc method of Smith (Harley and Smith, 1956), for suitable thalli, is satisfactory for many situations.

Chlorophyll contents of thalli have been widely measured. The method of Hill and Woolhouse (1966) for extraction is excellent. Levels found in lichens with *Trebouxia* are in the order of 0.15–1.0 mg/g thallus dry weight (Wilhelmsen, 1959; Kärenlampi, 1970; Farrar, unpublished), whereas in *Chlorella* grown in culture up to 6 per cent dry weight of the alga is chlorophyll (Bogorad, 1962). Even allowing for the small amount of algae in the thallus, this still means that lichens have less chlorophyll per algal cell than similar non-lichenized algae grown in optimal conditions.

A further complication in measuring photosynthesis in lichens is non-photosynthetic (dark) fixation of carbon, which can be

5–10 per cent of light fixation rates (Drew, 1966; Farrar, unpublished). This high value is probably partly due to the large excess of fungal material, as the incorporation pattern that Drew found using [$^{14}$C]bicarbonate, with most of the label in aspartic acid, and other organic acids including malic, parallels that found by Harley (1964) and Carrodus (1967) in mycorrhizal roots of beech.

*Fate of photosynthetically fixed carbon*

There are two main aspects of the fate of carbon fixed by lichens: firstly, the early products of algal photosynthesis and the transfer of fixed carbon to the fungus, and secondly, the long-term fate of carbon thus fixed and partitioned between the symbionts. The first of these is among the best understood areas of lichen physiology, as a result of the work of Smith and his associates, and more recently that of Feige and his associates (1967, 1969, 1970*a*; Simonis and Feige, 1967; Feige and Simonis, 1969). General reviews can be found in Richardson, Hill, and Smith (1968), and Smith, Muscatine and Lewis (1969).

It is now well established that a large proportion of the carbon fixed by the alga passes to the fungus in the form of a single, simple, carbohydrate, which is rapidly converted to a distinct carbohydrate by the fungus. In a range of species, Hill and Smith (1972) showed that 40–70 per cent of a pulse of fixed carbon moved to the fungus as carbohydrate. The nature of the mobile carbohydrate is determined by the genus of alga present (*see* Table 1).

*Table 1 The carbohydrate moving to the fungus from various genera of algae (based on Richardson, Hill and Smith, 1968)*

| | Algal genus | Mobile carbohydrate |
|---|---|---|
| *green algae* | *Trebouxia* | ribitol |
| | *Myrmecia* | ribitol |
| | *Coccomyxa* | ribitol |
| | *Trentepohlia* | erythritol |
| | *Hyalococcus* | sorbitol |
| *blue-green algae* | *Nostoc* | glucose |
| | *Calothrix* | ?glucose/glucan |
| | *Scytonema* | glucose |

Although this broad picture of transfer of carbohydrate between the symbionts is clear, several difficulties remain. Both the rate of carbohydrate transfer and the mechanism remain unknown. Further, the possibility of other compounds being transferred in small quantities cannot be excluded. Indeed, in lichens with blue-green algae, it is known that nearly all the nitrogen fixed by the alga is transferred to the fungus (see below), but the identity of the mobile nitrogen compounds is unknown. As yet, there is no means of detecting small quantities of other compounds moving in the presence of the main mobile carbohydrate.

The techniques used so far do not allow accurate estimation of the overall rate of carbohydrate transfer. Simply following the rate at which $^{14}C$ moves fails to allow for the dilution of fixed $^{14}C$ into a pre-existing pool of the mobile carbohydrate, and if this pool is large then estimates of transfer rates based on $^{14}C$-transfer will be far too low.

A method used to estimate rate of transfer (and also used for identifying the mobile carbohydrate) is the 'inhibition technique', in which the lichen is incubated on a solution of 1 per cent carbohydrate containing [$^{14}C$]bicarbonate. If the carbohydrate in the medium is the same as, or an analogue of, the mobile carbohydrate, then $^{14}C$-labelled mobile carbohydrate can be detected in the medium in large quantities. The rate of $^{14}C$ appearance in the medium is not a good indication of the rate of carbohydrate transfer. Its specific activity depends partly on the amount of mobile carbohydrate already in the alga, which will dilute fixed $^{14}C$ to an unknown extent. A modification of the inhibition technique involves using a metabolic analogue (such as 2-desoxyglucose instead of glucose), which can be separated from the mobile carbohydrate in the medium by gas chromatography, and thus allows estimation of the mobile carbohydrate lost to the medium directly. This inhibition technique also has the disadvantage that the lichen is 'inhibited' in a 1 per cent solution of a biologically active compound or its potentially toxic analogue—a most unnatural state that may have significant effects on metabolism.

Examination of the situation in two distinct cases—*Peltigera polydactyla* and *Xanthoria aureola*—will clarify the situation. In *Peltigera*, the *Nostoc* symbiont fixes [$^{14}C$]bicarbonate into a wide variety of compounds. Radioactivity can be detected in the first fungal compound to become labelled, mannitol, after 2 minutes. After 1 hour, about 70 per cent of the fixed $^{14}C$ is in mannitol. Gas chromatography has shown that the lichen contains a large pool of mannitol but very little free glucose. During inhibition on 1 per cent glucose, [$^{14}C$]glucose is found in the medium, and it has been estimated that 1 mg glucose/g dry wt/hour is released into a 2-desoxyglucose medium (Smith and Drew, 1965; Drew, 1966; Drew and Smith, 1967; Hill, 1970; Hill and Smith, 1972). In *Xanthoria aureola*, the *Trebouxia* symbiont again fixes [$^{14}C$] bicarbonate into a wide variety of compounds. Label is not detected in the fungal compounds until after 30–40 minutes when labelled arabitol and mannitol appear. During inhibition on ribitol, labelled ribitol accumulates in the medium. After 24 hours 60–70 per cent of the label is found in the fungal polyols. Analysis of the soluble carbohydrates indicates that a large pool of ribitol is present; in *Hypogymnia physodes* (which also contains *Trebouxia*) it occupies about 1 per cent dry wt of the thallus (Bednar and Smith, 1966; Richardson and Smith, 1968; Richardson, 1967; Farrar, unpublished). Thus although the movement of $^{14}C$ between the symbionts is much slower in *Xanthoria* than in *Peltigera*, the pre-existing pool of mobile carbohydrate is far bigger, and in neither case is there a reliable estimate of the rate of carbohydrate transfer.

The importance of rates of transfer is that it is commonly assumed that the main (or perhaps sole) source of carbon for the fungus is carbon fixed by the alga. If rates of transfer are low, then this would be of considerable significance in restricting lichen growth. Thus the rate of transfer would have to be greater than the respiration rate, at a realistic temperature, to provide the fungus with a carbon surplus. In this context it should be noted that transfer drops off in the dark (Hill, 1970), so transfer rates in the light would have to be significantly greater than respiration rates.

The mechanism of carbohydrate transfer is as yet unknown, and may differ between lichens. The working of the inhibition technique suggests that the alga simply releases the carbohydrate, which is subsequently absorbed by the fungus; this is probably a gross oversimplification, however. Hill (1972) considers that

*Nostoc* synthesizes a glucan extracellularly, which is broken down by the fungus. It should be noted that the effect on the fungus of different carbohydrates is unknown, but it is possible that the algal genus present exerts considerable control over fungal development by the nature of the carbohydrate it supplies.

The longer-term fate of fixed carbon has not been examined in great detail. After exposing *Peltigera polydactyla* to a pulse of $^{14}CO_2$, Drew (1966) found that, after 3 and 6 days of dark starvation, 15 per cent of the label was in insolubles, and that most of the label remained in mannitol. In *Hypogymnia physodes*, Farrar (unpublished) found about 30 per cent of a one-hour pulse of $^{14}C$ remained in the alga after 24 hours, rather more than would be expected on a proportional share basis. Up to 72 hours, most of the label remained in polyols, but 15 per cent had moved to insolubles. After 7 days in the light at 20°C, 70 per cent of a pulse of $^{14}C$ had been respired; hence estimates of the amount of label remaining in various fractions must be based on actual counts, rather than percentage distribution between fractions. Over 24 hours, only 2 per cent of the fixed carbon was incorporated into protein. Thus we are still uncertain of the long-term fate of carbon in the thallus; the few observations available indicate that a high proportion of the carbon may be respired, much remains in polyols, and comparatively little enters insolubles.

### *Soluble carbohydrates: occurrence and utilization*

It is clear from the preceding section that polyols are of central importance in lichen metabolism; in all species studied they are the main fungal repository for fixed carbon, and in lichens with green algae it is as a polyol that carbon moves between the symbionts. It was also noted above that in *Peltigera polydactyla*, mannitol is the main respiratory substrate, and in *Hypogymnia physodes*, it is arabitol. Further indication of their importance comes from their wide distribution among lichens and their abundance within the thallus. Mannitol occurs in all lichens examined for it, and many species contain three different polyols. These compounds commonly occupy 3–12 per cent dry weight of the thallus, being (along with their glycosides) by far the most common soluble carbohydrates (Lewis and Smith, 1967; Culberson, 1969). The types of polyol present are to some extent determined by the genus of alga, but within these broad limits there is still wide variation. It is believed that ribitol is a purely algal polyol, and mannitol and arabitol are fungal polyols in lichens: in any one thallus, each polyol will probably be confined to one symbiont.

The functions mentioned above could all be performed by ordinary sugars, and yet in lichens polyols are seemingly far more important. There is likely, then, to be some function that polyols can perform in lichens rather better than ordinary sugars. Several roles have been suggested. Lewis and Smith (1967) observed that they are efficient stores of reducing power; Green (1970) has implicated them in protecting macromolecules during water stress, by replacing water molecules normally bonded to the polymers; and Lewis and Smith (1967) have suggested an osmoregulatory role. It is probable that all of these are important, and that polyols are ideal multi-purpose molecules for plants such as lichens, some fungi, bryophytes, and brown algae. In view of the very low water content of air-dry lichen thalli, protection of macromolecules is a particularly likely role. It should be borne in mind that the different polyols may have different roles in the same lichen. Thus in *Hypogymnia physodes*, ribitol is the algal polyol which moves to the fungus, arabitol the main respiratory substrate in the fungus, and the function of mannitol remains obscure, although it behaves differently from ribitol and arabitol (Farrar, unpublished). In this context the rise of mannitol levels during respiration of arabitol may be significant; it is possible that only part of the arabitol molecule is respired, mannitol being synthesized from the remnants. Such a dual polyol system would combine efficient storage of reducing power with maximum osmotic potential and stress protection. It is also probable that the same polyol can have different functions in different lichens: mannitol seems to be the main respiratory substrate in *Peltigera polydactyla*, whereas it is not so in *Hypogymnia physodes*. Some of the observed changes in polyol levels will be mentioned below: it could be added that the present author believes that lichens need to maintain a high level of polyols in the thallus, and that it would not be surprising to find strong correlations between polyol metabolism and ecological tolerances.

Free sugars are found in the thallus to only a limited extent (Solberg, 1970*a*). Whereas glucose is of major importance to *Nostoc*-containing lichens for carbon transport between the symbionts, it is only present in *Peltigera polydactyla* at levels below 0.05 per cent dry weight (Smith, 1963*b*). Gas chromatography of many lichens reveals a large number of small peaks besides the common compounds, indicating that a wide variety of polyols and sugars may occur at low levels (Farrar, unpublished). Disaccharides are usually at rather higher levels than hexoses and pentoses, sucrose and trehalose in particular being frequent.

Work on soluble carbohydrates can thus produce extremely useful information about lichen behaviour, especially as the polyols are symbiont-specific and can thus be used to study the response of each symbiont to experimental treatment, in the intact thallus. It must be emphasized that careful technique is needed to distinguish between certain of the compounds; in particular, polyols can only be successfully separated after conversion to suitable derivatives. Gas chromatography is most useful for routine chromatography of sugars. Although carbohydrate metabolism is fundamental, we know little about the control of carbohydrate metabolism by mechanisms such as catabolite repression (Anderson and Woods, 1969). For example, it is possible that a reduction in photosynthesis could be caused by a change in fungal metabolism which would alter source-sink relationships in the thallus.

### *Insoluble carbohydrates*

(The term 'insoluble' is used throughout to denote 80 per cent methanol—or ethanol—insoluble.)

Insoluble carbohydrates are very abundant in lichens, occupying 30 per cent by weight of the *Peltigera polydactyla* thallus (Smith, 1962), for example. However, little is known of their synthesis or function. Culberson (1969) lists the polysaccharides reported from lichens, and J.-Cl. Boissière (1969), M.-Cl. Boissière (1969), and Green (1970) have confirmed earlier findings. Several kinds of glucose polymers, chitin, and a variety of uncharacterized, mixed, branched, polymers of glucose, galactose, and mannose, have been reported. Various electron micrographs have indicated the presence of starch in the chloroplast of lichenized *Trebouxia* (Jacobs and Ahmadjian, 1969; Harris and Kershaw, 1971; Peveling, 1970), but starch has not been chemically isolated.

Observations of the above electron microscopists indicate that changes in starch abundance depend upon environmental conditions. As the amount of fungal and extracellular carbohydrate greatly exceeds the algal starch, it is difficult to detect changes in levels of starch in the alga using isotopic methods. Farrar (unpublished) found incorporation of $^{14}C$ into both a hot-water soluble, and an alkali-soluble, fraction in *Hypogymnia physodes*, but no loss of label from these fractions under a variety of conditions. As starch-sugar interconversions could be most important for metabolic control or osmoregulation in the alga, further more critical work is obviously needed.

*Nutrient uptake*

Lichens are extremely efficient accumulators of both inorganic and low molecular weight organic compounds. Two completely distinct processes obtain—active uptake, which is accompanied by enhanced respiration and is sensitive to both temperature and inhibitors, and passive adsorption of cations onto cell walls, which is temperature-independent and equally rapid in live and dead thalli.

Uptake and utilization of exogenously applied sugars has been studied in *Peltigera polydactyla* by Harley and Smith (1956), Smith (1960*b*, 1963*b*), and Drew (1966), and in *Xanthoria aureola* by Richardson and Smith (1966) and Richardson (1967). The most remarkable aspect is the very high rate of accumulation from concentrated solutions, discs of *Peltigera* taking up 25 per cent of their own weight of glucose in 24 hours from a 2 per cent solution at 20°C. Uptake had a high RQ, and was inhibited by low pH and sodium fluoride, and so was definitely active. Smith found evidence of a surface enzyme which hydrolysed sucrose, glucose being preferentially absorbed from the resultant mixture of glucose and fructose. Drew found that *Peltigera* took up galactose, mannitol and fructose rather more slowly than glucose and mannose. Most of the glucose taken up was converted into mannitol, and if labelled glucose was supplied, 20 per cent of the activity was respired in 24 hours in the dark. Richardson showed that *Xanthoria* took up arabitol, ribitol, xylitol, and mannitol, at similar rates; xylitol does not occur naturally in lichens. Feige (1970*b*) has shown that *Cladonia convoluta* can absorb and metabolize both glucose and glycerol. The whole problem of sugar uptake is a vexed one; its importance to lichen biology lies in the role of sugars in the algal-fungal interaction, and in possible heterotrophic sources of carbon in nature. The mechanism of uptake is unknown; the possibility of sodium-linked uptake must be considered (Schultz and Curran, 1970).

Amino acids and amides are also strongly accumulated, and this may be of significance in nature as Smith (1960*b*) has shown that, in the habitat of *Peltigera polydactyla*, the run-off after light rain contained both organic and inorganic nitrogen, with organic nitrogen in greater quantity. He has shown (Smith, 1960*a,b*) that *Peltigera polydactyla* from this habitat accumulated asparagine, glutamine, and glutamic and aspartic acids rapidly, and ammonium rather less rapidly, whilst nitrate was accumulated very slowly.

Phosphate is accumulated rapidly from both concentrated and dilute solutions (Smith, 1960*c*; Feige, 1967; Farrar, unpublished) by a range of species. Farrar has shown that in *Hypogymnia physodes* the uptake is very rapid and is DNP-inhibited, and that the phosphate absorbed from a $10^{-4}$M solution cannot be exchanged out by immersion in further phosphate solutions. This non-exchangeability may be of some importance in nature.

An interesting aspect of uptake is the observed synergism and competition between distinct types of molecule. Smith has shown that, in *Peltigera polydactyla*, ammonium uptake was greatly enhanced by the presence of glucose, whereas both asparagine and phosphate uptake were depressed. As uptake is unlikely to be limited by low energy supply (witness the high rate of glucose uptake) and the molecules are so different that competition for uptake sites is not likely, there may be competition for factors involved in maintaining charge separations and electrochemical gradients. In view of these complications, it is essential in experiments to buffer carefully and to control all of the cations and anions present, as well as the compound being accumulated; thus phosphate uptake may be different if the phosphate is applied as the sodium rather than the potassium salt.

It is thus clear that lichens can actively accumulate small organic molecules and some anions and non-metallic cations from solution. The uptake mechanism is far from clear, as is the relation between the amounts of nutrients needed by the lichen for optimal growth, and the amounts available in nature. Most nutrient accumulation in the field presumably occurs from very dilute solutions, but nearly all of the laboratory experiments have been confined to uptake from concentrated solutions. It would seem necessary to determine whether accumulation is as efficient from very dilute media.

It has been known for some years that some fungal cell walls and ascospore walls will strongly bind metal cations and dyes such as methylene blue, in a completely non-metabolic and reversible way. For a given concentration, the cations can be arranged in order of binding power, any cation being able to elute out a cation lower in the series. The series closely resembles the Hofmeister (lyotropic) series (Sussman and Lowry, 1955; Lowry, Sussman and von Boventer, 1957). Elution and absorption further depend upon concentration and pH, although the processes are temperature- and energy- independent. The cations are thought to bind onto anionic sites on the cell wall, and the pK of elution is characteristic of a particular binding site, such as protein carboxyls, sulphonates or phosphates. Rothstein and Larrabee (1948) and Rothstein and Meir (1951) find that uranyl ions, whilst being strongly absorbed onto the wall, can reversibly inhibit glucose uptake. In general, however, the wall represents a large sink for rendering potentially highly-toxic cations harmless. Tuominen (1967) found that the strontium uptake in *Cladonia stellaris* could best be explained in the same terms, i.e. the uptake was strongly pH-dependent and the lichen acted as a cation-exchanger broadly following the same series of binding power as the fungal systems (see above). Examining a range of species, he found that there was a rough correlation between binding power and habitat, and he considered usnic acid not to be involved in the process. In a later paper (Tuominen, 1968) he showed that dead *Cladonia stellaris* could passively 'transport' caesium and strontium ions up the thallus as a consequence of the binding characteristics. Handley and Overstreet (1968) found $^{137}Cs$-uptake by *Ramalina menziesii* to be temperature-independent, competition with other metals to correspond with the lyotropic series, and uptake to be greater under nitrogen than under air, in living thalli. Brown and Slingsby (1972) investigated the compartmentalization of lead and potassium in *Cladonia rangiformis* from a lead-rich site. They eluted out the metals in the thallus with HCl and with nickel solutions, and concluded that all of the lead was bound to insoluble anionic sites in an exchangeable form, and that whilst some of the potassium was bound like the lead, the bulk was present intracellularly in a freely diffusible form normally contained by the permeability barriers of the cell. They further mention unpublished data which indicate that zinc behaves more like potassium than like lead.

In many of the early reports of high quantities of metals and radionuclides in lichen thalli (Lounamaa, 1956, 1965; Maquinay *et al.*, 1961; Lange and Zeigler, 1963; Noeske *et al.*, 1970; Gorham, 1959; Salo and Miettinen, 1964), the authors simply ashed or counted the lichen with no attempt to determine the localization of the metals. Further, for at least two of these papers (Mićović and Stefanović, reported in Hale, 1967, and Lounamaa, 1956) it can be seen that the accumulation of the metal relative to substrate concentration shows a crude relationship with the lyotropic series. Without knowing the available (rather than total) ion contents of the substrate and of the run-off water, it is impossible to evaluate the significance of relevant accumulation figures.

It seems, then, that most of the non-metabolic cations in lichen thalli will be bound to anionic sites in the cell wall, where they will have little or no effect on cell metabolism. This may be of great significance to a long-lived organism with no obvious morphological barriers to the entry of toxins, acting as a 'filter' to remove cations from rainwater. Some heavy metals will still enter the living cell, especially when high amounts are involved. With work of this kind it is vital to differentiate between active and passive accumulation (by temperature sensitivity and killed controls), and between the various intra- and extracellular compartments in which the metals can be found. In the absence of further data, it would seem necessary to study uptake and elution characteristics of each cation in each lichen species under investigation.

### *Phosphate metabolism*

Uptake of phosphate, as mentioned above, is rapid and active. The metabolism of absorbed phosphate seems to be equally rapid. Feige (1967) has examined in some detail the fate of accumulated phosphate in several species of lichens, by the use of $^{32}PO_4$. In *Cladonia convoluta* many labelled compounds could be detected within 12 min of applying label, much of the label being in sugar phosphates and some in nucleotide phosphates, and PGA. A prolonged incubation in the light or dark after labelling caused a large drop in soluble phosphates and a rise in insolubles, phosphatidylethanolamine and phosphorylcholine becoming heavily labelled. Experiments with *Peltigera aphthosa* followed a broadly similar pattern. The phosphorus content of 8 lichens (species of *Cladonia* and *Cetraria*) was approximately 0.05 per cent of the dry weight, about 50 per cent being in an insoluble fraction which contained nucleotide phosphates and polyphosphate, and 13 per cent as inorganic phosphate. Farrar (unpublished) has shown that uptake in the dark by *Hypogymnia physodes* is equal to that in the light, even after 24 hours' pre-incubation in darkness. At 20°C, within five seconds of applying labelled phosphate in the light, 10 organic compounds could be detected. Rapid incorporation into an insoluble fraction, believed to be polyphosphate, was also seen, the incorporation into this fraction being increased by 'chasing in' unlabelled phosphate solution. The presence of polyphosphate is interesting. It may be characteristic of plants living in environments prone to water stress, and it can be used as a store of inorganic phosphate, which can be utilized in times of need (Aitcheson, 1970). The presence of large quantities in the thallus would indicate that phosphorus is not limiting in nature, and yet phosphorus is in very low supply in rainwater, compared with, say, nitrogen.

Two problems associated with phosphate work should be noted. Firstly, the localization of accumulated phosphate is not known: it is assumed to be largely fungal because of the quantities involved. How much phosphate the alga gets is unknown at present. Secondly, care must be exercised during extraction, as breakdown of organic phosphates can occur at low pH, high temperature, or due to the liberation of phosphatases.

*Sulphur metabolism*

Very little is known about the metabolism of sulphur compounds in lichens. This lack of knowledge is regrettable in view of the proposed sensitivity of lichens to atmospheric sulphur dioxide. Without more detailed knowledge of the way in which the lichen uses sulphur and sequesters it in the thallus under normal conditions, it is extremely difficult to interpret experiments in which sulphur oxides are applied and their effects monitored by changes in some physiological parameter not obviously connected with sulphur metabolism *per se*.

Gilbert (1969) has shown that accumulation of sulphur from city air by live thalli of *Usnea filipendula* is six times greater than that by dead thalli; both the dead thalli and cotton wool, however, also accumulated appreciable amounts of sulphur. Hence most sulphur absorption under these conditions was metabolic, but some was non-metabolic. Lindberg (1955) reports the presence of choline sulphate from three species of *Roccella*. Feige (1969) labelled *Cladonia convoluta* with $^{35}SO_4^{2-}$ for periods up to 3 hours. After this time most of the radioactivity was still in the form of sulphate, and four other compounds were detected. Choline sulphate accounted for 60 per cent of the label in organic compounds, ethanolamine sulphate for 5 per cent, and the rest was divided more or less equally between two unknowns. It is perhaps significant that both phosphate and sulphate accumulate in lecithins and cephalins; this may mean that lipid metabolism is of more importance than has been supposed, or that this is a means of sequestering small molecules harmlessly in the cell until such time as they may be needed.

Two more points on experimental studies of sulphur metabolism need to be made. Firstly, although $^{35}S$ is quite a convenient isotope, methods for identifying sulphur compounds in plant extracts are still unsatisfactory. Secondly, as the oxidation state of inorganic sulphur oxides is markedly pH-dependent, it would seem necessary to know both the effect of external buffering on the effective cell pH of lichens, and the capacity of the lichen for oxidation-reduction reactions, and the rate at which these can occur.

*Nitrogen metabolism*

A striking aspect of nitrogen metabolism is the capacity of at least some lichens with blue-green algae to fix atmospheric nitrogen at very high rates, and to make it available to the fungus. Bond and Scott (1955), Scott (1956), and Henrickson and Simu (1971) have demonstrated fixation in a variety of *Nostoc*-containing lichens, Fogg and Stewart (1968) have demonstrated it *in situ* in Antarctica, and Rogers *et al.* (1966) consider that in arid Australian soils, nitrogen fixation by lichens may be an important contribution to the nitrogen balance. More detailed work has been done recently on fixation by cephalodia of *Peltigera aphthosa* (Millbank and Kershaw, 1969; Kershaw and Millbank, 1970; Millbank, 1972) using $^{15}N$ and acetylene reduction methods. The *Nostoc* in the intact thalli fixed nitrogen at substantially higher rates than cultured blue-green algae, although the heterocyst frequency was low. This suggests that ordinary vegetative cells fix $N_2$ in the thallus. The fixation was more rapid at 25°C than 12°C, and was very sensitive to physical damage of the cephalodia. Almost all of the fixed nitrogen passed to the fungus, a very low proportion remaining in the *Nostoc* cells. Further, the nitrogen was passed more or less entirely into the fungus, the *Coccomyxa* symbiont only receiving about 3 per cent of what would be expected on a proportional share (by weight) basis. Millbank and Kershaw consider that the application of nitrate at low levels, which increased the apparent health of *Peltigera aphthosa*, is necessary as a nitrogen source for the *Coccomyxa*. This area of lichen metabolism potentially has much to tell us about the relationships of the symbionts, and is obviously of great ecological significance to *Nostoc*-containing lichens capable of nitrogen fixation.

Amino-acid metabolism and protein synthesis have received scant attention. Apart from the uptake work mentioned above, Smith (1960*a*,*b*) examined the distribution of nitrogen in various fractions extracted from *Peltigera polydactyla*. About 60 per cent of the nitrogen was insoluble, i.e. in proteins and nucleic acids, and after 6 days' starvation in the dark, soluble nitrogen increased at the expense of insoluble nitrogen, but only to a small extent. Absorption of large amounts of nitrogen compounds resulted in very little increase in protein, the nitrogen remaining in soluble form. Solberg (1970) surveyed the amino-acid composition of a range of Norwegian lichens and noted that glutamic acid was the most abundant. Farrar (unpublished) has investigated protein synthesis in *Hypogymnia physodes*; [$^{14}$C]leucine, supplied carrier-free, was rapidly taken up and about 50 per cent incorporated into a methanol-insoluble, alkali-soluble protein fraction within 24 hours. Of the remaining 50 per cent, much was lost (presumably by respiration) and much transaminated. No decrease of counts in the protein fraction was seen over the course of 7 days. Further, by dual labelling with [$^{3}$H]leucine and [$^{14}$C]bicarbonate, it was possible to show that only 2 per cent of photosynthetically fixed carbon moved into protein in 24 hours. Rates of turnover of proteins are as yet unknown; it is possible that they are faster than has often been thought. As the rate of protein turnover has considerable bearing on questions such as growth rate, accurate measurements would be most useful.

#### *Lipid metabolism*

Apart from a few casual microscopic observations, there is no information on lichen lipids apart from the scant references made above. Clearly, such a major sector of metabolism deserves more attention.

### Effects of environmental variables

The terrestrial environment is one of continuous change and flux: onto the daily rhythm of light and dark are superimposed less predictable changes in water availability and nutrient supply, and these in their turn interact with temperature, and the slow turn of seasons to result in an environment in which nothing is constant and little predictable. Different groups of organisms have come to terms with this in different ways; mammals have complex mechanisms to maximize homeostasis; flowering plants have a morphology adapted to the needs of light gathering and control of water loss; some fungi sporulate at the onset of unfavourable conditions. Lichens, on the other hand, have few obvious morphological adaptations, and are completely open to the environment. How, then, do they cope with the changes they meet, and how, in turn, does having to face environmental extremes place constraints on lichen metabolism? We are not yet in a position to answer these questions fully, but a great deal of data exist on how lichens react to various environmental changes, and some suggestions as to the integration of this data can be made. It will nevertheless become clear that both the complexity of the interactions between variables, and the significance of environmental fluctuations to lichen thalli, have been seriously underestimated.

There are several difficulties inherent in these studies. Firstly, the method of assessing the response of the lichen must be suitable and meaningful. Secondly, the simulation of environmental variables in the laboratory must be realistic before extrapolations to the field situation are made. And thirdly, care is needed to differentiate between temporary and reversible changes induced by the treatments given, and permanent and irreversible damage to the lichen system. As will become apparent, in comparing the results of other workers it is necessary to examine the exact conditions under which their experiments were carried out.

*Fluctuations*

Several lines of evidence indicate that fluctuations in major environmental variables are of great importance in maintaining healthy lichen thalli. Ahmadjian (1967) discusses the role of fluctuations in the synthesis of lichens from their symbionts, where alternate wetting and drying is necessary for successful lichenization. This is not necessarily relevant to mature thalli, as the physiology of the young synthetic thallus is rather distinct (Hill and Ahmadjian, 1972), but will probably be of more relevance to lichen establishment in the wild. Several workers have cultured lichens in phytotrons, and all found growth to be more successful when conditions were varied. Pearson (1970) grew *Hypogymnia physodes*, *Xanthoria parietina*, and *Peltigera polydactyla*, and by using dry weight and manometric determinations of photosynthesis as indicators of viability, found that *Hypogymnia* and *Xanthoria* became unhealthy in constant conditions whereas *Peltigera* remained rather more viable. All three species were healthier in treatments where temperature, light, and relative humidity were varied more or less independently. Dibben (1971) grew six species from macerates of thalli under 18 different combinations of environmental conditions, and again found that fluctuating temperature, relative humidity, and light, were necessary for successful growth of *Pycnothelia* and species of *Cladonia*. Harris and Kershaw (1971) found that *Parmelia sulcata* and *Hypogymnia physodes* soon died under continuous light, but under 12-hour light and dark periods, and with alternate days wet and dry, growth was maintained for 4 months, during which time *Parmelia* grew 15 per cent and *Hypogymnia* 7 per cent as assayed by dry weight.

Electron microscopy has also indicated possible effects of various environmental conditions. Variations have been claimed in size and number of pyrenoglobuli, starch granules, and lipid-like granules (Brown and Wilson, 1968; Jacobs and Ahmadjian, 1969; Peveling, 1970; Harris and Kershaw, 1971). These authors differ somewhat in their findings, possibly due to the widely differing, and loosely defined, conditions imposed on the lichens, and in part to the differential response of different species. However, they all agree that varying conditions are reflected in ultrastructural changes.

There is thus direct evidence that fluctuating conditions are necessary for the growth of many lichens. However, it must be noted that some lichens (those that live in more constant environments, such as aquatic lichens and lichens of moist ground in shaded woods) may tolerate, or even need, nearly constant conditions. Kershaw and Millbank (1969) kept *Peltigera aphthosa* in a more or less constant humidity and temperature regime with a 16-hour day; the lichen was successfully maintained thus, and Millbank (1972) found that it gave consistent and repeatable experimental results. Ried (1960*d*) has shown that the aquatic lichen *Verrucaria elaeomelaena* is tolerant of prolonged submersion and is highly intolerant of drying. In general, however, some variation does seem necessary; in the last two cases light at least was varied diurnally, and in the majority of species studied, i.e. lichens from typical habitats, fluctuations in all of the main variables seem necessary for optimal growth. The effects of variations in the main environmental variables will now be considered in turn.

### *Water*

Lichens have no major morphological adaptations for retaining water, and the water content of most thalli thus mirrors the water content of the immediate environment. It is now well established that the rate of many physiological processes in lichens is closely tied to the water content of the thallus, most metabolic activity being suspended when the thallus is dry. It need hardly be emphasized that a dry lichen is, in biological terms, very dry indeed, with a water content of only 1–15 per cent of the dry weight (Smith, 1962; Lange, 1969*b*) and commonly at the lower end of this range. Most organisms would be irreparably damaged if dried only once to this level. Much of the work on variations in water content has involved the use of gas exchange as a measure of lichen response; information on other aspects of metabolism would be most valuable. Also, it has been normal practice to equilibrate the lichen to a certain water content and then measure its gas exchange; the lichen may not behave in the same way at the same water content whilst being dried out or rewetted. It should also be noted that different authors use different means of expressing water content—as the relative humidity of the air with which the lichen is in equilibrium, as a percentage of the maximum water content, or as the amount of water expressed as a percentage of the dry weight of the thallus.

*Variation in water content.* In most lichens so far examined, gas exchange rises as water content increases, both respiration and photosynthesis increasing non-linearly until they reach their maximum values at a water content rather below maximum. Above this water content, NAR drops but respiration rate stays steady. The shape of the curves of respiration and NAR against water content act as useful 'fingerprints', the shape, and in particular the position of maximum NAR, showing strong correlations with ecology. The results of most authors hold to this broad pattern; deviations usually occur either because the lichen concerned has a distinct ecology, or because the experimental conditions vary between authors.

Ried (1960*a,c,d*) examined the zonation of lichens in and above streams, taking lichens from each of the four main zones defined and investigating their gas exchange relative to water content. The aquatic lichen *Verrucaria elaeomelaena* showed maximum NAR in fully saturated thalli, respiration being maximal at 40 per cent maximum water content and above. At the other extreme, *Umbilicaria cylindrica* (from the driest zone) showed maximum NAR at 65 per cent saturation, and maximum respiration at 85 per cent. When fully saturated, NAR was only one-tenth of the maximum rate in this species. Lichens from the other zones showed intermediate behaviour. In all of Ried's species, at very low water contents the thalli showed a negative assimilation rate. Ried also noted that in general, the thicker and denser thalli had a lower optimal water content.

Later workers have added data rather than concepts. Bliss and Hadley (1964) also found NAR to be negative at low water contents in three species of arctic lichens. Lange (1969*a*,*b*) found that the desert lichen *Ramalina maciformis* reached maximum NAR and respiration at low water contents, and that the NAR did not fall as water content increased. Harris (1971*b*) used infra-red gas analysis on three species of corticolous lichens, at 20°C. Although the pattern he found was broadly similar, he did not find negative NAR's at low water contents, and respiration only became maximal at 100 per cent water content. Indeed, he attributed the fall in NAR at high moisture content to increased respiration. The variance between this finding and those of other authors may be largely a matter of temperature; respiration seems to become increasingly important as the temperature increases (see below).

A further concept of some importance has come out of this work. Harris (1971*b*) finds, like Ried, that different species, in this case on trees, show behaviour related to their habitat. Thus *Parmelia sulcata* at the tops of trees has its maximum NAR at a lower water content than *Parmelia caperata* at the bases. He also finds that both *Parmelia sulcata* and *Parmelia caperata* show intraspecific variation related to habitat. For example, *Parmelia caperata* from tree-tops has its maximum NAR at 55 per cent, and that from tree bases at 75 per cent, maximum water content. Such intraspecific variation has also been reported for geographical variation in *Parmelia caperata* in southern England (Kershaw and Harris, 1971*b*), for *Cladonia stellaris* in open and shaded situations (Kershaw and Rouse, 1971), and for several other species in varying habitats in Ontario (Kershaw, 1972).

*Prolonged soaking.* Prolonged soaking is a highly unnatural condition for most lichens, and as has just been seen, optimal assimilation rates are usually achieved in less than saturated thalli. However, it is convenient for many kinds of laboratory experiments to use thalli either floating on, or submerged in, aqueous media; virtually all of the information presented in the first half of this review, for example, comes from experiments involving saturated thalli kept in constant light or dark at 20°C. This set of conditions is only one, and an uncommon one, of the many to which a lichen is exposed, and so the relevance of many of these experiments to the lichen in the field may be limited, and great caution must be observed in assessing their suitability. It would be well, therefore, to examine in some detail the effects of prolonged soaking on lichens, as there are several implications for experimental design.

Ensgraber (1954) noted an increase in RQ from 0.87 to unity in *Hypogymnia physodes* over a period of days, when it was kept moist following a dry period. Ried (1960*d*) has found that whereas the aquatic lichen *Verrucaria elaeomelaena* showed normal gas exchange after 3 weeks' submersion, *Parmelia saxatilis* showed negative net assimilation within a week. Other species showed intermediate behaviour. He also showed that *Rhizocarpon geographicum* had greater resistance to prolonged submersion at 9°C than at 17°C. Using [$^{14}C$]bicarbonate fixation to assay true photosynthesis, Farrar (unpublished) has shown that *Hypogymnia physodes*, kept soaked in the dark or light, shows a steady fall in the capacity to photosynthesize after more than 24–48 hours at 20°C, or 72–96 hours at 5°C. After some 7 days in the dark at 20°C, photosynthesis was below the level of dark fixation. Both *Xanthoria aureola* and *Peltigera horizontalis* showed reduced photosynthesis after similar treatment, and both were especially sensitive to soaking in the dark. In the same experiments, Farrar measured phosphate uptake using $^{32}PO_4$, and found that, whereas in *Hypogymnia* and *Xanthoria* reduction in phosphate uptake was equivalent to reduction in photosynthesis, in *Peltigera* phosphate uptake persisted at a high level for much longer than photosynthesis. He interpreted this as indicating that in *Peltigera*, the alga was more sensitive to the treatments than the fungus, perhaps because it lacks a large pool of soluble sugars. Part of the reduction in photosynthesis may be ascribed to the observation that chlorophyll levels drop by 33 per cent in *Hypogymnia* after 72 hours' soaking in the dark at 20°C, but only by 10 per cent at 5°C.

Other changes also occur in the soaked lichen. Polyol levels drop on soaking, rather more rapidly in the dark than in the light. Richardson and Smith (1966) found that pentitols dropped to zero in *Xanthoria aureola* after 48 hours in the dark, with mannitol levels also dropping steadily but more slowly. In *Lecanora conizaeoides* (Richardson, 1967) identical treatment for ten days resulted in a much smaller net loss of polyols, with a slight rise in mannitol. Drew (1966) found that in *Peltigera polydactyla*, the drop in mannitol on soaking in the dark was much greater at 20°C than at 5°C. In *Hypogymnia physodes*, pentitols (especially arabitol) drop markedly over a period of seven days, with a small rise in mannitol; the drop was greater in the dark than in the light (Farrar, unpublished).

Additional information has come from pre-incubating the lichen on a source of radioactive carbon, and then watching the loss of radioactivity over a period of days. *Peltigera polydactyla* loses 20 per cent of the label, applied as glucose, in 24 hours (Smith, 1963*b*). Drew (1966) found that more of the label applied, as glucose, to *Peltigera polydactyla* entered insoluble fractions in the light than in the dark, and less was respired. Farrar (unpublished) has found that *Hypogymnia physodes* respires 70 per cent of photosynthetically fixed label in seven days when soaked in the light at 20°C.

It can thus be concluded that, for non-aquatic lichens, prolonged soaking induces considerable changes in both symbionts, including reduction in photosynthesis, chlorophyll levels, phosphate uptake, and pentitol or polyol levels. It seems that at 20°C these changes begin after 24 hours, and at 5°C, after about four days.

*Effect of drying.* The effect of drying the desert lichen *Ramalina maciformis* has been investigated by Lange (1969*b*). He found the changes in NAR and respiration corresponded closely with those expected from experiments where the lichen was first equilibrated to various water contents. No change in the polyol content of *Hypogymnia physodes* during or after drying (Farrar, unpublished), and only slight changes in the distribution of a carbon pulse were noted. Harris (1972) found a strong correlation between the vertical evaporation gradient in trees and vertical distribution of species, indicating that the relative amount of time a thallus spends at various water contents as it dries may be of considerable importance.

The dry thallus may be capable of gas exchange (low rates being reported for the desert lichen *Chondropsis semiviridis* (Rogers, 1971)), but any metabolism must be proceeding at a very low rate. No reports of metabolism proceeding in the dry thallus exist. In *Hypogymnia physodes* dried and then kept dry for 72 hours, both chlorophyll levels and the amount of photosynthetically-applied label decreased by 30 per cent; it is not clear to what extent these changes occurred during drying, or in the dry state (Farrar, unpublished).

*Rewetting a dry thallus.* The dry lichen is capable of absorbing enough water from moist air to restart metabolism. Bertsch (1966) found that species of *Evernia* and *Ramalina* in equilibrium with saturated air achieved 90 per cent of their maximum NAR, and compensation points were reached even in unsaturated air. *Ramalina maciformis* behaves similarly (Lange and Bertsch, 1965; Lange 1969*b*) as do a variety of fruticose European lichens (Buttner, 1971). Thus, resaturation of the thallus with water vapour leads to a positive carbon balance. The nature of respiration when a lichen is rewetted this way is unknown.

The situation is very different when rewetting with liquid water occurs. Three distinct types of gas exchange follow rewetting, resulting in a very unfavourable carbon balance. These three types are as follows: 1) 'Wetting burst'—a large burst of gas 80 per cent of which is carbon dioxide, equivalent to a C loss of several hours' normal respiration, released within 90 seconds of rewetting the thallus. 2) 'Resaturation respiration'—a high but steadily decreasing rate of respiration, which is cyanide-sensitive, has a distinct RQ, and lasts for from one to nine hours. 3) 'Basal respiration'—this obtains both during and after resaturation respiration.

The wetting burst is a strange phenomenon, and at the time of writing it is not known whether it is purely physical, or partly metabolic. Smith (in press) studied the burst in *Peltigera polydactyla* and *Xanthoria aureola*, and has also found that treating the lichen with cyanide before drying does not affect the burst.

In *Hypogymnia physodes*, radioactive carbon dioxide can be trapped in the burst from a lichen pre-incubated in [$^{14}$C]bicarbonate (Farrar, unpublished). The amount of carbon lost corresponds to the loss in carbon from pentitols on wetting and drying, and the burst could be eliminated by wetting the lichen for just two minutes and immediately redrying it, when on subsequent rewetting no burst was observed. It is therefore possible that the burst itself is purely a physical process, but that the carbon lost in it has a metabolic origin, from the period when the lichen is moist before drying. It is obviously necessary to establish whether the lost carbon has a metabolic origin, as such a large amount is involved. It should also be noted that if a lichen is rewetted in a closed atmosphere (for example, a Warburg flask) a most distorted view of gas exchange will be produced. Smith adopted the procedure of closing the Warburg tap two minutes after tipping water onto the lichen, in order to circumvent this problem. It also makes assessment of the speed of recovery of true photosynthesis very difficult, as applied $^{14}CO_2$ will be diluted by the large amount of carbon dioxide emitted.

Resaturation respiration was first studied by Ried (1953), who examined the gas exchange of three species of lichens after drying them thoroughly for 24 hours. *Rhizocarpon geographicum*, from a dry habitat, showed respiration rising to about twice normal levels and lasting for an hour. The aquatic lichen *Verrucaria elaeomelaena* showed a maximum of six times its normal respiration and never fully recovered. *Lecidea soredizodes*, which was ecologically intermediate, showed four times the normal respiration and returned to normal in four days. Ried (1960*b*) further examined the gas exchange of several lichens after periods of desiccation longer than they were likely to experience in the field, and concluded that the magnitude of resaturation respiration was correlated with drought resistance. He suggested that the resaturation respiration was of more significance than drought resistance *per se*.* Ried also noted that after prolonged desiccation, net assimilation built up slowly, and that in the light respiration was higher than in the dark. Resaturation respiration was noted by

* However, Rogers (1971) considered that length of the drought period was important in limiting the distribution of the desert lichen *Chondropsis semiviridis* in Australia.

Lange (1969*b*) in *Ramalina maciformis*, following rewetting with liquid water, although, as mentioned above, rewetting with water vapour had no such effect. It has also been demonstrated in *Peltigera polydactyla* and *Xanthoria aureola* dried beyond a certain critical water content (Smith, in press). Again an ecological correlation was found, as in *Xanthoria* from a dry habitat, the resaturation respiration was lower in both intensity and duration than in *Peltigera* from a moist woodland floor. Smith also showed this period of respiration to be azide and cyanide sensitive and to have a changed RQ. When experimental design involves rewetting a dry lichen, therefore, measurements of gas exchange are complicated by both the wetting burst and by resaturation respiration. The latter is especially difficult to evaluate, as its significance is not known, and its duration is dependent on the species, and probably also on habitat within that species.

A further point of interest is the speed with which phosphate uptake recovers after rewetting in *Hypogymnia physodes* (Farrar, unpublished). Organic compounds can be found after one minute, and active uptake obtains at 30 seconds; total uptake in the hour following rewetting was slightly lower than in soaked controls. This measure of recovery from drying apparently presents fewer problems than gas exchange measurements, as long as suitable controls (such as killed lichens, low temperatures, and inhibitors) are used. Recovery from the dry state is a most important aspect of lichen biology. Many lichens are repeatedly dried and rewetted in nature, and the speed with which a positive carbon balance, active uptake and a metabolic permeability barrier can be re-established after rewetting must be of considerable importance ecologically.

*Repeated wetting and drying cycles.* Smith (in press) subjected *Peltigera polydactyla* to a harsh regime of two hours' soaking in the dark followed by 22 hours in a desiccator over calcium chloride. Over four such cycles the mannitol content dropped by 75 per cent, and resaturation respiration was considerably reduced in size and duration. *Hypogymnia physodes* under a similar regime showed a net loss in polyols (Farrar, unpublished), with arabitol dropping the most. Further, over three such cycles over 50 per cent of pre-applied $^{14}C$ was lost. Photosynthetic ability was not much affected by three cycles, and nor were chlorophyll levels, but after seven cycles both phosphate uptake and photosynthesis were greatly impaired, decreasing to half control levels for lichens in the dark, and to 10 per cent of control for those in low light. These severe regimes thus greatly affect lichen metabolism; it should be noted that the high losses of carbon observed cannot be explained by basal and resaturation respiration alone, and hence the wetting burst may be involved.

*Temperature*

Lichen metabolism is greatly influenced by temperature, and some good correlations between temperature and ecology are emerging. The essence of the effect of temperature is that it affects different processes to different extents. In the case of NAR the optimum is not necessarily where photosynthesis is maximal, as at that point respiration may be disproportionately high. Working with a variety of species, Stalfelt (1939) showed that $Q_{10}$'s for NAR and respiration changed with temperature, and the $Q_{10}$ for respiration was in general much greater than that for NAR; the result was that assimilation was proportionately much higher than respiration at 0–10°C than 15–25°C. Also Bliss and Hadley (1964) found that in three species of arctic lichens photosynthesis is disproportionately higher than respiration at 10°C than at 20°C. Lange (1965; 1969*a,b*) has examined a variety of lichens for gas exchange at different temperatures and at different light intensities. Several important points emerge. Firstly, respiration increases markedly (and non-linearly) with temperature, so that fall-off in NAR at high temperatures is largely due to high respiration rather than low photosynthesis. Secondly, for some species the temperature for maximal NAR is lower at reduced light intensities. And thirdly, the temperature at which maximum NAR occurs shows strong geographical correlations, being at about 5°C for arctic lichens, and at over 20°C for some tropical species. For these latter species, respiration still increases markedly with temperature, so photosynthesis must increase at high temperatures. The lowest temperature at which a carbon surplus is achieved shows a very clear relation to geographical distribution. Gannutz (1969) has similarly shown a relationship between the temperature for optimum NAR and geographical distribution. Heikkilä and Kallio (1966) found arctic specimens of *Botrydina* and *Coriscium* to have low optimum temperatures for net assimilation, and Kallio and Heinonen (1971) found that the optimum temperature for assimilation in *Nephroma arcticum* was greater in late summer than in winter. Stalfelt (1939) found that, in a variety of species, the $Q_{10}$'s of NAR and respiration were different in January and May, and that in January, optima were lower than in May.

The question of photosynthesis at low temperatures is a vexed one. Carbon dioxide fixation and a positive net carbon balance has been reported at temperatures down to −24°C (Lange, 1962, 1965; Lange and Metzner, 1965); Kallio and Heinonen (1971) found that NAR at −5°C for lichens such as *Cetraria nivalis* and *Nephroma arcticum* was independent of light intensity above a small limiting value, and thus may be qualitatively distinct from assimilation at higher temperatures. The need for critical work, including labelling experiments, is obvious. Several other effects of temperature have been noted above—slower fall in polyols during dark starvation, slower active uptake, slower onset of harmful effects of submersion, all at low temperatures. It remains to be added that Lange considers some lichens to be adapted to low temperatures, as it is under these conditions that they appear to be most active in the field. It is therefore regrettable that most experimental work has been done at 18–25°C because for temperate lichens, 5–10°C would be far more realistic. In interpreting experimental results, it must be remembered that the effects of temperature are non-linear, and no $Q_{10}$ can be assumed; nor can it be assumed that all processes are equally affected; NAR and respiration certainly are not. Finally the temperature of the thallus may well be different from the ambient temperature, especially if it is drying out.

Lichens are remarkably resistant to extremes of temperature. Most lichens are far too cold-resistant to be limited in their distribution by low temperatures; two Antarctic lichens withstood direct plunging of hydrated thalli into liquid nitrogen, but *Roccella phycopsis* was exceptional in being damaged at −20°C. Most lichens are intermediate in behaviour between these extremes (Lange, 1962; Lange, 1969*b*; Lange and Metzner, 1965; Kappen and Lange, 1970*a*,*b*, 1972; Kallio and Heinonen, 1971; Heikkilä and Kallio, 1966). Lichens are also fairly resistant to high temperatures, at least when dry; the hydrated thallus is very much less resistant (Lange, 1969*b*). Normally, lichens will be dry at high temperatures so this will be of little consequence: Lange found that artificially moistening a lichen at high temperature led to a net carbon loss, which he ascribed to the effect of respiration (Lange, Schulze, and Köch, 1970*a*). Rogers (1971) considered the heat-sensitivity of hydrated thalli of *Chondropsis semiviridis* to limit its distribution in Australia.

*Light*

The interaction of light with several other variables has been noted above, including the increased respiratory loss following rewetting a desiccated lichen in the light rather than the dark, and the different optimum temperatures for carbon assimilation at different light intensities. Ahmadjian (1967) reviews data on light intensity optima. Harris has recently shown (Harris, 1969) that in *Parmelia caperata* light compensation points for a twenty-four-hour period vary by an order of four throughout the year. It is possible that light saturation values will show an ecological correlation; thus Harris finds corticolous *Parmelia* species to saturate at 16 000 lux, whereas the desert lichen *Ramalina maciformis* saturates at 48 500 lux (Lange, Schulze and Köch, 1970*a*). It is likely to be the light compensation point at a realistic temperature that is ecologically important to the lichen.

It would be well to consider the effect of light on processes other than gas exchange: unfortunately little work has been forthcoming. The transport of glucose between the symbionts of *Peltigera polydactyla* falls off in the dark (Hill and Smith, 1972), as does the movement of ribitol in *Hypogymnia physodes* (Farrar, unpublished) and nitrogen fixation in *Collema tuniforme* and *Peltigera rufescens* (Henricksson and Simu, 1971). Both Feige (1967) and Farrar (unpublished) found little difference in the fate of a pulse of [$^{32}$P]phosphate in the light or dark. It is not clear how differently lichens behave at various light intensities, but probably many changes remain undetected. It should be pointed out that the effects of a sudden change from the light to the dark —the usual practice in laboratory and phytotron work—may have rather different effects from a slow fading and brightening of light, as is usual in nature. Farrar (unpublished) found that in

*Hypogymnia physodes*, photosynthesis in the hour following one hour in the dark was one-third of that in controls kept in the light, whereas phosphate uptake was not greatly affected.

By now it should have become clear that none of the variables considered—water, temperature, and light—can be meaningfully considered in isolation. Although useful ecological correlations can be extracted from one alone, it is the interaction of the three which is of importance to the lichen in the field; and in order to extrapolate from the laboratory to the field, or to make detailed correlations with distribution patterns, all three must be considered together. It should also be noted that no extrapolations from one set of conditions to another can be made, as none of the relationships between variables and behaviour are linear.

### *pH and nutrients*

Much casual observation, but little critical work, relates lichen distribution to nutrient supply and acid- or base-status of the substrate. The two may well be closely linked, at least in some situations, as has been indicated by Haynes and Morgan-Huws (1970).

Photosynthesis in *Usnea subfloridana* is strongly inhibited at pH 8 and above, but is not affected by low pH values down to 2.5 (Hill, 1971). Respiration in a variety of lichens drops off above pH 8 and below pH 3 to 4 (Baddeley, Ferry, and Finegan, 1971), but it is not clear what kind of respiration was being measured. *Xanthoria aureola* leaks $^{14}C$ to the medium below pH 4 (Hill and Smith, 1972), and the loss of $^{14}C$ by *Peltigera polydactyla* during inhibition is pH-sensitive. This is explained by the differing sensitivities of the algae to pH, but as the authors point out, the pH of the buffer and the pH at any given site (for example, the site of carbon release by the alga) are not necessarily the same. As lichens are such avid accumulators of small molecules, it is necessary to use buffers with minimum biological activity. Further, in experiments where various species are being compared, bringing them to the same pH may amount to treating them differently, as each species will be displaced from its natural pH to a different extent.

One of the few experiments on feeding lichens with nutrients was performed by Scott (1960), where he fed discs of *Peltigera praetextata* on various levels of nitrate, keeping them at constant high humidity for periods up to 14 weeks. The discs receiving more than 0.25 g/l of nitrogen broke down, with the phycobiont outgrowing the mycobiont. From this and from the importance of low nutrients in establishing lichen syntheses (Ahmadjian, 1967) it has been argued that lichens need a low supply of nutrients, or else the symbiosis may break down. It is better to interpret these results as indicating that when a lichen is placed in grossly unnatural conditions it will not survive, but that the particular set of conditions employed may favour one of the symbionts. The effect of various nutrient regimes on lichens under more natural environmental conditions has not been investigated; nor have the N requirements of the so-called 'nitrophilous' species. The nutrient status and requirements of lichens are thus little understood. It is the opinion (no more) of the present author that because lichens are slow-growing they need little nutrient, rather than their growth being limited by low nutrient supply.

*The field situation and seasonal variation*

It is only by reference to the field situation that laboratory work on plant physiology has ultimate validity, and it is only through laboratory work that the field situation becomes comprehensible. Any results from laboratory work on lichens have to be compatible with a wide range of field observations, such as the slow growth rates and distribution patterns of these plants. There have, however, been comparatively few studies where the aim was to link field and laboratory work; these will be considered first. The gas exchange of the desert lichen *Ramalina maciformis* was investigated in the field by infra-re dgas analysis following careful laboratory experiments (Lange, 1969*a*,*b*; Lange, Schulze, and Köch, 1968, 1970*a*). The lichen was measured under ambient conditions in summer, and it was found that as temperature and light increased at dawn, the dew-soaked lichen developed a positive carbon balance, which dropped off as the temperature rose and the lichen dried out, to spend most of the day dry and inactive; following the onset of darkness, the thallus absorbed sufficient water vapour from dewfall to restart metabolism, and respired during the night. On balance the lichen showed a slight carbon surplus at the end of 24 hours, but this was very dependent on morning evaporation conditions. Productivity of the lichens was significantly increased by experimentally lowering the temperature; lower temperatures would obtain naturally in winter. Thus a desert lichen was adjusted to utilization of water vapour and the cool periods of early morning. Other species behave in a similar way, and it has been shown that actual growth rates approximate to expected ones in *Caloplaca aurantia* (Lange, Schulze and Köch, 1970*b*; Lange and Everari, 1971). Schulze and Lange (1968) have also shown a carbon surplus in *Hypogymnia physodes* in the field at low temperatures, and again found that these conditions gave a net gain in carbon. Simulation studies, utilizing computer techniques, have been used by Kershaw and Harris (1971*a*,*b*) and Harris (1972) to relate experimental behaviour of *Parmelia caperata* to observed growth rates in the field, a two-year growth period being simulated. The data show a good correspondence between vertical distribution of lichens and their behaviour at different water contents, and thus evaporation rates appear to be significant. The simulated net increase was of the order of twice the observed growth rate; this may be partly due to not taking rewetting phenomena into account. The use of simulation studies enables critical processes to be highlighted, and is a good test of laboratory assumptions.

Some observations on chlorophyll variation and contents of metabolically important elements are also valuable (Hill and Woolhouse, 1966; Kärenlampi, 1971). Hill and Woolhouse examined populations of *Xanthoria parietina* growing in marine, and inland corticolous and saxicolous communities, and found significant differences in thallus thickness, dry weight per unit area, and contents of chlorophyll, parietin, and potassium in lichens from different sites, giving more indication of the variability of lichen species.

Seasonal variation is now well documented. It seems that temperate European lichens can best utilize the cool moist days of late winter and early spring, and are under greatest stress in summer, when warm dry days keep photosynthesis to a minimum, whilst warm nights with dewfall maximize respiration. Some of the observations on seasonal variation are summarized in Table 2, in a simple comparative fashion.

*Table 2 Seasonal variation in a range of lichen characters in Europe*

| Character | Month | | | Reference |
|---|---|---|---|---|
| | *May–June* | *Sept.* | *Dec.–Feb.* | |
| algal cells/unit area | | high | low | Harris, 1971 |
| photosynthesis/unit area | | high | low | Harris, 1971 |
| photosynthesis/unit weight | low | | high | Stalfelt, 1939 |
| light compensation values | | low | high | Harris, 1971 |
| chlorophyll level | low | | high | Wilhelmsen, 1959 |
| optimum temp. for NAR | high | | low | Stalfelt, 1939 |
| dry wt/unit area | high | low | low | Smith, 1962 |
| total carbohydrate/unit area | high | low | | Smith, 1962 |
| glucose absorption/unit area | high | low | | Smith, 1962 |
| soluble carbohydrate/unit area | | high | low | Smith and Ozin, unpublished |

These variations are probably a result of changing climate, rather than seasons *per se*; thus Richardson (1967) followed changes in polyol content in *Xanthoria aureola* for 18 months, and found poor correspondence between winter levels in successive years. It would thus seem necessary to exercise great caution both in comparing observations on seasonal variation made in different years, and in extrapolating from data based on a single year's observations.

A further kind of experimental work in the field is the transplant experiment. As has been shown above, lichens are very exactly adjusted to the conditions under which they live; whether this is genetic or phenotypic variation, and how much a lichen can adapt itself to new conditions, is not known. Thus if a lichen is transplanted and dies, it may simply be that the set of environmental conditions to which it has been moved are beyond the range of conditions to which it can adapt. It will also be noted that it is impossible to do a satisfactory control transplant; the reciprocal transplant is hardly a control (but see ch 3, 17).

## Integration and implications

How may the main concepts to emerge from the literature on lichen physiology be integrated into a general picture of lichen growth? Let us start with the indisputable—the observation that, compared with other plants, lichens grow very slowly. This does not seem to be because any of the metabolic processes occur more slowly in lichens than in other plants—nearly all processes examined proceed very quickly and efficiently, with the exception of the shunting of carbon and nitrogen into proteins, and other 'growth processes'. Why, then, is the fixed carbon not moved into protein and polysaccharide faster? As we have seen, most remains in polyols, and subsequently is lost by respiration, especially following rewetting a dry lichen. And so what is the function of the polyols? They are not acting purely as respiratory substrates to provide energy for growth processes as these are proceeding very slowly; yet they are being respired and turned over, and they are both ubiquitous and abundant. It has been seen that they are run down during periods of stress, and it would be reasonable to assume (from work on other groups as well as lichens) that they are involved in the mechanisms by which the lichen survives periods of stress, especially dehydration. It is also clear that lichens are frequently placed in stress conditions due to the continual fluctuations in their natural environment, and that polyols would be expected therefore to be continually turned over in the field, and much fixed carbon therefore lost.* Thus it may be that the primary sinks for fixed carbon in lichens are the mechanisms by which resistance to environmental fluctuations and stress is mediated, and these include polyols. Slow growth of lichens would then be primarily due to both the short percentage of time during which net carbon assimilation is possible, and to partitioning of fixed carbon such that little was put into growth processes because most was needed for stress resistance. Slow growth would thus be a necessary concomitant of survival in adverse habitats, due to the small percentage of fixed carbon retained in the thallus for long periods.

This hypothesis can be further related to other aspects of lichen biology. It is implied here that net carbon balance is a critical feature of lichen growth, and this balance would not be appreciated in many experimental routines as the lichen is not stressed during them. Further it provides a means of explaining how long-term but small changes in the environment can affect lichen

* The very high resistance to extreme conditions by lichens is well documented, and polyols may be active here also.

growth, as they may tip the balance between a carbon surplus and a net loss. A slightly drier environment, which may either lower the amount of time the lichen is at optimal water content, or may increase the number of times the lichen is wetted and dried, with ensuing carbon loss, would tip the balance in this way. Similarly, having to utilize fixed carbon to sequester a pollutant may tip the balance adversely.

If lichens are slow-growing because they need to use carbon for stress resistance, then they would need comparatively small amounts of nutrients. The supply of nutrients by rain and by leachates would thus be more than adequate for growth, and indeed the storage of large amounts of unnecessary inorganic molecules could be something of a nuisance. Phosphate can be stored as polyphosphate; most nitrate remains as soluble compounds in which carbon is tied up. Clearly, good evidence on nutrient requirements is needed. The presence of the cation absorption mechanisms on the cell walls may be a means of sieving water for potentially toxic cations, and so reducing the chance of their being accumulated.

It is sometimes contended that the lichen symbionts are delicately balanced, and that the symbiosis will maintain its integrity only if certain conditions necessary to keep the balance (such as low nutrient status or alternating conditions that favour each of the symbionts in turn) are fulfilled. However, it seems rather that the symbiosis is extremely stable, withstanding a good deal of environmental stress; the environment of most lichens fluctuates too unpredictably to be a balancing factor. Lichens are, however, most intolerant of constant conditions, especially high humidity and light; they may further be intolerant of various changes in their environment such as increased dryness, or pollutants.

This is a personal synthesis of the existing evidence, and of how the lichen may be prone to certain types of environmental change. A brief review of the salient points concerning experimental design and interpretation should also be made. These points are especially relevant when quantification of any kind is envisaged, and when laboratory work is to be related to field observations.

1. The behaviour of the lichen is determined both by the

conditions in which it is placed and the recent environmental history of the thallus. Thus a lichen that has just been dark starved will behave very differently from one kept dry and suddenly rewetted. As lichens collected from the field will have been exposed to unknown conditions it is essential to give a realistic pretreatment to the material; even then some variability between collections (especially between collections at different times of the year) is to be expected. These differences in behaviour may be short-term and reversible, or the lichen may have been permanently damaged. It is also of importance to measure all of the variables a lichen is being exposed to experimentally.

2. Lichens seem to be closely adapted to the environment in which they live, particularly with respect to water content. In comparing lichens (even of the same species) from two different habitats, under identical conditions, one is in effect treating them differently, as they are being exposed to conditions which deviate from their normal environmental conditions to different extents. Comparison between them is thus complex, except in the broadest of terms. This makes the interpretation of transplants in particular very difficult.

3. Lichens live in and are adjusted to a whole range of fluctuating conditions. When they are experimentally exposed to just one combination of variables, and the effect of any other factor examined, this is a grossly oversimplified situation. It may be that the factor being examined has its effect when the lichen is exposed to a different combination of variables, or that although it has an effect, this combination of variables plays so minor a part in the biology of the lichen that it is irrelevant. For example, the period immediately following rewetting a dry lichen may be one at which the lichen is especially sensitive to pollutants, but it has not been examined.

4. The variables that are of importance to lichens are not those commonly measured in the field, and so it is difficult to relate lichen distribution patterns to environmental variables. Thus it is not so much rainfall, or even mean relative humidity, which is of importance to lichens, but the percentage of time the lichen is at various water contents, the state of other variables at the same time (thus if the lichen is always wet at night it will lose carbon, or if usually cool when moist it may have a larger carbon surplus),

and the frequency with which the water content drops below a certain point which will result in the rewetting phenomena being invoked. These considerations are especially important when productivity studies are envisaged; it is not possible to calculate annual growth from a knowledge of gas-exchange rates and climatic conditions, as many of the things controlling carbon uptake and loss will be omitted from consideration.

5. The choice of parameters used to assess the response of a lichen to its environment is difficult. In particular, differentiating both between reversible and irreversible effects, and also between small changes that are important in the long term rather than the short term, are two major problems. Gas exchange, although the most commonly used, is not the easiest to interpret, and use of other parameters may be profitable. The effects of the normal variables on the parameter must be known before more exotic variables such as pollutants can be profitably investigated.

It is hoped that this survey of lichen physiology will be of some use in designing experiments, especially those concerned with the effects of pollution; if the reader leaves it more confused than when he started, I must apologize for a less than clear presentation of the data. Perhaps the main conclusion to be drawn from the literature is that we know, as yet, very little about lichen physiology.

*Note added in proof:*
Further work by the author on the rewetting of dry thalli has shown that the wetting burst (see p. 262) is a purely physical phenomenon, and occurs in dead thalli and dried filter paper. The carbon dioxide is assumed to be selectively absorbed onto macromolecules. In *Hypogymnia physodes* the burst is accompanied by leakage of phosphorus and carbon, the latter in sufficiently large amounts to account for the heavy loss of polyols observed (see p. 265).

## References

Ahmadjian, V. (1967). *The lichen symbiosis*. Waltham, Mass.: Blaisdell.

Aithcheson, P. A. (1971). *Polyphosphate metabolism in* Chlorella vulgaris. D.Phil. thesis, University of Oxford.

Anderson, R. L. and Wood, W. A. (1969). Carbohydrate metabolism in micro-organisms. *Ann. Rev. Microbiol.* **23,** 539–78.

Baddeley, M. S., Ferry, B. W. and Finegan, E. J. (1971). A new method of measuring lichen respiration: Response of selected species to temperature, pH and sulphur dioxide. *Lichenologist* **5,** 18–25.

Bednar, T. W. and Smith, D. C. (1966). Studies in the physiology of lichens. VI. Preliminary studies of photosynthesis and carbohydrate metabolism of the lichen *Xanthoria aureola. New Phytol.* **65,** 211–20.

Beevers, H. (1961). *Respiratory metabolism in plants.* Evanston, Illinois: Row, Peterson & Co.

Bertsch, A. (1966). Über den $CO_2$-Gaswechsel einiger Flechten nach Wasserdampfaufnahme. *Planta* **68,** 157–66.

Bliss, L. C. and Hadley, E. B. (1964). Photosynthesis and respiration of alpine lichens. *Am. J. Bot.* **51,** 870–4.

Bogorad, L. (1962). Chlorophylls. In: Lewin, R. A. (ed.) *Physiology and biochemistry of the algae,* 385–408. London and New York: Academic Press.

Boissière, J.-Cl. (1969). La chitine chez quelques lichens: mise en évidence, localisation. *Mém. Soc. bot. Fr.* **1968,** 141–50.

Boissière, M.-Cl. (1969). Les hémicelluloses chez quelques lichens: composition, localisation. *Mém. Soc. bot. Fr.* **1968,** 151–9.

Bond, G. and Scott, G. D. (1955). An examination of some symbiotic systems for fixation of nitrogen. *Ann. Bot.* **19,** 67–77.

Brown, D. H. and Slingsby, D. R. (1972). The cellular location of lead and potassium in the lichen *Cladonia rangiformis* (L.) Hoffm. *New Phytol.* **71,** 297–305.

Brown, R. M. and Wilson, R. (1968). Electron microscopy of the lichen *Physcia aipolia* (Ehrh.) Nyl. *J. Phycol.* **4,** 230–40.

Butin, H. (1954). Physiologisch-ökologische Untersuchungen über den Wasserhaushalt und die Photosynthese bei Flechten. *Biol. Zbl.* **73,** 459–502.

Büttner, R. (1971). Untersuchungen zur Ökologie und Physiologie des Gasstoffwechsels bei einigen Strauchflechten. *Flora, Jena* **160,** 72–99.

Carrodus, B. B. (1967). Absorption of nitrogen by mycorrhizal roots of beech. II. Ammonium and intrate as sources of nitrogen. *New Phytol.* **66,** 1–4.

Culberson, C. F. (1969). *Chemical and botanical guide to lichen products.* Chapel Hill, N.C.: University of North Carolina Press.

Dibben, M. J. (1971). Whole-lichen culture in a phytotron. *Lichenologist* **5,** 1–10.

Dormaar, J. F. (1968). Infra-red absorption spectra of mineral matter in saxicolous lichens and associated mosses. *Can. J. Earth Sci.* **5,** 223–30.

Drew, E. A. (1966). *Some aspects of the carbohydrate metabolism of lichens.* D.Phil. thesis, University of Oxford.

Drew, E. A. and Smith, D. C. (1966). The physiology of the symbiosis in *Peltigera polydactyla* (Neck.) Hoffm. *Lichenologist* **3,** 197–201.

Drew, E. A. and Smith, D. C. (1967*a*). Studies in the physiology of lichens. VII. The physiology of the *Nostoc* symbiont of *Peltigera polydactyla* compared with cultured and free-living forms. *New Phytol.* **66,** 379–88.

Drew, E. A. and Smith, D. C. (1967*b*). Studies in the physiology of lichens. VIII. Movement of glucose from alga to fungus during photosynthesis in the thallus of *Peltigera polydactyla*. *New Phytol.* **66,** 389–400.

Feige, B. (1967). *Untersuchungen zum Kohlenstoff- und Phosphatstoffwechsel der Flechten unter Verwendung radioaktiver Isotope.* Doctoral thesis, Universität Würzburg.

Feige, B. (1969). Stoffwechselphysiologie Untersuchungen an der tropischen Basidiolichene *Cora pavonia* (Sw.) Fr. *Flora, Jena* **160A,** 169–80.

Feige, B. (1970*a*). Untersuchungen zur Stoffwechselphysiologie der Flechte unter Verwendung radioaktiver Isotope. *Votr. bot. Ges.* (*Dt. bot. Ges.*), *n.f.* **4,** 35–44.

Feige, B. (1970*b*). Zur Verwertung uniform $^{14}C$-markierten Glukose und uniform $^{14}C$-markierten Glycerins durch die Flechte *Cladonia convoluta* (Lam.) P. Cout. *Z. Pflanzenphysiol.* **63,** 211–13.

Feige, B. and Simonis, W. (1969*a*). Untersuchungen zur Physiologie der Flechten *Cladonia convoluta* (Lam.) P. Cout. I. Allgemeines und Methodik der Untersuchungen. *Flora, Jena* **160A,** 552–60.

Feige, B. and Simonis, W. (1969*b*). Cholinsulfat in der Flechte *Cladonia convoluta* (Lam.) P. Cout. *Planta* **86,** 202–4.

Fogg, G. E. and Stewart, W. D. P. (1968). In situ determination of biological nitrogen fixation in Antarctica. *Br. Antarct. Surv. Bull.* **15,** 39–46.

Gannutz, T. P. (1969). Effects of environmental extremes on lichens. *Mém. Soc. bot. Fr.* **1968,** 169–79.

Gibbs, M. (1962). Respiration. In: Lewin, R. A. (ed.) *Physiology and biochemistry of the algae*, 361–90. London and New York: Academic Press.

Gilbert, O. L. (1969). The effect of $SO_2$ on lichens and bryophytes around Newcastle upon Tyne. In: *Air pollution, Proceedings of the first European Congress on the influence of air pollution on plants and animals, Wageningen 1968*, 223–35. Wageningen: Centre for Agricultural Publishin,g and Documentation.

G orham E. (1959). A comparison of lower and higher plants as accumulators of radioactive fallout. *Can. J. Bot.* **37,** 327–9.

Green, T. G. A. (1970). *The biology of lichen symbionts.* D.Phil. thesis, University of Oxford.

Hale, M. E. (1967). *The biology of lichens.* London: Arnold.

Handley, R. and Overstreet, R. (1968). Uptake of carrier-free $^{137}Cs$ by *Ramalina reticulata*. *Pl. Physiol.* **43,** 1401–5.

Harley, J. L. (1964). Incorporation of carbon dioxide into excised beech mycorrhizas in the presence and absence of ammonium. *New Phytol.* **63,** 203–8.

Harley, J. L. and Smith, D. C. (1956). Sugar absorption and surface carbohydrase activity of *Peltigera polydactyla* (Neck.) Hoffm. *Ann. Bot.* **20,** 513–43.

Harris, G. P. (1971). The ecology of corticolous lichens. II. The relationship between physiology and the environment. *J. Ecol.* **59,** 441–52.

Harris, G. P. (1972). The ecology of corticolous lichens. III. A simulation model of productivity as a function of light intensity and water availability. *J. Ecol.* **60,** 19–40.

Harris, G. P. and Kershaw, K. A. (1971). Thallus growth and the distribution of stored metabolites in the phycobionts of the lichens *Parmelia sulcata* and *Parmelia physodes. Can. J. Bot.* **49,** 1367–72.

Haynes, F. N. and Morgan-Huws, D. I. (1970). The importance of field studies in determining the factors influencing the occurrence and growth of lichens. *Lichenologist* **4,** 362–8.

Heikkilä, H. and Kallio, P. (1966). On the problem of subarctic basidiolichens. *Rep. Kevo Subarctic Res. Stn.* **3,** 48–74.

Henricksson, E. and Simu, B. (1971). Nitrogen fixation by lichens. *Oikos,* **22,** 119–21.

Hill, D. J. (1970). *The carbohydrate movement between the symbionts of lichens.* D.Phil. thesis, University of Oxford.

Hill, D. J. (1971). Experimental study of the effect of sulphite on lichens with reference to atmospheric pollution. *New Phytol.* **70,** 831–6.

Hill, D. J. (1972). The movement of carbohydrate from the alga to the fungus in the lichen *Peltigera polydactyla. New Phytol.* **71,** 31–40.

Hill, D. J. and Ahmadjian, V. (1972). Relationship between carbohydrate movement and the symbiosis in lichens with green algae. *Planta* **103,** 267–77.

Hill, D. J. and Smith, D. C. (1972). Lichen physiology. XII. The 'Inhibition technique'. *New Phytol.* **71,** 15–30.

Hill, D. J. and Woolhouse, H. W. (1966). Aspects of the autecology of *Xanthoria parietina* (agg.). *Lichenologist* **3,** 207–14.

Jackson, W. A. and Volk, R. J. (1970). Photorespiration. *Ann. Rev. Pl. Physiol.* **21,** 385–432.

Jacobs, J. R. and Ahmadjian, V. (1969). The ultrastructure of lichens. I. A general survey. *J. Phycol.* **5,** 227–40.

Kallio, P. and Heinonen, S. (1971). Influence of short-term low temperature on net photosynthesis in some subarctic lichens. *Rep. Kevo Subarctic Res. Stn* **8,** 63–72.

Kappen, L. and Lange, O. L. (1970*a*). Kalteresistenz von Flechten aus verschiedenen Klimagebieten. *Votr. bot. Ges.* (*Dt. bot. Ges.*), *n. f.* **4,** 61–5.

Kappen, L. and Lange, O. L. (1970*b*). The cold resistance of phycobionts from macrolichens of various habitats. *Lichenologist* **4,** 289–93.

Kärenlampi, L. (1970). Distribution of chlorophyll in the lichen *Cladonia alpestris. Rep. Kevo Subarctic Res. Stn* **7,** 1–8.

Kershaw, K. A. (1972). The relationship between moisture content and net assimilation rate of lichen thalli and its ecological significance. *Can. J. Bot.* **50,** 543–55.

Kershaw, K. A. and Harris, G. P. (1971*a*). Simulation studies and ecology: A simple defined system and model. In: Patil, G. P., Pielou, E. C. and

Waters, W. E. (ed.) *Statistical ecology*, **3,** 1–21. University Park, Penna.: Pennsylvania State University Press.

Kershaw, K. A. and Harris, G. P. (1971*b*). Simulation studies and ecology: Use of the model. In: Patil, G. P., Pielou, E. C. and Waters, W. E. (ed.) *Statistical ecology*, **3,** 23–42. University Park, Penna.: Pennsylvania University Press.

Kershaw, K. A. and Millbank, J. W. (1969). A controlled environment lichen growth chamber. *Lichenologist* **4,** 83–7.

Kershaw, K. A. and Millbank, J. W. (1970). Nitrogen metabolism in lichens. II. The partition of cephalodial-fixed nitrogen between the mycobiont and phycobionts of *Peltigera aphthosa*. *New Phytol.* **69,** 75–9.

Kershaw, K. A. and Rouse, W. R. (1971). Studies on lichen-dominated systems. I. The water relations of *Cladonia alpestris* in spruce-lichen woodland in northern Ontario. *Can. J. Bot.* **49,** 1389–99.

Lange, O. L. (1962). Die Photosynthese der Flechten bei teifen Temperaturen und nach Frostperioden. *Ber. dt. bot. Ges.* **75,** 351–2.

Lange, O. L. (1965). Der $CO_2$-Gaswechsel von Flechten bei teifen Temperaturen. *Planta* **64,** 1–19.

Lange, O. L. (1969*a*). Die funktionellen Anpassungen der Flechten an die ökologischen Bedingungen arider Gebieten. *Ber. dt. bot. Ges.* **82,** 3–22.

Lange, O. L. (1969*b*). Experimentell-ökologische Untersuchungen an Flechten der Negev-Wüste. I. $CO_2$-Gaswechsel von *Ramalina maciformis* (Del.) Bory unter kontrollierten Bedingungen im Laboratorium. *Flora, Jena* **158B,** 324–59.

Lange, O. L. and Bertsch, A. (1965). Photosynthese der wüstenflechte *Ramalina maciformis* nach Wasserdampfaufnahme aus dem Luftraum. *Naturwissenschaften* **52,** 215–16.

Lange, O. L. and Evernari, M. (1971). Experimentell-ökologische Untersuchungen an Flechten der Negev-Wüste. IV. Wachstumsmessungen an *Caloplaca aurantia* (Pers.) Hellb. *Flora, Jena* **160,** 100–6.

Lange, O. L. and Metzner, H. (1965). Lichtabhangiger Kohlenstoffeinbau in Flechten bei teifen Temperaturen. *Naturwissenschaften* **52,** 191–2.

Lange, O. L., Schulze, E.-D. and Köch, W. (1968). Photosynthese von Wüstenflechten am natürlichen Standort. *Naturwissenschaften* **55,** 658–659.

Lange, O. L., Schulze, E.-D. and Köch, W. (1970*a*). Experimentall-ökologische Untersuchungen an Flechten der Negev-Wüste. II. $CO_2$-Gaswechsel und Wasserhaushalt von *Ramalina maciformis* (Del.) Bory am natürlichen Standort während der sommerlichen Trockenperiode. *Flora, Jena* **159,** 38–62.

Lange, O. L., Schulze, E.-D. and Köch, W. (1970*b*). Experimentell-ökologische Untersuchungen an Flechten der Negev-Wüste. III. $CO_2$-Gaswechsel und Wasserhaushalt von Krusten- und Blattflechten am natürlichen Standort während der sommerlichen Trockenperiode. *Flora, Jena* **159,** 525–38.

Lange, O. L. and Ziegler, H. (1963). Schwermetallgehalt von Flechten aus dem *Acarosporetum sinopicae* auf Erzschlackenhalden des Harzen. *Mitt. flor.-soz. Arbeit.* **10**, 156–83.

Lewis, D. H. and Smith, D. C. (1967). Sugar alcohols (polyols) in fungi and green plants I. Distribution, physiology, and metabolism. *New Phytol.* **66,** 143–84.

Lindberg, B. (1955). Studies on the chemistry of lichens. 8. Investigation of a *Dermatocarpon* and some *Roccella* species. *Acta chem. scand.* **9,** 917–19.

Lounamaa, K. J. (1956). Trace elements in plants growing wild on different rocks in Finland. A semi-quantitative spectrographic survey. *Ann. bot. soc. zool.-bot. fenn. 'Vanamo'* **29**(4), 1–196.

Lounamaa, K. J. (1965). Studies on the content or iron, manganese, and zinc in macrolichens. *Ann. Bot. Fenn.* **2,** 127–37.

Lowry, R. J., Sussman, A. S. and Boventer, B. von (1957). Physiology of the cell surface of *Neurospora* ascospores. III. *Mycologia* **46,** 609–621.

Maquinay, A. I., Lamb, I. M., Lambinon, J. and Ramaut, J. L. (1961). Dosage du zinc chez un lichen calaminaire Belge: *Stereocaulon nanodes* Tuck. f. *tyroliense* (Nyl.) M. Lamb. *Physiologia Pl.* **14,** 284–9.

Millbank, J. W. (1972). Nitrogen metabolism in lichens. IV. The nitrogenase activity of the *Nostoc* phycobiont in *Peltigera canina*. *New Phytol.* **71,** 1–10.

Millbank, J. W. and Kershaw, K. A. (1969). Nitrogen metabolism in lichens. I. Nitrogen fixation in the cephalodia of *Peltigera aphthosa*. *New Phytol.* **68**, 721–9.

Noeske, O., Lauchli, A., Lange, O. L., Vieweg, G. H. and Zeigler, H. (1970). Konzentration und Lokalisierung von Schwermetallen in Flechten der Erzschlackenhalden des Harzes. *Votr. bot. Ges.* (*Dt. bot. Ges.*), *n.f.* **4,** 67–79.

Pearson, L. C. (1970). Varying environmental factors in order to grow lichens intact under laboratory conditions. *Am. J. Bot.* **57,** 659–64.

Peveling, E. (1970). Das vorkommen von Stärke in *Chlorophyceen*-Phycobionten. *Planta* **93,** 82–5.

Quispel, A. (1960). Respiration of lichens. In: Ruhland, W. (ed.) *Handbuch der Pflanzenphysiologie*, **12**(2), 455–60. Berlin: Springer.

Richardson, D. H. S. (1967). *Studies in the biology and physiology of lichens with special reference to* Xanthoria parietina *(L.) Th. Fr.* D.Phil. thesis, University of Oxford.

Richardson, D. H. S. (1971). Lichens. In: Booth, C. (ed.) *Methods in microbiology*, **4,** 267–93. London and New York: Academic Press.

Richardson, D. H. S., Hill, D. J. and Smith, D. C. (1968). Lichen physiology. XI. The role of the alga in determining the pattern of carbohydrate movement between lichen symbionts. *New Phytol.* **67,** 469–86.

Richardson, D. H. S. and Smith, D. C. (1968). Lichen physiology. IX. Carbohydrate movement from the *Trebouxia* symbiont of *Xanthoria aureola* to the fungus. *New Phytol.* **67,** 61–8.

Ried, A. (1953). Photosynthese und Atmung bei xerostabilen und xerolabilen Krustenflechten. *Planta* **41,** 436–8.

Ried, A. (1960*a*). Thallusbau und Assimilationshaushalt von Laub- und Krustenflechten. *Biol. Zbl.* **79,** 129–51.

Ried, A. (1960*b*). Nachwirkungen der Entquellung auf den Gaswechsel von Krustenflechten. *Biol. Zbl.* **79,** 659–78.

Ried, A. (1960*c*). Stoffwechsel und Verbreitungsgrenzen von Flechten I. Flechtenzonierungen an Bachufern und ihre Beziehungen zur järlichen Überflutungsdauer und zum Mikroklima. *Flora, Jena* **148,** 612–38.

Ried, A. (1960*d*). Stoffwechsel und Verbreitungsgrenzen von Flechten II. Wasser- und Assimilationshaushalt, Entquellungs-und Submersion-resistenz von Krustenflechten benachbarter Standorte. *Flora, Jena* **149,** 345–85.

Rogers, R. W. (1971). Distribution of the lichen *Chondropsis semiviridis* in relation to its heat and drought resistance. *New Phytol.* **70,** 1069–78.

Rogers, R. W., Lange, R. T., and Nicholas, D. J. D. (1966). Nitrogen fixation by lichens of arid soil crusts. *Nature, Lond.* **209,** 96–7.

Rothstein, A. and Larrabee, C. (1948). The relationship of the cell surface to metabolism II. *J. cell. comp. Physiol.* **32,** 247–59.

Rothstein, A. and Meir, R. (1951). The relationship of the cell surface to metabolism IV. *J. cell. comp. Physiol.* **38,** 245–70.

Salo, A. and Miettinen, J. K. (1964). Strontium-90 and caesium-137 in arctic vegetation during 1961. *Nature, Lond.* **201,** 1177–9.

Schultz, S. G. and Curran, P. F. (1970). Coupled transport of sodium and organic solutes. *Physiol. Rev.* **50,** 637–718.

Schulze, E.-D. and Lange, O. L. (1968). $CO_2$-Gaswechsel der Flechte *Hypogymnia physodes* bei teifen Temperaturen in Frieland. *Flora, Jena* **158B,** 180–4.

Scott, G. D. (1960). Studies of the lichen symbiosis. I. The relationship between nutrition and moisture content in the maintenance of the symbiotic state. *New Phytol.* **59,** 374–81.

Simonis, W. and Feige, B. (1967). Untersuchungen über den Intermediarstoffwechsel zurischen Alge und Pilze bei *Peltigera aphthosa* (L.) Willd. *Flora, Jena* **158B,** 599–603.

Smith, D. C. (1960*a*). Studies in the physiology of lichens. I. The effects of starvation and of ammonia absorption upon the nitrogen content of *Peltigera polydactyla. Ann. Bot.* **24,** 52–62.

Smith, D. C. (1960*b*). Studies in the physiology of lichens. II. Absorption and utilisation of some simple organic nitrogen compounds by *Peltigera polydactyla, Ann. Bot.* **24,** 172–85.

Smith, D. C. (1960*c*). Studies in the physiology of lichens. III. Experiments with dissected discs of *Peltigera polydactyla. Ann. Bot.* **24,** 186–99.

Smith, D. C. (1962). The biology of lichen thalli. *Biol. Rev.* **37,** 537–570.

Smith, D. C. (1963*a*). Experimental studies of lichen physiology. *Symp. Soc. gen. Microbiol.* **13,** 31–50.

Smith, D. C. (1963*b*). Studies in the physiology of lichens. IV. Carbohydrates in *Peltigera polydactyla* and the utilization of absorbed glucose. *New Phytol.* **62,** 205–16.

Smith, D. C. and Drew, E. A. (1965). Studies in the physiology of lichens. V. Translocation from the algal layer to the medulla in *Peltigera polydactyla. New Phytol.* **64,** 195–200.

Smith, D. C., Muscatine, L. and Lewis, D. (1969). Carbohydrate movement from autotrophs to heterotrophs in parasitic and mutualistic symbiosis. *Biol. Rev.* **44,** 17–90.

Smyth, E. S. (1934). A contribution to the physiology and ecology of *Peltigera canina* and *Peltigera polydactyla. Ann. Bot.* **48,** 781–818.

Solberg, Y. J. (1970). Studies on the chemistry of lichens. VIII. An examination of the free sugars and ninhydrin-positive compounds of several Norwegian lichen species. *Lichenologist* **4,** 271–82.

Stalfelt, M. G. (1939). Der Gasaustausch der Flechten. *Planta* **29,** 11–31.

Sussman, A. S., Boventer, B. von and Lowry, R. J. (1957). Physiology of the cell wall of *Neurospora* ascospores. IV. *Pl. Physiol.* **32,** 586–90.

Sussman, A. S. and Lowry, R. J. (1955). Physiology of the cell surface of *Neurospora* ascospores I. *J. Bact.* **70,** 674–85.

Tuominen, Y. (1967). Studies on the strontium uptake of the *Cladonia alpestris* thallus. *Ann. Bot. Fenn.* **4,** 1–28.

Tuominen, Y. (1968). Studies on the translocation of caesium and strontium ions in the thallus of *Cladonia alpestris. Ann. Bot. Fenn.* **5,** 102–11.

Wilhelmsen, J. B. (1959). Chlorophylls in the lichens *Peltigera, Parmelia,* and *Xanthoria. Bot. Tidskr.* **55,** 30–6.

# 13: Sulphur Dioxide and Photosynthesis in Lichens

D. H. S. RICHARDSON and K. J. PUCKETT

## Introduction

Little is known about the effects of sulphur dioxide on the photosynthetic process in plants, which is remarkable since some five million tons of this compound is emitted every year in Britain alone. Some 3.9 million tons of this is deposited on land, mostly on plant surfaces (Meetham, 1950). Most studies that have been done have documented leaf damage in particular species, under different environmental conditions during acute fumigations in which typical intercostal or marginal necrotic zones appear (Daines, 1968; Katz, 1949). The effects of fumigations which do not cause these lesions have been little studied although Spedding (1969) investigated the rate of radioactive sulphur dioxide ($[^{35}S]O_2$) uptake.

### *The properties of sulphur dioxide gas*

Sulphur dioxide, a colourless heavy gas with an acrid smell, dissolves readily in water. One volume of water dissolves 45 volumes of gas at 15°C. The boiling point of sulphur dioxide is −10°C and it is hence liquefied easily by low temperature or 2.5 atm. of pressure. In air, the gas slowly oxidizes to sulphur trioxide. Traces of copper (Durrant, 1959) or manganese (Coughanowr, 1956) greatly speed up this process. Thus sulphur dioxide is oxidized to sulphate some 500 times as rapidly (1 per cent per minute) in fog droplets containing $MnSO_4$ as catalyst, as in air in sunlight (0.1 to 0.2 per cent per hour). The presence of ozone and olefines also leads to increased rates of oxidation (Cox and Penkett, 1971; Atkins *et al.*, 1972).

### *Properties of dissolved sulphur dioxide*

Sulphur dioxide has been used for many years to preserve food against micro-organism attack. The ability of sulphur dioxide to do this is affected by the pH of the solution containing the gas. Thus Cruess *et al.* (1931) found that 1000 ppm were required to inhibit bacteria at pH 7 but yeasts and moulds were still unaffected. However, at pH 4, Rahn and Conn (1944) showed that 4 ppm were able to inhibit *Saccharomyces ellipsoides* whilst 100 ppm effectively inhibited bacteria. A study of the properties of sulphur dioxide in solution show that it can assume a number of ionic states which are in equilibrium, depending on the pH of the solution. At low pH, free sulphurous acid is present; at intermediate pH the bisulphite ion predominates whilst at high pH the sulphite ion is found (*see* Puckett *et al.*, 1973). The characteristics of these different forms of dissolved sulphur dioxide can be understood by examining their standard electrode potentials. These demonstrate that free sulphurous acid is a fairly effective oxidizing agent whereas sulphite is a good reducing agent (Latimer, 1952). Indeed dilute solutions of sulphur dioxide are better oxidizing agents than solutions of sulphur trioxide of similar molarity.

The following equations and standard electrode potentials demonstrate this observation. The more positive the $E_0$ value, the more readily does a reaction go from left to right as written. The $E_0$ values confirm that sulphurous acid is a fairly good oxidizing agent (it is itself reduced) and that sulphite is a fairly good reducing agent (it is itself oxidized). However, the effective reduction potentials will depend on concentration factors and pH as discussed by Puckett *et al.* (1973). The phytotoxicity of sulphur dioxide does not depend solely on these properties. Recent studies of *Pinus strobus* indicate that where sulphur dioxide and ozone are present simultaneously, the damage to the pine needles is greater than that caused by either gas separately (Dochinger *et al.*, 1970).

(*a*) in acid solutions:

I*a* $SO_4^{2-} + 4H^+ + 2e \rightleftharpoons H_2O + H_2SO_3$ $E_0$ 0.17V

II*a* $H_2SO_3 + 4H^+ + 4e \rightleftharpoons 3H_2O + S$ $E_0$ 0.45V

III*a* $2H_2SO_3 + 2H^+ + 4e \rightleftharpoons S_2O_3^{2-}$ (thiosulphate) $+ 3H_2O$ $E_0$ 0.40V

IV*a* $4H_2SO_3 + 4H^+ + 6e \rightleftharpoons S_4O_6^{2-}$ (tetrathionate) $+ 6H_2O$ $E_0$ 0.51V (*b*) in basic solutions:

| | | | |
|---|---|---|---|
| I*b* | $SO_4^{2-} + H_2O + 2e \rightleftharpoons SO_3^{2-} + 2OH^-$ | $E_0$ | −0.93V |
| II*b* | $SO_3^{2-} + 3H_2O + 6e \rightleftharpoons 6OH^- + S^{2-}$ | $E_0$ | −0.66V |
| III*b* | $2SO_3^{2-} + 3H_2O + 4e \rightleftharpoons S_2O_3^{2-} + 6OH^-$ | $E_0$ | −0.58V |

## Methods

Three types of technique have been used to study the effects of sulphur dioxide on photosynthesis of cryptogams. Samples have been exposed in closed vessels, in moving streams of air or in aqueous solutions to which a certain proportion of sulphur dioxide has been added. After exposure a number of parameters have been examined to determine the effects on the plant—see Table 1. Each of these techniques, as applied to date, has certain limitations and these are discussed below.

### *Closed vessels*

Rao and LeBlanc (1965), Pearson and Skye (1965) and Coker (1967) enclosed samples of cryptogams in sealed vessels of various shapes and then generated sulphur dioxide gas inside these by adding acid to sodium sulphite. The amount of sulphur dioxide produced from a known weight of sulphite can be calculated and hence the desired concentration formed in the vessel. In these early experiments, no mixing devices were used and because sulphur dioxide is heavier than air it almost certainly accumulated in the lower part of the vessel to produce a concentration in excess of that calculated. In the experiments of Pearson and Skye (1965) this might have been offset by the sulphur dioxide dissolving in the moist plastic foam placed beneath the lichens. Hence the actual concentration to which the lichens were exposed is unknown. Rao and LeBlanc (1965) tried to control the humidity in the experimental chamber by means of saturated solutions of potassium acetate, potassium nitrate and sodium carbonate. The generated sulphur dioxide would again dissolve in these to an unknown extent. In addition, as Gilbert (1968) points out, the minimum concentration used in these studies was 5 ppm which was almost 500 times that needed to eliminate all epiphytes on trees around Newcastle in Britain.

*Table 1 A summary of the conditions and techniques used to examine the effec[t of] sulphur dioxide on photosynthesis in cryptogams*

| Author | Exposure chamber | Exposure time | Conc. of $SO_2$ | Light | Ten[p.] |
|---|---|---|---|---|---|
| Rao & LeBlanc (1965) | Sealed desiccator jars | 24 hr | 5 ppm | ? | 25° |
| Pearson & Skye (1965) | Sealed flasks 580 ml | 1–15 days | 0.01–10% | 3000 lux | 17°C |
| Coker (1967) | Sealed plastic boxes 500 ml | 44 hr | 5–120 ppm | ? | ? |
| Gilbert (1968) | Petri dishes | 48 hr | 20–600 ppm | ? | ? |
| Syratt & Wanstall (1969) | Continuous flow chamber | 24 hr | 5 ppm 1–10 ppm | 500 W mercury vapour | ? |
| Nash (1971) | Continuous flow chamber | 24 hr | 0.5 0.1 ppm | 4500 lux | ? |
| Hill (1971) | Sealed flasks 50 ml $SO_2$ in solution | 3 hr and 24 hr | 0.2–1 mM metabi-sulphite | 10 000 lux | 20°C |
| Puckett *et al.* (1973) | Sealed 2″ × 1″ specimen tubes $SO_2$ in solution | 6 hr | 0.75–750 ppm | 8500 lux | 18°C |
| Showman (1972) | Continuous flow chamber | 24 hr | 2 ppm–6 ppm | ? | 24°C |

| % | Form of sulphur dioxide | Method of generation | Parameters measured | Species |
|---|---|---|---|---|
| | Gas | Sodium sulphite plus sulphuric acid | Sulphate conc<br>Free $Mg^{2+}$ ions<br>Chlorophyll | *Xanthoria fallax*<br>*X. parietina*<br>*Parmelia caperata*<br>*Physcia millegrana* |
| 0 | Gas | Sodium sulphite plus sulphuric acid | Net photosynthesis (Warburg apparatus)<br>Morphology | *Parmelia sulcata* |
| 0 | Gas | Sodium sulphite plus lactic acid | Sulphate accumulation<br>Chlorophyll content<br>Free $Mg^{2+}$ ions | *Radula complanata*<br>*Orthotrichum lyellii*<br>*Orthotrichum diaphanum* |
| | In solution, pH 6.2, 4.2, 3.2 | Sulphur dioxide in water | Regeneration of bryophyte protonema after 3 weeks | *Bryum argenteum*<br>*Ceratodon purpureus*<br>*Hypnum cupressiforme*<br>*Polytrichum commune* |
| 0<br>–100 | Gas | Cylinder sulphur dioxide | Chlorophyll breakdown<br>Respiration<br>Sulphate accumulation | *Dicranoweisia cirrata*<br>*Metzgeria furcata*<br>*Hypnum cupressiforme* |
| | Gas | Cylinder sulphur dioxide | Chlorophyll breakdown | *Parmelia caperata*<br>*Physcia millegrana* |
| - | In solution | Sodium metabisulphite in water | [$^{14}C$]-fixation | *Usnea subfloridana*<br>*Hypogymmia physodes*<br>*Lecanora conizaeoides* |
| - | In solution | Sulphur dioxide in water buffered to pH 6.6, 4.4, 3.2 | [$^{14}C$]-fixation<br>Chlorophyll breakdown | *Umbilicara muhlenbergii*<br>*Cladonia stellaris*<br>*Cladonia deformis*<br>*Stereocaulon paschale* |
| ) | Gas, 138 ppm in solution | Cylinder sulphur dioxide | Respiration rates<br>Net photosynthetic rates<br>Chlorophyll | *Cladonia cristatella*<br>*Caloplaca holocarpa*<br>*Lecanora dispersa* |

*Moving gas streams*

In more recent experiments carried out by Syratt and Wanstall (1969), Nash (1970) and Showman (1972), plant samples were placed in an experimental chamber through which a stream of sulphur dioxide-contaminated air was passed. With the aid of capillary flow systems and mixing chambers the contaminated air was humidified to the desired extent. Such apparatus allows the effect of sulphur dioxide gas and humidity to be more accurately assessed. However, in nature fumigations often coincide with dew or rain which is more difficult to simulate with this technique.

*Aqueous solutions*

Aqueous solutions of sulphur dioxide are easy to prepare and enable the interacting effects of pH and concentration of toxicant to be determined. However, it is difficult to equate a level of sulphur dioxide in solution with that in air. This problem arises because sulphur dioxide is very soluble in water and continually dissolves so that in shallow or thin films of water a concentration is built up which is far higher than that in air. Saunders (1970) has tentatively suggested that 100 $\mu g/m^3$ of sulphur dioxide in air would give rise to a solution containing 35 ppm in water. However, the fate of sulphur dioxide from the time emitted into the air and its deposition on foliage is complex and not fully understood (*see* Liss, 1971; Kellog *et al.*, 1972; Saunders, ch 2).

Gilbert (1968) cultured moss protonema on petri dishes and then treated the protonema with solutions of sulphur dioxide which had been buffered to a variety of pH conditions. After exposure the plates were washed and regeneration of the protonema assessed after subculture. This technique has not been used on lichen samples but now that limited growth can be obtained in filtered air growth chambers, it has potential (Kershaw and Millbank, 1969; Harris and Kershaw, 1971).

Both Hill (1971) and Puckett *et al.* (1973) studied the effect of sulphur dioxide in aqueous solutions on net photosynthesis using radioactive sodium bicarbonate ($NaH^{14}[C]O_3$). The disadvantage of determining net fixation in saturated lichen thalli, in solution, is that it may be depressed by up to 50 per cent of the maximum (Ried, 1960*a*; Kershaw, 1972). Genera such as *Umbilicaria* with thick thalli show the greatest reduction and this has been attributed to problems of diffusion of carbon dioxide between the dense water-swollen fungal hyphae.

A further problem of studying the effects of aqueous sulphur dioxide in studies on net photosynthesis is that the acidity of the solution precludes the simultaneous use of radioactive sodium bicarbonate. This is because under conditions of low pH, [$^{14}CO_2$] is displaced from the bicarbonate solution into the atmosphere above. This disadvantage can be overcome if the lichen samples are first exposed to the sulphur dioxide solution, then carefully washed with distilled water before being placed in the solution containing the radioactive sodium bicarbonate. However it means that experiments are limited to periods over thirty minutes because of the extra manipulations; a problem which is compounded by the inherent variability of lichen samples so that many replicates are required for each treatment. In fact it would be very meaningful to study the effects of aqueous sulphur dioxide on net [$^{14}C$]-fixation over ten minutes or less.

## Results

### *Symptoms exhibited by fumigated samples*

Lichens fumigated experimentally in the field with sulphur dioxide showed a series of macroscopic changes: *Parmelia sulcata* turned reddish, *Hypogymnia physodes* white, and *Evernia prunastri* black (Skye, 1968). In the laboratory, 5 ppm of this gas caused bleaching of the chlorophyll in the lichen algae and development of brown spots. Rao and LeBlanc (1965) showed that these spots were phaeophytin resulting from chlorophyll breakdown and it proved possible to identify excess free magnesium ions in extracts of exposed thalli. The amount of damage to the lichen algae can be assessed by determining the proportion of chlorophyll to phaeophytin. Nash (1971) observed that the proportion decreased greatly in sensitive species such as *Parmelia caperata* but to a lesser extent in *Physcia millegrana*. It is interesting that he noted that the absolute amounts of chlorophyll plus phaeophytin varied considerably between different specimens of the same species (from 15 to 32 per cent) and even more from species to species (up to 100 per cent) so that total amounts of chlorophyll may be less informative than the above ratio. Puckett *et al.* (1973) have observed, from studies *in vitro* and *in vivo* with chlorophyll extracted from lichens, that sulphur dioxide at moderate concentrations induces the conversion of chlorophyll to phaeophytin at pH 2.2 but not at pH 3.2 and above. They therefore suggest that only under very acid intracellular conditions is this conversion to phaeophytin significant. Other studies by Coker (1967) on bryophytes noted that there was a distinct colour change within 10 minutes in sensitive species such as *Radula complanata* when fumigated with sulphur dioxide. In damaged plants, excess free magnesium ions and sulphur compounds were identified in the leaves, while much of the chlorophyll was converted to phaeophytin. Samples maintained at 45 per cent relative humidity were less damaged than those at 100 per cent relative humidity. It was suggested that this was due to cells at the lower relative humidity being in an inactive state. *Hypnum cupressiforme* seemed able to withstand short periods of exposure to 10 ppm but other mosses were damaged by 5 ppm of sulphur dioxide. Syratt and Wanstall (1969) showed that chlorophyll degradation was severe even in *Hypnum cupressiforme* and other mosses at 10 ppm, while at 5 ppm of sulphur dioxide *Hypnum* showed more degradation than *Dicranoweisia* or *Metzgeria*. These two bryophytes were able to convert sulphite to sulphate in relatively large quantities whereas *Hypnum* could not. In addition they suggest that the higher chlorophyll content in *Dicranoweisia* might enable it to withstand bursts of high intensity sulphur dioxide. Presumably under such conditions, the mechanism for oxidation of sulphite could not cope with all the pollutant but enough chlorophyll would remain for the plant to survive.

Sulphur dioxide also affects other aspects of lichen metabolism. A field study by Gilbert (1968) indicated that respiration might be affected under naturally-occurring conditions. Samples of *Ramalina farinacea* and *Lecanora conizaeoides* were transferred together with the substratum onto a roof in the city of Newcastle where the sulphur dioxide concentration averaged 0.09 ppm. Controls were set up on a village roof in a pollution-free area. Lichens moved from the natural habitat to the control site showed a respiratory increase of about 30 per cent while chlorophyll levels varied. Transfer to the polluted site resulted in drastic changes in *Ramalina farinacea* as 84 per cent of the chlorophyll had disappeared in five weeks and respiration was 20 per cent of normal. However, *Lecanora conizaeoides*, a pollution-tolerant species, showed no drastic changes after being moved. More recently Baddeley *et al.* (1971, 1972) have shown that lichen respiration is generally inhibited by low, experimentally applied concentrations of sulphur dioxide in solution. The effects of sulphur dioxide on lichen respiration are discussed more fully in chapter 14.

In addition to effects on respiration, photosynthetic fixation is reduced by the presence of sulphur dioxide. Pearson and Skye (1965) observed that fumigated thalli showed net respiration (negative net assimilation rate) in laboratory experiments. Hill (1971) found that metabisulphite affected net radioactive carbon fixation by lichen samples floated on radioactive sodium bicarbonate ($NaH\ {}^{14}[C]O_3$) solutions in the light. Lichens differed in their response. Net photosynthetic fixation was completely inhibited in *Usnea subfloridana* by 0.4 mM-metabisulphite whereas twice this concentration was required to prevent fixation in *Lecanora conizaeoides*. Puckett *et al.* (1973) have obtained similar results using another pair of lichens, one of which was pollution-sensitive and the other pollution-insensitive (Table 2). These workers, however, used dissolved sulphur dioxide gas in their experiments. Hill also showed that sulphate in concentrations up to 0.4 mM had little effect on fixation in contrast to metabisulphite. Sulphur dioxide can apparently cause a reduction in net fixation under conditions where no chlorophyll breakdown can be detected (Showman, 1972) which might suggest that conversion of chlorophyll to phaeophytin after fumigation is a secondary effect. Showman (1972) also found that cultured *Trebouxia* phycobionts from different lichens were equally sensitive to sulphur dioxide damage, suggesting that it is the lichen fungi which afford protection in pollution-tolerant lichen species.

### *Interaction between sulphur dioxide and pH*

In an early study, Brooks (1943) found that the toxicity of sulphite solutions to the algae *Nitella*, *Spirogyra* and *Hydrodictyon* was

*Table 2 The percentage change in net photosynthetic* $^{14}$*[C]-fixation by lichen samples incubated in solutions of sulphur dioxide buffered at pH 3.2, 4.4, 6.6 as compared with controls without sulphur dioxide. Each percentage change represents the mean of six replicates. Standard deviations of percentage change are shown for* Umbilicaria muhlenbergii

(*a*) *Stereocaulon paschale*

| pH | ppm sulphur dioxide 0.75 | 7.5 | 75 | 750 | Net [$^{14}$C]-fixation of control in cpm |
|---|---|---|---|---|---|
| 3.2 | +6 | +3 | −94 | −95 | $4.57 \times 10^5$ |
| 4.4 | +22 | +31 | −42 | −82 | $4.86 \times 10^5$ |
| 6.6 | +16 | +20 | −6 | −19 | $5.95 \times 10^5$ |

(*b*) *Umbilicaria muhlenbergii*

| pH | ppm sulphur dioxide 0.75 | 7.5 | 75 | 750 | Net [$^{14}$C]-fixation of control in cpm |
|---|---|---|---|---|---|
| 3.2 | $-9 \pm 5.7$ | $-53 \pm 8.7$ | $-98 \pm .05$ | $-98 \pm .51$ | $10.29 \times 10^6$ $\pm 8.7\%$ |
| 4.4 | $+5 \pm 10.3$ | $+14 \pm 13.4$ | $-91 \pm 1.9$ | $-96 \pm .36$ | $6.7 \times 10^6$ $\pm 11.8\%$ |
| 6.6 | $-16 \pm 10.8$ | $-19 \pm 9.3$ | $-17 \pm 9.8$ | $-67 \pm 5.1$ | $9.8 \times 10^6$ $\pm 13.9\%$ |

Samples composed of $10 \times 5$ mm discs of *Umbilicaria muhlenbergii* or 200 mg fresh weight of *Stereocaulon paschale*. Samples shaken in aqueous solutions containing 0.75–750 ppm $SO_2$ buffered to the indicated pH for 6 hours in the light. Samples were then washed in distilled water and allowed to photosynthesize in $2'' \times 1''$ specimen tubes (sealed with a glass coverslip) containing 3 ml distilled water and 10 μCi of NaH $^{14}[C]O_3$. After 18 hours' incubation with an incident light of 8500 lux, the samples were killed and extracted in boiling ethanol. The total amount of fixed $^{14}$[C] per sample was determined using a Picker Liquamat 200 Scintillation Counter.

greater if the pH was low. For example *Spirogyra* sp. and *Hydrodictyon* sp. were uninjured by four hours' exposure to pH 8.3 but were killed in four hours at pH 5.3 or 4.2 in a solution of 0.0053 N sulphite (equivalent to 170 ppm sulphur dioxide in solution). *Nitella* was a little more resistant. Thomas *et al.* (1950) confirmed this and explained the increased toxicity at low pH as being due to increased sulphite uptake. They also found that plants take up only 10 to 50 per cent as much sulphite in the dark as in the light. Brooks (1943) also acidified the water in which these algae grew with hydrochloric acid and found they could survive at pH 4 although at pH 3 they were injured. Since this water contained 0.00145 N sulphate, the plants are evidently insensitive to sulphate as compared with sulphite at low pHs.

Gilbert (1968) working on bryophytes recognized that sulphur dioxide affects plants principally in the dissolved form and examined the effects of aqueous solutions of this substance on the regenerative ability of these plants. Results showed that strong solutions of sulphur dioxide were not damaging providing that the pH was high. Specimens exposed under these conditions where the sulphur dioxide was in the form of sulphite were able to regenerate, photosynthesis presumably returning to normal. At lower pHs the bisulphite ion is formed and was toxic to the gametophores of sensitive species and to all protonema at 20 ppm sulphur dioxide in solution. Finally undissociated sulphurous acid was most toxic. No protonema survived 20 ppm and even gametophores of resistant species were killed at 40–70 ppm sulphur dioxide in solution. It is important to realize that these concentrations are as sulphur dioxide in solutions and could result from very much lower aerial concentrations. Gilbert recognized that short fumigations at high sulphur dioxide concentrations do not necessarily resemble field conditions where long fumigations at low intensities are more common. However, these experiments explained that basic substrata or those with a high buffering capacity can support the growth of epiphytic mosses much closer to a pollution source because they reduced the toxicity of sulphur dioxide.

Lichens have been used to investigate the interacting effect of sulphur dioxide and pH on net carbon fixation. Hill (1971) found that solutions of sodium metabisulphite buffered to pH 4 and below were toxic to lichens but not if buffered to pH 5 and above. Puckett has investigated the effects of sulphur dioxide concentration and pH on net carbon fixation in *Stereocaulon paschale* and *Umbilicaria muhlenbergii* and some results are shown in Table 2. These indicate that concentrations as high as 750 ppm produced only a 20 per cent reduction in net carbon fixation in the former species providing that the pH was maintained at 6.6. This lichen seems to be pollution-tolerant and grows within 5 miles of a nickel smelter at Sudbury, Ontario. *Umbilicaria muhlenbergii* which grew only at a distance of more than 15 miles was more seriously affected. Lower concentrations of sulphur dioxide caused greater reductions in net fixation of both lichens if the pH was 3.3 or 4.4. More detailed results of studies on these and other lichens are to be found in the work of Puckett *et al.* (1973).

## Discussion and conclusions

Ecological studies indicate that the distribution of epiphytic vegetation in industrial areas is best correlated with sulphur dioxide levels (Hawksworth, 1971; ch 3, 4 and 5). Both Berge (1968) and Thomas and Hendricks (1956) differentiate between chronic and acute sulphur dioxide damage on higher plants but this distinction has not been made for epiphytes such as lichens. Chronic injury is caused either by a single fumigation of intensity less than is necessary to cause acute damage or by continued absorption of sublethal amounts of sulphur dioxide until the buffer capacity of the leaf is exceeded or toxic amounts of sulphur accumulated. Chronic damage may be defined as an interference with the biochemistry of the cell without induction of dramatic visible symptoms.

A number of laboratory studies have been done on the effects of sulphur dioxide on plants but there is still a lack of detailed information on the mode of action at the cellular level. Work on higher plants (summarized by Daines, 1968) has shown that there may be a temporary and partial inhibition of photosynthesis in the presence of low concentrations of sulphur dioxide. If the leaves are not damaged permanently then the normal level or even a slightly higher level of photosynthesis may be regained after the fumigation ceases. Comparable results have been obtained with lichens exposed to aqueous sulphur dioxide (Puckett, unpublished). It seems that such inhibitions do not seriously affect higher plants (Daines, 1968) but in lichens it is likely that several chronic fumigations of this sort may interfere with the flow of nutrients, such as carbohydrates, between the symbionts resulting in the breakdown of the symbiosis. Thus the disappearance of lichens from industrial areas with low prevailing sulphur dioxide concentrations may be explained by effects on the physiology of the symbiosis.

The action of sulphur dioxide on photosynthesis in plants depends on the intensity of fumigation. Results to date suggest that a sequence of increasing damage could occur as follows:

1. A temporary inhibition of photosynthesis with subsequent recovery;
2. A permanent reduction in photosynthesis but with no chlorophyll breakdown;
3. A permanent reduction in photosynthesis associated with chlorophyll breakdown.

Laboratory studies on lichens have shown the existence of each of these stages. Thus Rao and LeBlanc (1965) noted the formation of phaeophytin in samples exposed to high (5 ppm) concentrations of sulphur dioxide in air. Showman (1972) found that under some conditions a decrease in net photosynthesis can occur without detectable chlorophyll breakdown, and Puckett (see above) observed temporary inhibition of photosynthesis.

It has been shown that sulphur dioxide is less toxic when buffered at high pH (Gilbert, 1968; Hill, 1971; Puckett *et al.*, 1973). The pH determines the proportion of the different ionic species (sulphurous acid; bisulphite; sulphite) in aqueous solutions. Each of these species has particular oxidation-reduction properties (as outlined in the Introduction) and also has different charges. Uncharged molecules can gain entry into cells more easily than charged ions and thus undissociated sulphurous acid would enter faster than sulphite ions and could therefore accumulate in toxic amounts more readily. It is important to note that under most biological conditions the bisulphite ion is the predominant ion to be found in solution. In addition to this, Puckett *et al.* (1973) have shown that sulphurous acid and bisulphite are more toxic to lichens than sulphite, though, except in the case of acute fumigations, these ionic forms may change when inside the cell due to its buffering capacity.

Puckett *et al.* (1973) came to the conclusion that the increased toxicity of sulphur dioxide to lichens observed at low pH (3.2–4.4) is associated in part with the destruction of chlorophyll by an irreversible oxidation process. This conclusion is based on studies *in vitro* and *in vivo* of the effects of sulphur dioxide on lichen and spinach chlorophyll. Oxidation of chlorophyll resulted from exposure to dissolved sulphur dioxide (7.5–750 ppm) at low pH values. They also calculated the probable, effective reduction potentials (oxidation-reduction properties) of bisulphite and sulphurous acid under these conditions. These workers concluded that chlorophyll oxidation

$$\text{chlorophyll} \rightarrow .\text{chl}^{+}$$

by sulphur dioxide could occur in the intracellular environment and be responsible for the reduced rate of net radioactive carbon ($^{14}C$) fixation observed. At a lower pH (2.0–3.0), phaeophytization becomes an important reaction and could be dominant under such conditions. At high and moderate pH, chlorophyll is not oxidized and inhibition of photosynthesis is only found at high sulphur dioxide levels where it could interfere with the electron transport chains involved in photosynthesis. It is of interest that Puckett *et al.* (1973) have shown an enhancement of net photosynthesis when lichens are exposed to low concentrations of sulphur dioxide at high pH. This trend is also seen in the data shown in Fig. 1 of the study by Hill (1971). This may possibly relate to the ability of sulphite and bisulphite ions to behave as electron donors (are themselves oxidized) under these conditions.

The results of the studies mentioned above suggest that sulphur dioxide might be expected to affect higher plants and lichens equally. However, many studies (summarized by Hawksworth, 1971; ch 3 and 10) have shown that epiphytes and especially lichens are far more sensitive. The reason for this seems to be due to the efficient absorption systems of lichens and the fact that they absorb over their entire surface whereas higher plants are protected by both cuticle and stomata. Therefore in lichens sulphur dioxide quickly reaches toxic levels during a fumigation, especially if the thallus is fully water-saturated, and damage or death of the plant quickly follows if the level of pollutant is high.

## References

Atkins, D. H. F., Cox, R. A. and Eggleton, A. E. J (1972). Photochemical ozone and sulphuric acid aerosol formation in the atmosphere over southern England. *Nature, Lond.* **235,** 372–6.

Berge, H. (1963). Phytotoxische Immisionen—Sorauer. *Handbuch der Pflanzenkrankheiten,* I. Berlin.

Brooks, P. M. (1943). Ph.D. thesis, University of Stanford.

Coker, P. D. (1967). The effects of sulphur dioxide on bark epiphytes. *Trans. Br. bryol. Soc.* **5,** 341–7.

Coughanowr, D. R. (1956). Oxidation of sulphur dioxide in fog droplets. *Diss. Abstr.* **16,** 1647–8.

Cox, R. A. and Penkett, S. A. (1971). Oxidation of atmospheric $SO_2$ by products of the ozone-olefin reaction. *Nature, Lond.* **230,** 321–322.

Cruess, W. V., Richert, P. H. and Irish, J. H. (1931). The effect of hydrogen-ion concentration on the toxicity of several preservatives to microorganisms. *Hilgardia* **6,** 295–314.

Daines, R. H. (1968). Sulphur dioxide and plant response. *J. occup. Med.* **10,** 516–34.

Dochinger, L. S., Bender, F. W., Fox, F. L. and Heck, W. W. (1970). Chlorotic dwarf of eastern white pine caused by an ozone and sulphur dioxide interaction. *Nature, Lond.* **225,** 476.

Durrant, P. J. (1959). *General and inorganic chemistry.* London: Longmans Green.

Gilbert, O. L. (1968). *Biological indicators of air pollution.* Ph.D. thesis, University of Newcastle upon Tyne.

Harris, E. P. and Kershaw, K. A. (1971). Thallus growth and the distribution of stored metabolites in the phycobionts of the lichens *Parmelia sulcata* and *P. physodes. Can. J. Bot.* **49,** 1367–72.

Hawksworth, D. L. (1971). Lichens as litmus for air pollution: A historical review. *Int. J. Environ. Studies* **1,** 281–96.

Hill, D. J. (1971). Experimental study on the effect of sulphite on lichens with reference to atmospheric pollution. *New Phytol.* **70,** 831–6.

Katz, M. (1949). Sulphur dioxide in the atmosphere and its relation to plant life. *Ind. Engng Chem. ind. Edn* **41,** 2450–66.

Kellog, W. W., Cadle, R. D., Allen, E. R., Lazrus, A. L. and Martell, E. A. (1972). The sulfur cycle. *Science, N.Y.* **175,** 587–96.

Kershaw, K. A. (1972). The relationship between moisture content and net assimilation rate of lichen thalli and its ecological significance. *Can. J. Bot.* **50,** 543–55.

Kershaw, K. A. and Millbank, J. W. (1969). A controlled environment lichen growth chamber. *Lichenologist* **4,** 83–7.

Latimer, W. M. (1952). *Oxidation potentials.* Ed. 2. Englewood Cliffs, N.J.: Prentice Hall.

Liss, P. S. (1971). Exchange of $SO_2$ between the atmosphere and natural waters. *Nature, Lond.* **233,** 327–9.

Meetham, A. R. (1950). Natural removal of pollution from the atmosphere. *Quart. J. R. Meterol. Soc.* **76,** 359–71.

Nash, T. H. (1971). *Effects of effluents from a zinc factory on lichens.* Ph.D. thesis, Rutgers University.

Pearson, L. and Skye, E. (1965). Air pollution affects pattern of photosynthesis in *Parmelia sulcata*, a corticolous lichen. *Science, N.Y.* **148,** 1600–2.

Puckett, K., J., Nieboer, E. Flora, W. and Richardson, D. H. S. (1973). Sulphur dioxide: Its effect on photosynthetic $^{14}C$ fixation in lichens and suggested mechanisms of phytoxicity. *New Phytol.* **72,** 141–54.

Rahn, O. and Conn, J. E. (1944). Effect of increase in acidity on antiseptic efficiency. *Ind. Engng Chem. ind. Edn* **36,** 185.

Rao, D. N. and LeBlanc, F. (1966). Effects of sulfur dioxide on the lichen algae with special reference to chlorophyll. *Bryologist* **69,** 69–75.

Ried, A. (1960). Stoffwechsel und Verbreitungsgrenzen von Flechten II. Wasser- und Assimilationshaushalt, Entquellungs- und Submersionsresistenz von Krustenflechten benachbarter Standorte. *Flora, Jena* **149,** 345–85.

Saunders, P. J. W. (1970). Air pollution in relation to lichens and fungi. *Lichenologist* **4,** 337–49.

Showman, R. E. (1972). Residual effects of sulfur dioxide on the net photosynthetic and respiratory rates of lichen thalli and cultured lichen symbionts. *Bryologist* **75,** 335–41.

Skye, E. (1965). Botanical indicators of air pollution. *Acta phytogeogr. suec.* **50,** 285–7.

Spedding, D. J. (1969). Uptake of sulphur dioxide by barley leaves at low sulphur dioxide concentrations. *Nature, Lond.* **224,** 1229–31.

Syratt, W. J. and Wanstall, P. J. (1969). The effect of sulphur dioxide on epiphytic bryophytes. In: *Air Pollution, Proceedings of the first European Congress on the influence of air pollution on plants and animals, Wageningen 1968*, 79–85. Wageningen: Centre for Agricultural Publishing and Documentation.

Thomas, M. D. and Hendricks, R. H. (1956). Effect of air pollution on plants. In: *Air pollution handbook:* Section **9.**

Thomas, M. D., Hendricks, R. H. and Hill, R. G. (1950). Sulphur metabolism of plants, Effects of sulphur dioxide on vegetation. *Ind. Engng Chem. ind. Edn* **42,** 2231.

Vas, K. and Ingram, M. (1949). Preservation of fruit juices with less sulphur dioxide. *Fd Mf.* **24,** 414–16.

# 14: Sulphur Dioxide and Respiration in Lichens

M. S. BADDELEY, B. W. FERRY and E. J. FINEGAN

Earlier chapters in this book testify to the wealth of evidence supporting the view that sulphur dioxide is the most important component of air pollution affecting the distribution of lichens in industrial countries. It is clear from this work that lichens are amongst the most sensitive of living organisms to sulphur dioxide, and that the level of sensitivity varies from species to species. The need for an understanding of the physiological mechanism of this phenomenon is perhaps long overdue, although a start has already been made on the problem during the last decade.

The physiological approach needs to relate as closely as possible to field conditions of exposure to sulphur dioxide but, as is usual with physiological work, in order to maintain precise control of experimental conditions, certain compromises between field and laboratory situations become necessary. In this respect the choice of sulphur dioxide concentrations and methods of exposure to sulphur dioxide in laboratory experiments are relevant and are discussed in more detail below.

Once the effect of realistic doses of sulphur dioxide on the physiology of intact lichen thalli in the laboratory has been demonstrated, and variation in field sensitivity between different species explained, it remains for the precise mode of action of sulphur dioxide on metabolism to be examined. Brief mention of this aspect of the problem is made in chapter 17.

This chapter is concerned, particularly, with the effect of sulphur dioxide on lichen respiration and full discussion of photosynthetic responses to sulphur dioxide is given in chapter 13. Some brief reference is made to photosynthesis in this chapter in order to compare the sensitivities of the two processes for a range of lichens, using the methods described.

## Methodology

### *Measurement of respiration in lichens*

A variety of methods have been used to measure respiration rates in lichens and these are discussed in some detail in chapter 12. In our work we have used an oxygen electrode to measure respiration rates and the considered advantages of this technique have been discussed previously (Baddeley, Ferry and Finegan, 1971). The method is unquestionably more sensitive than most other techniques which have been used, but has the one disadvantage, that measurements have to be made with infiltrated samples of thallus in an aqueous medium. Most lichens produce maximum respiration rates in the water-saturated state, although there is some indication, from our experiments, that respiration rates fall after prolonged periods (several hours) of immersion in an aqueous medium.

### *Experiments with sulphur dioxide*

Details of the experimental procedures developed, using sulphur dioxide in buffered solutions, have been outlined elsewhere (Baddeley, Ferry and Finegan, 1972). The experiments were designed to accommodate some variations in the conditions of exposure to sulphur dioxide in the field. Clearly, this is an instance where a compromise has to be reached between experimental design and control in the laboratory and conditions pertaining in the field, about which relatively little is known. The experimental procedures ranged from short-term exposures of 15 min to prolonged exposures of 18 hr to single concentrations of sulphur dioxide. Moderately long-term exposures of 4 hr to gradually increasing sulphur dioxide concentrations were also used. The pre-experimental conditions were varied, the lichens being maintained dry for 24 hr before the short-term exposures (Drop-in-dry procedure) and moist for 24 hr before the moderately long-term (Subsequent-additions procedure) and prolonged (Overnight-incubation procedure) exposures.

All experiments were conducted in buffered solutions for reasons made clear below. McIlvaine's phosphate-citrate buffer was used as it allows pH adjustment over the range of interest (pH 3.2 to 6.2). Compared with deionized water, McIlvaine's buffer, at comparable pH values, gives a somewhat higher respiration rate, which is to be expected as it contains biologically-active material. A few experiments conducted with phthalate buffer, which is biologically inert, gave identical results at pH 4.2 compared with those obtained with McIlvaine's buffer, suggesting that the biological activity of the latter does not affect the results obtained.

The choice of 25°C as a working temperature is open to comment. A number of lichens tested showed near maximal respiration rates at 25°C and rather reduced rates at lower, more natural, temperatures. There is clearly a need for caution in extrapolating from results obtained at 25°C to the natural situation where temperatures within the range 10–20°C are operative, and it would be interesting to obtain results at these lower temperatures.

*Sulphur dioxide in solution*

Sulphur dioxide is very soluble in aqueous solution and can be easily weighed into water or buffer by bubbling the gas through the solution. Alternatively solid sulphite (sodium salt) can be used. Irrespective of which source of ionic sulphur is used, an equilibrium mixture of sulphur-containing ions is attained very rapidly in solution, the precise mixture being pH-dependent. Metabisulphite (sodium salt) does not equilibrate so rapidly and is therefore, perhaps, unsuitable for these experiments. Bisulphite ions predominate at pH 3.5, undissociated sulphurous acid becoming more important at lower pH and sulphite ions more important at higher pH values (Vas and Ingram, 1949).

The natural pH range for corticolous lichen substrates, and therefore the range used in these experiments, is considered to be from pH 3.2 to 6.2 (Barkman, 1958). Buffer at pH 4.2 was chosen as an initial working medium, this being the approximate pH of moderately acid bark of non-eutrophiated trees such as oaks. Also, at this pH there is virtually no oxidation of ionic sulphur (bisulphite) to sulphate.

Experiments at higher pH values, involving the use of buffers at pH 5.2 and 6.2, need to allow for the oxidation of ionic sulphur (bisulphite and/or sulphite) to sulphate, the rate of oxidation being much higher at pH 6.2. This is particularly important in experiments involving the use of the oxygen electrode which measures respiration rates by following oxygen uptake in solution. Clearly at these higher pH values there is a need for some standardization in experiments with regard to this gradual oxidation to sulphate. Also there is a slow loss of sulphur dioxide from solution (Saunders, 1971), and therefore freshly-prepared sulphur dioxide solutions, made up in pH 4.2 buffer, were always used and were kept in closed brown glass bottles.

The range of sulphur dioxide concentrations tested in these experiments was 1 to 112 ppm in solution. With some lichens, effects on respiration were observed with concentrations as low as 3.5 ppm applied for 15 min, while in other instances there was still some appreciable respiration at 112 ppm after 18 hr exposure. The question of what represents the realistic upper limit of naturally-occurring sulphur dioxide in solution is discussed more fully below.

## Effects of sulphur dioxide on lichen respiration

Prior to 1971, two papers refer very briefly to the effects of sulphur dioxide on lichen respiration (Pearson and Skye, 1965; Schubert and Fritsche, 1965). More recently, two further papers give rather more detailed information on the effects of sulphur dioxide on respiration for a range of corticolous lichens (Baddeley, Ferry and Finegan, 1971, 1972). In these latter experiments all lichens tested showed reduced respiration rates over the range 1 to 112 ppm sulphur dioxide in solution, irrespective of the experimental procedure employed (see above). In some instances, however, low concentrations (up to 10 ppm) gave slightly enhanced rates. In general terms the range of concentrations resulting in 50 per cent reductions in respiration rates for different species gives an indication of the mildness or severity of the sulphur dioxide treatment employed in the various experimental procedures. For the Drop-in-dry procedure the range is 10–40 ppm and this would be considered a relatively mild treatment. For the Subsequent-additions procedure the range is 7–30 ppm and for the Overnight-incubation procedure 4–20 ppm, both of which would be considered relatively severe treatments.

How realistic these concentration ranges are, particularly with regard to their upper limits, is open to debate. From the discussion of Saunders and Wood (ch 2) it is clear that naturally-occurring concentrations of sulphur dioxide in air and in solution (in rain, mist and also surface water on substrates and vegetation) fluctuate considerably. It is also clear that routine measurements of 'sulphur dioxide' levels in air do not necessarily represent accurately levels of sulphur dioxide alone, but may include sulphate which is considerably less toxic to lichens, and to which sulphur dioxide is converted at a fairly rapid rate in many environmental situations. Saunders and Wood estimate that sulphur dioxide, at a concentration of 100 $\mu g/m^3$ (0.035 ppm) in air, would be equivalent to an aqueous solution containing 35 ppm sulphur dioxide. Concentrations of 100 $\mu g/m^3$ in air, but normally including sulphate, are not at all uncommon in polluted areas (*see* ch 3). It could be argued, therefore, that concentrations up to about 30 ppm sulphur dioxide in solution occur in nature. Sulphur dioxide oxidizes, to varying degrees, to sulphate in air and where it contacts basic (lichen) substrates, the rate of oxidation to sulphate would certainly be very appreciable. It should be noted however, as Saunders and Wood point out, that sulphur dioxide gas may dissolve directly into the water of moist lichen thalli and therefore escape the influence of the substrate. In such circumstances the buffering capacity of the lichen itself would be particularly important.

The precise levels of sulphur dioxide to which lichens are exposed in nature are not known and the value of 30 ppm in solution may be a substantial overestimate. It seems reasonable to assume that the sensitivity of a lichen to sulphur dioxide depends on how much it can ultimately absorb and also on the maximum rate at which it can absorb this amount, this rate being dependent on how rapidly the sulphur dioxide is 'inactivated' in the lichen tissues. The essential difference then, between laboratory and field situations, would seem to be the rate of uptake of sulphur dioxide. Perhaps the concentrations of sulphur dioxide used in the laboratory often result in rates of absorption being in excess of rates of 'inactivation', a situation probably not normal in nature. A number of workers have suggested that different levels of sulphur dioxide initiate damage to different metabolic processes in lichens and that, in the usual field situation, it is the lower damaging sulphur dioxide concentrations which are most important.

*Sensitivity range of lichens to sulphur dioxide*

The varying sensitivities of different lichen species in the field is now well documented (*see* ch 3, 4 and 5), and it might be expected that sensitivites in the laboratory would, to an extent, parallel these. This would seem to be the case, as far as respiratory sensitivity is concerned, providing comparisons are made between species of similar habitat and within a single geographical (climatic) region.

The relative sensitivities of a range of species growing on non-eutrophiated oaks in the Weald of Kent and Sussex (England) are given in Table 1. The relative sensitivity values are derived from sulphur dioxide-response curves of the type shown in Fig. 1 and are calculated by summing the sulphur dioxide concentrations required to give a 50 per cent reduction in respiration rate in each of the experimental procedures (D.I.D., S.A. and O.I.) and dividing by 100. The data are based on experiments carried out at pH 4.2, the approximate pH of non-eutrophiated oak bark. The apparent positions on the scale, based in most cases on reasonably complete data, are also given for a number of other species of this habitat from other geographical areas. Where sensitivities of a single species from two different geographical regions differ, this is thought to be due to either climatic differences between the regions or to the occurrence of ecotypes or races which differ in their sensitivity to sulphur dioxide. There is evidence for a decreased sensitivity in material collected from North Wales compared with material from the south of England.

A number of environmental factors associated with climate are believed to affect sensitivity to sulphur dioxide and these would include water relations (and drought) and temperature, and would involve seasonal changes. Some discussion of these is included in chapter 12.

The evidence for the existence of physiologically distinct ecotypes or races is slight. Gilbert (1971) noted that *Parmelia saxatilis*, growing on wall-tops in Northumberland, England, occurred in small pockets within the inner limit of its normal range with respect to pollution from Blyth power station. He suggested that these pockets might be populations with enhanced resistance to sulphur dioxide. Harris (1971) has reported ecotypes, differing with regard to certain physiological characteristics, of species growing at varying heights on oaks (*Quercus*

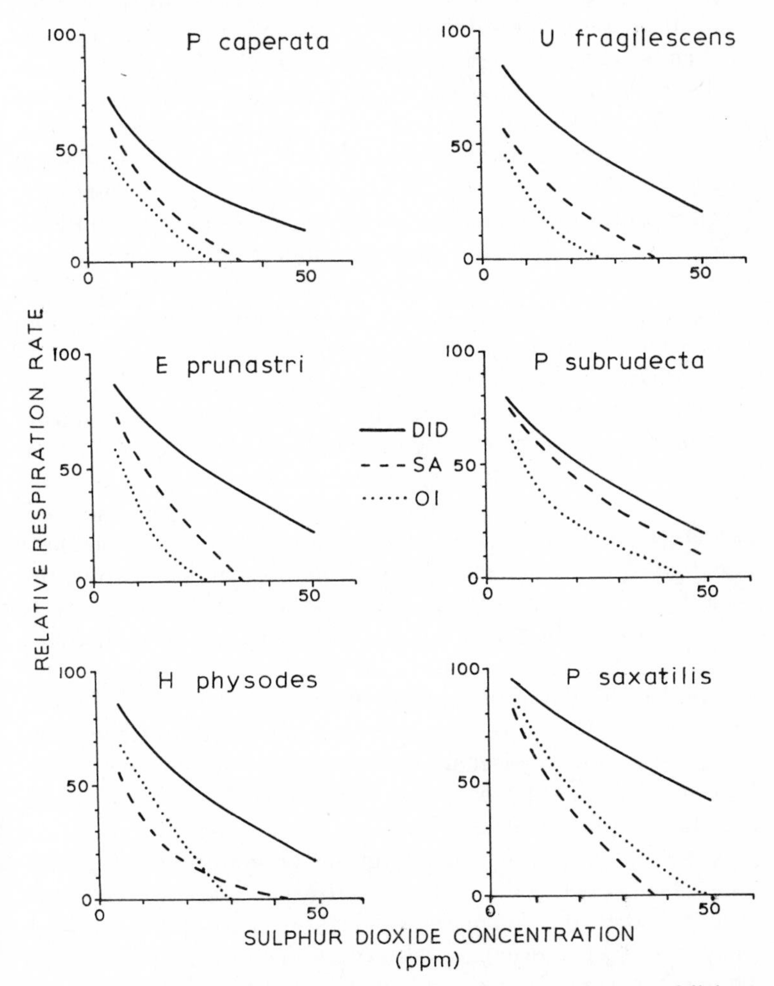


Fig. 1 Sulphur dioxide response curves for various species of lichens growing on non-eutrophiated oaks. For conditions of the experiments, see text

*robur*) in Devonshire. Species of non-lichenized fungi generally show a considerable capacity for physiological variation and it might be assumed that lichens would be similar in this respect.

*The physiological state of lichens exposed to sulphur dioxide*

Lichens will tend to accumulate sulphur dioxide in some form, even in areas of low sulphur dioxide levels in air, and the rate of accumulation will be proportional to levels of sulphur dioxide in the air. Gilbert (1969) has, for example, shown this to be so for *Parmelia saxatilis* growing on wall-tops in Northumberland, England. There seems to be little evidence that, once sulphur is present in lichen tissues, it is released again to any significant extent into the environment. The effect of naturally accumulated sulphur within the thallus on the respiratory response of lichens to sulphur dioxide under laboratory conditions cannot easily be assessed. One possibility is that lichen samples, collected from somewhat polluted sites, and containing fairly high levels of accumulated sulphur, will appear over-tolerant of sulphur dioxide. Such misleading results have been obtained with *Evernia prunastri* collected from a site in the Weald of Kent, England, at the limit of its range into polluted areas.

All of the data included in Table 1 (and Table 2 below) and in two other papers (Baddeley, Ferry and Finegan, 1971, 1972) are based on experiments with lichens from normal, healthy populations taken from areas with low mean winter sulphur dioxide levels in air ($<30$ $\mu g/m^3$). Comparisons were only made between species of a uniform habitat and from a single geographical region. In addition, for some experiments, collections of different species were made at the same time in an attempt to standardize the general physiological state of the lichens at the time of the experiments. Samples collected were stored, dry, in polythene bags for up to two weeks, depending on the species.

A further aspect of physiological standardization concerns the parts of lichen thalli used in experiments. Many workers have observed that the younger marginal lobes of foliose lichens show the first morphological symptoms of sulphur dioxide damage. In contrast, Gilbert (1971) has noted that the central portions of *Parmelia saxatilis* thalli growing on wall-tops disappear first in areas of moderate pollution, leaving crescent-

*Table 1 The relative respiratory sensitivities to sulphur dioxide of lichens of non-eutrophiated bark (mostly of oak) in England and Wales. Tested at pH 4.2*

| Relative Sensitivity Scale (see text) | Species in the Kent & Sussex Weald | Species in other southern counties | Species in Northumberland and N. Wales |
|---|---|---|---|
| 0 | | | |
| .10 | | | |
| .20 | | **Parmelia perlata* (H) | |
| | | **Usnea rubiginea* (D) | |
| | | **Usnea articulata* (D) | |
| | *Parmelia caperata* | | |
| | | *Usnea ceratina* (Dt) | |
| .30 | | | |
| | | *Parmelia crinita* (H) | |
| | *Usnea fragilescens* | **Parmelia laevigata* (D) | |
| | | **Platismatia glauca* (H) | |
| .40 | *Hypogymnia physodes* | *Lobaria amplissima* (Dt) | |
| | *Evernia prunastri* | *Lobaria scrobiculata* (D) | |
| | *Parmelia subrudecta* | | |
| | | *Lobaria laetevirens* (D) | |
| | | | *Parmelia perlata* (NW) |
| .50 | | | *Parmelia caperata* (NW) |
| | | *Lobaria pulmonaria* (Dt) | *Usnea subfloridana* (NW) |
| .60 | | | |
| | | **Usnea subfloridana* (H) | |
| .70 | *Parmelia saxatilis* | | |
| | | | *Usnea subfloridana* (N) |
| | | | *Alectoria fuscescens* (N) |
| .80 | | | |
| | | | *Platismatia glauca* (NW) |
| .90 | | | |
| 1.00 | | | |
| | | | *Platismatia glauca* (N) |
| 1.10 | | | |
| | | | *Parmelia saxatilis* (NW) |

H: Hampshire; D: Devonshire; Dt: Dorset; N: Northumberland; NW: North Wales
* based on incomplete sets of experiments

shaped marginal parts. Not all of these effects necessarily reflect differing sensitivities of older and younger parts of thalli to sulphur dioxide, for microshelter over the thallus surface might be involved.

*Table 2 The relative respiratory sensitivities to sulphur dioxide of lichens of eutrophiated trees in the Kent and Sussex Weald. Tested at pH 4.2*

| Relative Sensitivity Scale (see text) | |
|---|---|
| 0 | |
| .10 | |
| .20 | |
| | *Xanthoria parietina* |
| .30 | *Physcia ascendens* |
| | *Anaptychia ciliaris* |
| .40 | |
| | *Parmelia acetabulum* |
| .50 | *Buellia canescens* |
| .60 | |
| .70 | *Physconia pulverulenta* |
| | *Ramalina fastigiata* |
| .80 | *Parmelia sulcata* |
| .90 | |
| | *Ramalina farinacea* |
| 1.00 | |

The importance of using standard pieces of thalli in laboratory experiments is obvious. A further problem worthy of attention is the sensitivity of diaspores compared with established thalli (*see* ch 15).

### *The importance of substrate*

Natural substrates vary with respect to a great many chemical and physical characteristics. Frequent emphasis is placed on the pH and buffering capacity of the substrate in discussions about sulphur dioxide and its effect on lichens. This would seem reasonable in view of the well-documented evidence on the relationship between pH and the form of sulphur dioxide in solution (see above). In the laboratory one cannot hope to simulate the complex of natural conditions which lichens experience during exposure to sulphur dioxide. However, pH is easily controlled and it is possible to adjust the pH in experiments to relate closely to that of the natural substrate (see above).

In contrast to the results obtained at pH 4.2 for species of non-eutrophiated oaks, lichens of eutrophiated trees do not show an acceptable correlation between laboratory sensitivities and field sensitivities when tested at this pH (Table 2). Preliminary results for these latter species indicate that a rather better correlation may be obtained at pH 5.2 or higher. At pH 5.2, for example, *Anaptychia ciliaris* and *Parmelia acetabulum* appear to be marginally more sensitive than *Xanthoria parietina*. All species of both eutrophiated and non-eutrophiated trees show reduced sensitivity to sulphur dioxide in solution at pH 5.2 compared with pH 4.2, but the alleviating effect of the higher pH on sensitivity is more pronounced for the lichens of eutrophiated trees.

*The effect of morphology on sensitivity to sulphur dioxide*

With the oxygen electrode, in view of the efficiency with which lichens absorb solutes, it is necessary to maintain a constant ratio of lichen tissue to solution volume in experiments. The ratio used was 50 mg water-saturated thallus to 7 ml solution. Variation in surface area available for absorption seems to be relatively unimportant in the conditions obtaining in the oxygen electrode, where lichen samples are infiltrated with solution and are kept constantly agitated. However, in the case of *Hypogymnia physodes* the peculiarly high sensitivity rating obtained in laboratory experiments might be explicable in terms of its hollow thallus. This is solution-filled under the experimental conditions but may never be so in field situations. Obviously, in the field situation the surface area available for sulphur dioxide absorption, coupled with the wettability of the thallus, may be a critical factor controlling rate of sulphur dioxide uptake. The problem of wettability has not been properly investigated although some lichens have been observed to be relatively water-repellent, perhaps notably *Lecanora conizaeoides*. However, preliminary results indicate that this species is, in fact, inherently very insensitive when tested in sulphur dioxide solutions buffered at pH 4.2 after treatment with a wetting agent (1 per cent 'Tween 80'). The wetting agent was shown not to be harmful to other, more easily wettable, species.

### *The significance of respiratory sensitivity to sulphur dioxide*

There are now four papers referring to the effects of sulphur dioxide on photosynthesis in lichens (Pearson and Skye, 1965; Rao and LeBlanc, 1966; Hill, 1971; Puckett, Nieboer, Flora and Richardson, 1973) but the methods used, to measure photosynthesis and to expose samples to sulphur dioxide, do not allow for easy comparison with our results on respiratory sensitivity. Some preliminary results on photosynthetic sensitivity, using the oxygen electrode and buffer at pH 4.2, suggest that photosynthesis is generally three to five times more sensitive to sulphur dioxide than respiration. However, the relative sensitivities of the different species are much the same irrespective of whether respiration or photosynthesis is used as a basis for measurement. Such data might suggest some similar mode(s) of action of sulphur dioxide on the two processes (*see* ch 17). It indicates also that respiratory sensitivity is probably as useful as photosynthetic sensitivity in relating physiological responses in the laboratory to field sensitivity.

Higher plants are generally much less sensitive to sulphur dioxide than lichens in the field, but infiltrated tissues tested for respiration rates in the laboratory are only marginally less sensitive. Presumably this is because the barrier to sulphur dioxide entry presented by the cuticle is by-passed. Lichens, bryophytes and non-lichenized fungi lack cuticles and are all of comparable sensitivity in the laboratory and in the field, except that non-lichenized fungi are generally protected by their substrates in the field.

These observations on the responses of non-lichen tissues to sulphur dioxide, in some cases involving the use of the oxygen electrode technique, coupled with the observations made in the first paragraph of this section, suggest that some physiological process, other than respiration or photosynthesis, possibly the sulphur dioxide uptake mechanism, might be of overriding importance. Different lichen species might vary with regard to the efficiency of their sulphur dioxide uptake mechanisms, and respiratory and photosynthetic responses would be likely to reflect these variations.

### *Recovery of physiological processes to normal levels following exposure to sub-lethal doses of sulphur dioxide*

In the field there is some evidence for the recovery of lichen transplants, transferred initially into polluted areas, and then removed to non-polluted areas at a later date. Using this technique, Gilbert (1970) showed some recovery in *Hypogymnia physodes*. It is necessary here to distinguish between recommencement of growth from physiologically-undamaged parts of a thallus exposed to sulphur dioxide, and recovery and resumed growth of physiologically-damaged thallus. In some preliminary experiments, using the oxygen electrode, lichen samples exposed to sulphur dioxide in the usual way (Drop-in-dry procedure, see above) were left to recover for periods of up to three weeks, either dry or dry with some periods of overnight wetting. In no instance was recovery, even from slightly injurious sulphur dioxide concentrations, detected, but the limitations of such short-term experiments are obvious.

At present it is not possible, from laboratory observations, to assess the importance of recovery capacity in explaining the relative field sensitivities of lichens to sulphur dioxide. The conditions for recovery in the field, in terms of moisture content of thallus, temperature and other factors, need to be simulated in laboratory experiments if useful data are to be obtained. The further use of the transplant technique, in conjunction with measurements of physiological activity of thalli, would seem to be a particularly promising approach.

## Conclusions

Methods of studying the effects of sulphur dioxide on lichen physiology, particularly respiration, in the laboratory, are discussed. Emphasis is placed on the problems involved in relating conditions in laboratory experiments to field situations and on the need to maintain strict control of conditions in laboratory experiments.

It has been possible to show, using an oxygen electrode

technique, that respiratory processes in lichens are sensitive to acceptably low levels of sulphur dioxide. Further the relative respiratory sensitivities of different species are shown to relate to field sensitivities, providing comparisons are made between species from a single geographical (climatic) region and from a similar habitat, and providing experiments are conducted at realistic pHs, e.g. pH 4.2, for species of non-eutrophiated oaks. In experiments at this pH, species of eutrophiated trees do not show a good correlation between laboratory and field sensitivities.

The importance of a variety of factors likely to influence sensitivity in laboratory and field situations are discussed. These include: the physiological state of lichen material at the time of exposure to sulphur dioxide; the variation in sensitivity between different parts of a thallus; the effect of lichen substrates and thalli on sulphur dioxide, particularly with regard to oxidation to sulphate; the influence of thallus morphology and wettability on sulphur dioxide uptake; the relative importance of respiratory sensitivity compared with photosynthetic sensitivity, and the possible importance of capacity to recover from sublethal doses of sulphur dioxide in the field.

## Acknowledgements

We particularly wish to thank Miss Belinda Wager, research assistant to one of us (B.W.F.), who carried out many of the experiments referred to in this work. Part of the work is being carried out during the tenure of a grant from the Science Research Council.

## References

Baddeley, M. S., Ferry, B. W. and Finegan, E. J. (1971). A new method of measuring lichen respiration: Response of selected species to temperature, pH and sulphur dioxide. *Lichenologist* **5**, 18–25.

Baddeley, M. S., Ferry, B. W. and Finegan, E. J. (1972). The effects of sulphur dioxide on lichen respiration. *Lichenologist* **5**, 283–91.

Barkman, J. J. (1958). *Phytosociology and ecology of cryptogamic epiphytes.* Assen, Netherlands: Van Gorcum.

Gilbert, O. L. (1969). The effect of $SO_2$ on lichens and bryophytes around Newcastle upon Tyne. In: *Air pollution, Proceedings of the first European Congress on the influence of air pollution on plants and animals,*

*Wageningen 1968*, 223–35. Wageningen: Centre for Agricultural Publishing and Documentation.

Gilbert, O. L. (1970). A biological scale for the estimation of sulphur dioxide pollution. *New Phytol.* **69,** 629–34.

Gilbert, O. L. (1971). Studies along the edge of a lichen desert. *Lichenologist* **5,** 11–17.

Harris, G. P. (1971). The ecology of corticolous lichens. II. The relationship between physiology and the environment. *J. Ecol.* **59,** 441–52.

Hill, D. J. (1971). Experimental study of the effect of sulphite on lichens with reference to atmospheric pollution. *New Phytol.* **70,** 831–6.

Pearson, L. and Skye, E. (1965). Air pollution affects pattern of photosynthesis in *Parmelia sulcata*, a corticolous lichen. *Science, N.Y.* **148,** 1600–2.

Puckett, K. J., Nieboer, E., Flora, B. and Richardson, D. H. S. (1972). Sulphur dioxide: Its effect on photosynthetic $^{14}C$-fixation in lichens and suggested mechanisms of toxicity. *New Phytol.* **72,** 141–54.

Rao, D. N. and LeBlanc, F. (1966). Effects of sulfur dioxide on the lichen algae, with special reference to chlorophyll. *Bryologist* **69,** 69–75.

Saunders, P. J. W. (1971). Modification of the leaf surface and its environment by pollution. In: Preece, T. F. and Dickinson, C. H. (ed.) *Ecology of leaf surface micro-organisms*, 81–9. London and New York: Academic Press.

Schubert, R. and Fritsche, W. (1965). Beitrag zur Einwirkung von Lufverunreinigungen auf xerische Flechten. *Arch. NatSchutz* **52,** 107–10.

Vas, K. and Ingram, M. (1949). Preservation of fruit juices with less $SO_2$. *Fd Mf.* **24,** 414–16.

# 15: Experimental Study of the Effects of Sulphur Dioxide on the Soredia of *Hypogymnia physodes*

J. MARGOT

The sensitivity of lichens to pollution results from accumulation mechanisms that are highly efficient in relation to very dilute substances in the air, or in rain water, on which lichens are totally dependent for their nutrition. Further, these plants are perennials and therefore continually suffer the influence of a polluted atmosphere.

Among the great diversity of atmospheric pollutants, sulphur dioxide remains one of the principal agents of contamination, not only by reason of its ubiquity but also because it is given off in large quantities.

The toxicity of the ionic forms of sulphur produced is due principally to their oxidation-reduction properties. In lichens, the damage occurs *in situ* and is directly correlated with the water content of the thallus. LeBlanc and his school have described this damage, but there is a lack of agreement between authors as to the rate of action of these ionic forms on different species. There is also a need for further study to establish criteria for evaluating the damage to lichens caused by pollution.

The importance of the relative humidity as a factor influencing the development of lichens has already been indicated; any variation in the surrounding environment induces an adjustment in the water content of the thallus and in this respect it behaves like a hygrometer.

The sensitivity of epiphytic lichens in a polluted environment is demonstrated by a reduction of growth and fertility, and also by a decline in the number of species, and their cover on the substratum, as the source of emission of the pollutant is approached. These different reactions, which are easily observed, have made it possible to establish a classification of species based either on a distance gradient from the source of the pollutant, or on a gradient of resistance with respect to global pollution, or again based on the growth rate or deterioration of the thallus.

A number of difficulties are recognized in the literature: first, the extremely slow growth of the thallus; second, particularly, the different types of damage observed for different pollutants, making the estimation of sensitivity complicated; finally, the differences in behaviour according to physiological strain, habitat and the physico-chemical nature of the bark of the tree which varies with age. One could not possibly quote here all those who have worked on this problem. Almost all of them, however, consider the creation of lichen-free zones round towns to be the direct result of toxic compounds in the atmosphere, whilst Rydzak imputes this disappearance to the dryness of the urban atmosphere. Several earlier chapters deal with the arguments for and against these theories in detail (ch 7, 11). The two factors may act jointly, and we must therefore consider them both in interpreting work on pollution.

In another connection, the culture of lichens in a controlled environment is not easy and makes worthwhile ecophysiological experiments difficult, if not impossible.

I have attempted to approach the problem by examining the behaviour of the vegetative reproductive structures, soredia, of *Hypogymnia physodes* in appropriate nutrient media after various treatments in an atmosphere artificially loaded with sulphur dioxide or after spraying with sulphate in solution.

## Materials and Methods

*Hypogymnia physodes* is a common foliose species bearing labriform soralia on the lower side of the raised tip of the peripheral lobes. The samples necessary for the experiments in the laboratory, and those treated directly in the natural habitat, were all taken from pure plantations of *Picea* at a mean altitude of 550 m, on a humid plateau in the Belgian Ardennes, where no recognized pollution exists.

The soredia or groups of soredia were sown by superficial scratching of the soralia on a substratum of sterilized agar containing a nutrient medium (Bold's mineral medium, Ahmadjian,

1967), some trace elements and a soil extract. Such a medium is suitable for the development of the alga and of the fungus. The culture boxes were then kept under an illumination of 2500 lux for 12 hours a day and in an almost saturated atmosphere (95 per cent) to avoid a too rapid desiccation of the medium.

After a month, the living soredia send out whitish hyphae and most of them become completely surrounded by a green circular colony, in which can be seen lichen algal cells. It is possible to count the colonies under a binocular microscope, and a normal sample shows a total 'germination' of 97 per cent. Among this 97 per cent it is easy to distinguish green colonies containing an algal element and a concealed fungal element, representing 70 per cent of the total 'germination' and soredia emitting hyphae only, which represent the remaining 27 per cent.

The increase in cell number of the algal symbiont, which is more sensitive to pollution than the fungus, constitutes the principal quantitative criterion. It should also be pointed out that the value attributed to the fungal element is inaccurate, since it is partly masked by the algae. Further, an initial mortality of 3 per cent already exists in the control sample, which is accentuated subsequently during the equilibration necessary for the conditioning of the thallus both in the laboratory and in the natural habitat. This effect must be separated from the mortality due to the artificially applied pollutant to which the thalli are subjected before the soredia are sown.

We are measuring quantitatively the effect of pollutants on the behaviour of the soredia in culture.

### *The soredia of* Hypogymnia physodes

These pieces of the thallus are more or less spherical and measure 25 to 100 μm in diameter. They become detached from the thallus spontaneously and thus perpetuate the symbiosis by vegetative means. The soredia contain one or more algal cells surrounded by a cluster of hyphae. They arise in the algal layer under the cortex, and develop by growth and rapid division of the algal cells. The hyphae penetrate between these autospores and separate them from each other. A soredium can give rise to new soredia, which accumulate under the cortex and, by exerting pressure, they rupture the cortex resulting in the liberation of a pulverized mass of soredia from which the individual soredia are dispersed.

The identity of the symbiotic elements of the lichen, and hence those of the soredia, has been established with the organisms produced from these soredia in culture. It consists of an ascomycete, the small hyphae (2–3 μm diameter) of which have chitinous walls which stain well with cotton blue. The algal component is a green alga of the genus *Trebouxia* consisting of spherical cells 10 to 15 μm in diameter, with cellulosic walls, containing a parietal layer of cytoplasm and a hyaline core with a nucleus and a huge chloroplast with a central pyrenoid, the little incised edge of which is irregular and extends to the membrane in places. The multiplication of the algal cells in the lichen is by formation of autospores (4, 8, 16 or more) which show more or less polyhedric divisions within a complete bounding membrane. Asexual reproduction by the formation of zoospores occurs in culture and in the wild, in which case the chloroplast is always located at the posterior-pole.

## The experiment

In the wide context of the use of lichens as bioindicators of air pollution, it is essential to state precisely the methods used for a more rigorous investigation involving accurate quantification.

The present technique is intended to provide such a contribution to aid interpretation in a wider context. The experiment is restricted to the effects of a widespread pollutant, sulphur dioxide and also sulphate, on a common epiphytic lichen which is slightly sensitive, namely *Hypogymnia physodes*.

The effect of exposing the thallus and hence the soredia to an external pollutant or a modification of the surrounding environment just before separating and sowing the soredia, results in a change in the quantitative composition of the subsequent culture. This change, it will be seen, is a precise response to the conditions imposed experimentally and relates to the resistance of the organism and the level of pollutant. The reaction is very sensitive and reproducible. Further, this method can be applied to other species and different pollutants, thus constituting a quantitative method for the establishment of specific levels of sensitivity.

In the laboratory, the thalli of *Hypogymnia physodes*, contained in a nylon mesh sachet, are suspended in humidifiers which provide a precise control of relative humidity. In the field, transparent plastic boxes of 800 $cm^3$ capacity were used. They were attached to *Picea* trunks, bearing the single lichen species, and were always oriented in the same direction. A special cement was used for the attachment, and also to secure the walls of the boxes to render them air tight; the lids remained detachable.

The sulphur dioxide (liquid sulphur dioxide, 64.07 of BDH Chemicals Ltd), diluted in air to the required proportion, was injected into the boxes using a syringe. The sulphate, as the ammonium, magnesium or zinc salt in solution in distilled water was sprayed directly onto the thallus until the thallus was saturated.

### *The effect of experimental confinement and the variation of relative humidity*

Before investigating the action of the pollutant, it is necessary to assess the effect of the experimental conditions. As a function of increasing length of continuous confinement at all levels of relative humidity in the absence of pollutant, the soredial cultures sown from the confined thalli show a regular and marked decline in growth (Fig. 1). The curves are almost parallel at least for total 'germination'; the effect is more marked with respect to the algal cells, which indicates that they are more sensitive than the mycobiont. The mortality caused by confinement is significant at all values of relative humidity, but it is also a function of the water content, reaching a maximum at low relative humidity (Fig. 1).

Continuous desiccation is therefore harmful to the lichen and to the soredia subsequently to be grown in culture. This effect must be taken into account in experiments on pollutants. Other treatments involving daily alternation of high and low relative humidities have much less effect on the lichen. It is even possible to overcome the reaction to confinement by this treatment.

On the trunk, in the surrounding relative humidity (that of the atmosphere or that of the closed boxes) the same reaction can be observed. The growth of the soredia in culture after treatment is decreased as a function of the length of the conditioning period, and also of the daily length of treatment (Figs. 2 and 3).

*The effect of artificially applied pollutants*

The pollutants were applied in the field, sulphur dioxide in gaseous form by an injection each day, and ammonium sulphate in solution, with which the lichens were sprayed once a day. The boxes were closed for 6 hours following the sulphur dioxide injections. Each experiment lasted for 8 days, and for each pollutant three concentrations were used: 0.05, 0.1 and 1.0 ppm in air for sulphur dioxide; 0.15, 0.75 and 1.5 meq/100 ml solution for sulphate.

The total mortality of the soredia is shown to be a function of the duration of treatment for all the concentrations of both pollutants (Fig. 4). In the case of sulphur dioxide it is necessary to subtract the effect of the 6 hours per day confinement from the overall results to give a realist value. The two pollutants induce a similar result, only the effective concentrations are different.

The behaviour of the soredial cultures is significant with respect to the algal colonies, and the following results present data for the mortality of the algal partner only. Also the mortality caused by the pollutant only is quoted, that caused by the confinement of the sample having been subtracted.

*The concentration of the pollutants*

Treatment with the pollutant was for 16 days before the soredia were sown, although different frequencies of application of the pollutant were used. In each case the first injection was given on day one. In this experiment, the mortality rate was directly related to the concentration of the pollutant (Fig. 5). The pollutant acts on the lichen according to its concentration, and independent of the number/frequency of the injections. On the other hand, the confinement effect increases with the time of conditioning, and is additional to that of the pollutant, but independent of it. In the present experiment, the duration of exposure and the relative humidity were as before.

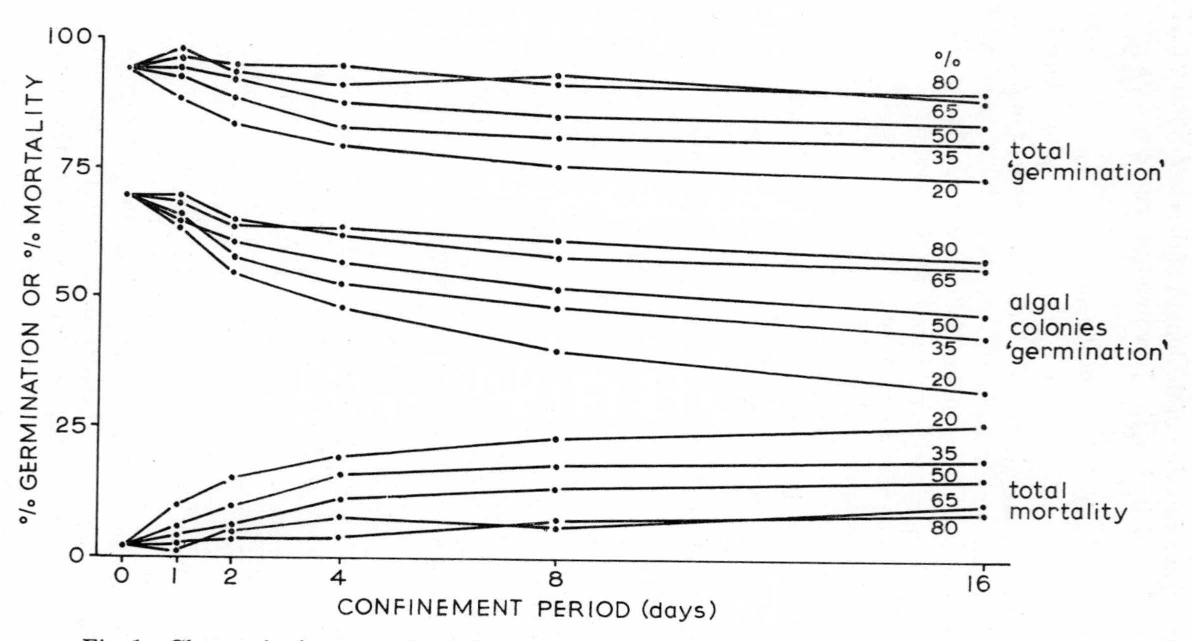


Fig. 1 Changes in the proportions of soredial cultures with the length of confinement at different relative humidities

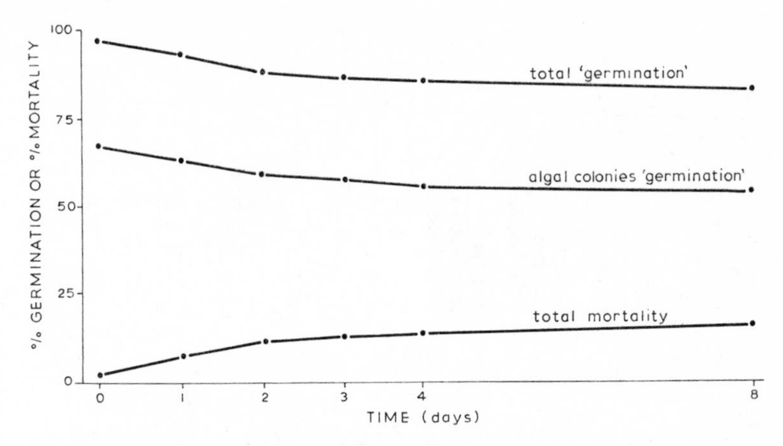


Fig. 2 Changes in the proportions of soredial cultures with the length of confinement in the closed experimental boxes in the field

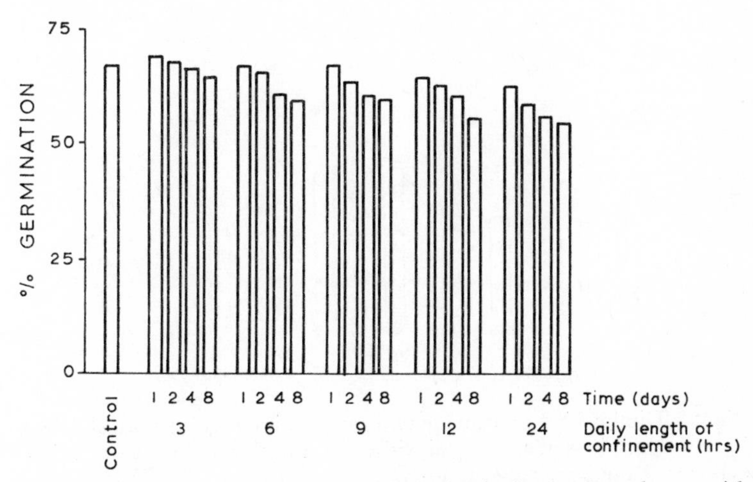


Fig. 3 Changes in the proportion of algal colonies in the cultures with the daily period, and number of days, of confinement in the closed boxes in the field

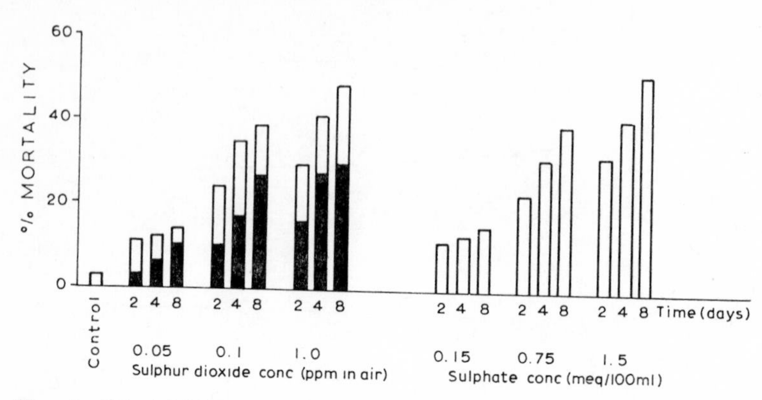


Fig. 4 Diminishing percentage of algal colonies in culture with the duration of pollutant treatment in the field. For the sulphur dioxide treatments the black part of the histograms represents the effect of the pollutant only, the white part the effect of confinement only. The two together give the total observed effect

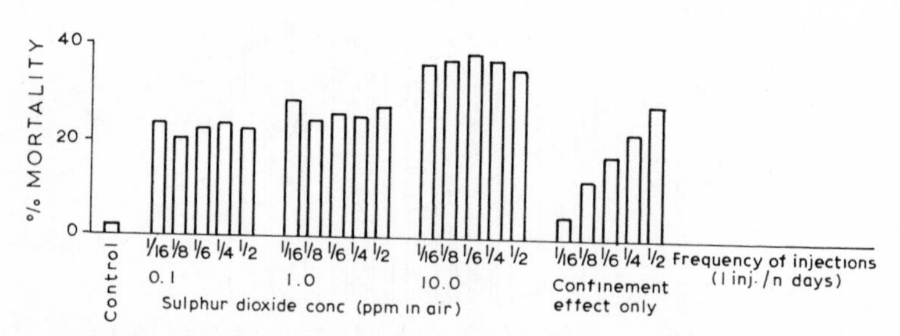


Fig. 5 Diminishing percentage of algal colonies in culture with increasing concentrations of sulphur dioxide. The effect of confinement has been subtracted and is shown separately

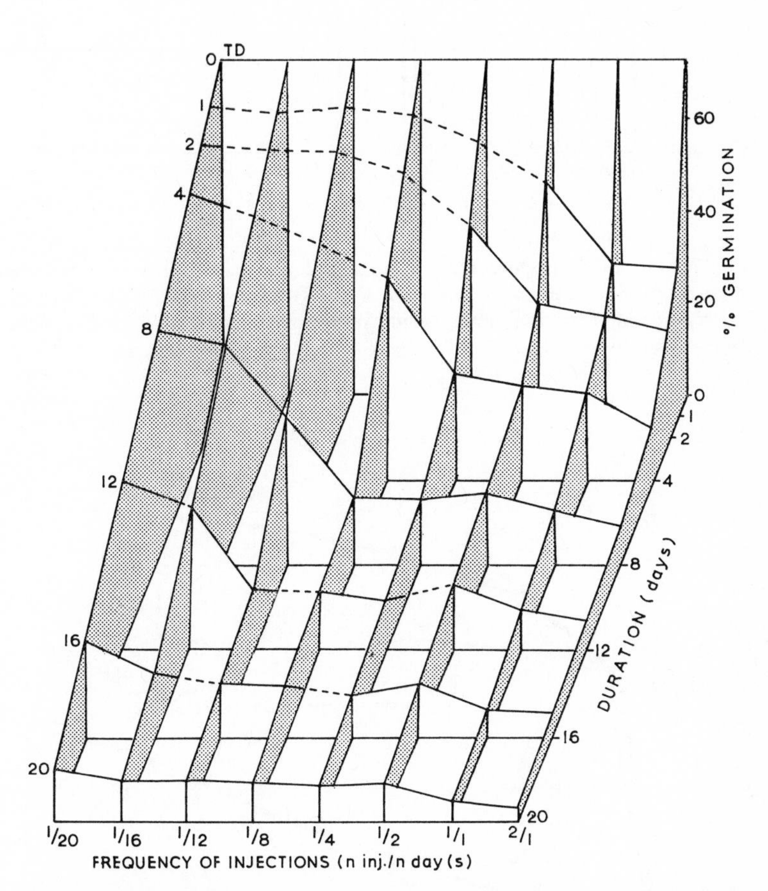


Fig. 6 Diminishing percentage of algal colonies in culture with varying frequency of injections of sulphur dioxide (10 ppm in air) and duration of pollutant treatment up to 20 days. No allowance is made for confinement

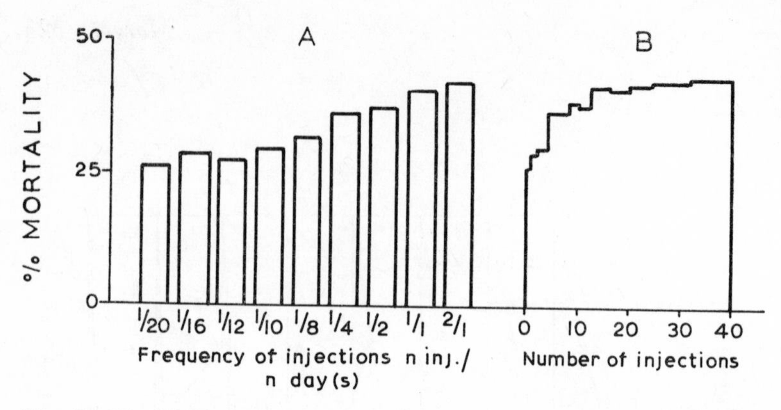


Fig. 7 Diminishing percentage of algal colonies in culture, (A) with the frequency of injections of pollutant and (B) with the actual number of these injections for the same period of time, i.e. for 20 days. The data relate directly to Fig. 6 but allowance is made for confinement

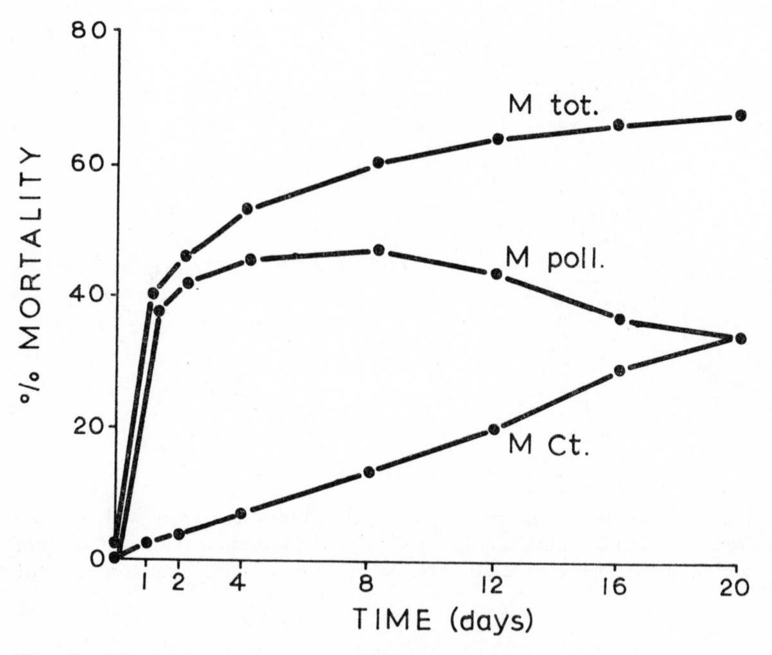


Fig. 8 Diminishing percentage of algal colonies in culture with the duration of pollutant treatment—sulphur dioxide at 10 ppm in air, one injection per day. Total mortality (M tot.) = mortality due to pollutant only (M poll.) + confinement effect (M Ct.)

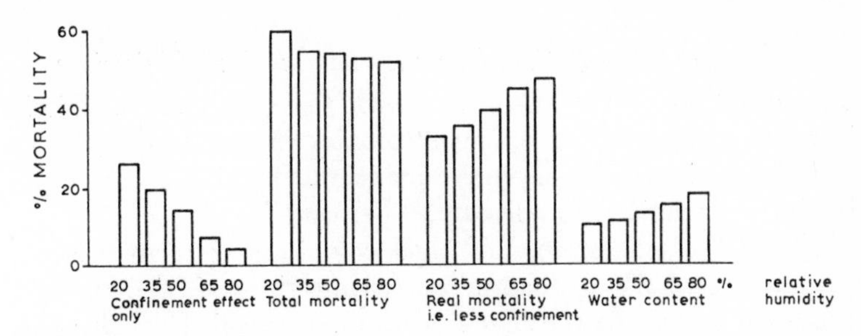


Fig. 9 Changes in the proportion of algal colonies in culture with relative humidity, when treated with sulphur dioxide (10 ppm in air) at one injection per day for one week

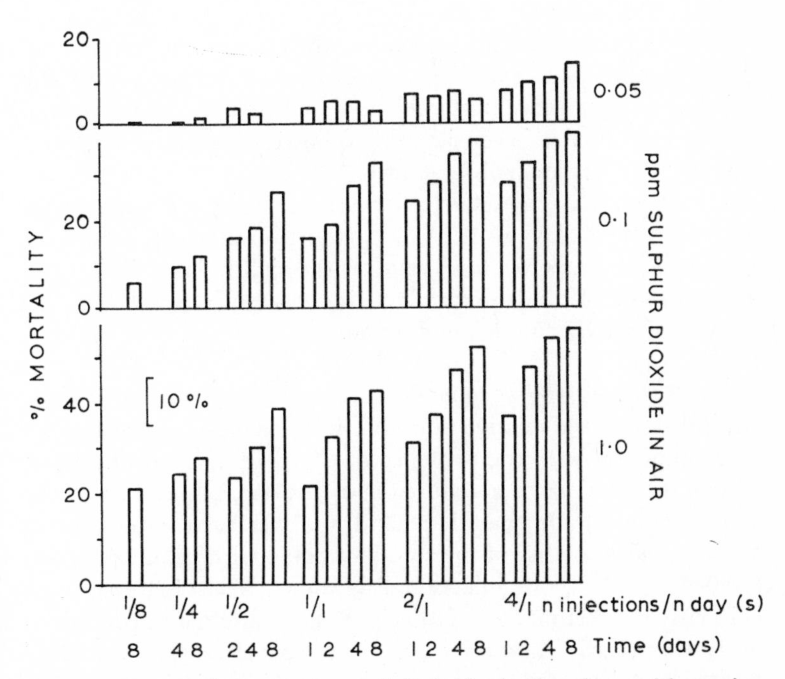


Fig. 10 Diminishing percentage of algal colonies in culture with varying concentration, frequency of application and duration of treatment of sulphur dioxide in the field. The effect of confinement has been subtracted

*Duration of the pollution, frequency and number of injections*

The duration of the treatment with the pollutants definitely influences the number of algal colonies in the culture, in an experiment in which sulphur dioxide was applied at 10.0 ppm in air, in a relative humidity of 30 per cent.

The decreased number of algal colonies was related to the frequency and also to the number of injections of the pollutant. For each treatment the first injection was applied on day one. On the graph (Fig. 6) the actual percentage of algal colonies is shown, indicating the combined effect of the pollutant, sulphur dioxide, and the effect of the confinement.

It is possible to distinguish the effect of the frequency of injections (Fig. 7A) and that of the number of injections (Fig. 7B) on the mortality of the algal cells. These experiments were for the same duration of 20 days.

The closer together the injections, the greater was the effect of the pollutant, the mortality rate of algae increasing with the number of injections. It should be noted that the toxic effect of the sulphur dioxide is considerable following the early injections, and that it decreases subsequently.

If one considers the effect of the use of a single frequency, of one injection a day over 20 days, the overall mortality of the algal cells increases to a high value at the eighth day (Fig. 8), and afterwards a diminishing effect is observed, which can be accounted for by confinement alone.

*Pollution and relative humidity*

An increase of the relative humidity in the conditioning chamber in conjunction with the presence of the pollutant and the effect of confinement, gave a reduction of the total mortality of the soredia (Fig. 9). On the other hand, the increased water content and the real mortality of the soredia treated with sulphur dioxide (10.0 ppm in air, one injection a day for a week) increase in an evidently parallel manner. Other pollutants applied in conditions of varying relative humidity react in the same way; an increased toxic effect is noted as the relative humidity is increased. It probably results from the fact that under low relative humidity, lichen metabolism is greatly if not completely retarded, which gives a certain protection with respect to the pollutant. This aspect is of first importance and must therefore be considered.

*Toxicity of sulphur dioxide to* Hypogymnia physodes

In the field, in natural conditions, without disturbing the ecology of the lichen, it has been possible to establish the scale of toxicity to sulphur dioxide of this species. This has been done by applying injections of sulphur dioxide at different frequencies (the first injection on day one), over an equal length of conditioning time, hence altering the number of injections. This can be repeated at different concentrations of the pollutant. The results shown in Fig. 10 give a series of actual mortality values of algal cells from soredial cultures sown after conditioning. The results vary from low levels of pollutant which have no harmful effect, to more frequent applications of the pollutant which kill nearly all of the algal colonies one would expect to find in a control sample. The results of such an experiment show that an application of 1.0 pp, sulphur dioxide in air, even at fairly distantly-spaced intervals, is harmful to this species. The application of 0.1 ppm is also harmful but to a lesser extent, and the damage increases with the increasing frequency of the injections. Applications of 0.05 ppm do not seem to be very harmful, and only produce a mortality of some 10 per cent at a rate of 4 injections a day for 8 days.

These results placing the threshold of sensitivity of *Hypogymnia physodes* at about 0.075 ppm sulphur dioxide in air conform reasonably with those of the literature which have been obtained by other methods (Tallis, 1964; ch 3).

Finally some trials similar to those carried out in this investigation have been carried out on other species of epiphytic lichens which possess soredia: *Platismatia glauca*, *Evernia prunastri*, *Pertusaria amara* and *Parmeliopsis ambigua*; all of these species respond in the same way but display a different threshold of sensitivity to the pollutant. The differences are statistically significant, and they therefore substantiate the method used as a quantitative measure of the toxi-sensibility of lichens to pollution.

This method can be extended either to verify results from

mapping studies, or by establishing a map based on results obtained from soredia carefully collected from appropriate sites.

## Conclusions

*Hypogymnia physodes*, an epiphytic lichen which is relatively insensitive to pollution, was selected for this study because its soredia germinate easily in culture, thus providing useful material for perfecting a technique for the quantification of lichen toxiphobia. The principal quantitative criterion employed was the multiplication of the algal cells. The identity of the symbiotic elements of the lichen with that of the culture has been verified.

The experimental confinement lowers the multiplication rate of the algal cells and must be deducted from the total mortality rate in order to provide a correct estimate of the toxicity of the pollutant. Whether applied in the form of gaseous sulphur dioxide or a solution of sulphate, the pollutant affects the lichen and its soredia, according to the concentration of the pollutant and according to the frequency and the number of the injections and also to the length of the conditioning time. A maximum effect for a given treatment is reached at some point, the pollutant being more harmful in conditions of high relative humidity.

The modification of the quantitative composition of the soredial cultures responds in a precise and reproducible way to the conditions in the experiments conducted in the laboratory and in the field, taking into account different ecological factors. This method is applicable to different species and also has some application in mapping studies of air pollution.

## Résumé

*Étude expérimentale des effets du sulphur dioxide sur les sorédies d'*Hypogymnia physodes

Les lichens marquent à l'égard des polluants atmosphériques une répulsion bien connue; cette toxiphobie se manifeste par une vitalité et une fertilité moindres comme aussi par une régression des espèces, de leur nombre et de leur recouvrement.

La croissance des thalles est lente et sa mesure longue; les autres méthodes d'estimation de la toxiphobie présentent également des difficultés liées au comportement variable d'une même espèce selon son habitat, selon le type de pollution ou selon les races physiologiques. Par ailleurs, la culture des lichens en milieu conditionné reste délicate et rend actuellement impossible toute expérimentation écophysiologique.

Devant ces difficultés, on a tenté d'aborder le problème par l'examen du comportement des éléments de reproduction végétative (sorédies) en culture, après divers traitements. Le pouvoir de multiplication de l'algue symbiotique, plus sensible aux polluants que le champignon, constitue le critère quantitatif principal (comptage des colonies).

En laboratoire, mais également sur le terrain, des thalles d'*Hypogymnia physodes* sont soumis à des pollutions artificielles par injections de sulphur dioxide ou par aspersions de sulfates en solution, dans des enceintes étanches.

Les essais portent non seulement sur le mode d'application, mais aussi sur l'intensité, la durée et la fréquence des pollutions, conjointement à une variation d'humidité relative de l'ambiance.

Le développement des colonies de *Trebouxia* dans les 'semis' de sorédies issues des thalles ainsi traités exprime les potentialités ou le pouvoir multiplicatif des gonidies et, par voie de conséquence, la nocivité réelle d'une pollution connue sur un élément symbiotique de la sorédie, au moment de sa libération du thalle.

## References

Ahmadjian, V. (1967). *The Lichen Symbiosis*. Waltham, Mass.: Blaisdell.

Tallis, J. H. (1964). Lichens and atmospheric pollution. *Admvt Sci., Lond.* **21**, 250–2.

# 16: Changes in the Lichen Flora of England and Wales Attributable to Pollution of the Air by Sulphur Dioxide

D. L. HAWKSWORTH, F. ROSE and
B. J. COPPINS

The lichen flora of England, like that of many countries in western Europe, has been studied since the late seventeenth century. During the last 280 years about 1000 books and papers containing records of English lichens have been published. Furthermore, many of the published reports are substantiated by specimens deposited in one or more of about thirty institutional herbaria in the British Isles. These herbaria also contain many collections which have not been mentioned in the literature. The largest collection is that of the British Museum (Natural History) which now includes about 80 000 specimens from England. Since the formation of the British Lichen Society in 1958, and particularly since 1967, considerable amounts of data have been accumulated in connection with the Society's Distribution Maps Scheme.

The availability of detailed records extending over many years enables maps showing the changes in distribution of particular species to be constructed and the past and present lichen floras of particular localities to be compared. This chapter is concerned with changes in the corticolous and lignicolous lichen flora of England and Wales which are considered to be attributable to sulphur dioxide pollution of the air. The reasons for preferring epiphytic species for such investigations have already been discussed (ch 3, p. 55). An additional factor, however, when considering changes in particular sites is the age of the trees. Lichenologists recording from trees 250–300 years old in 1972 will be examining the same trees studied by lichenologists last century. Consequently any comparison between the past and present lichen floras of such trees is more significant than observations on either less permanent or younger substrates.

This chapter outlines the various types of changes which are now known to have occurred. So many data are currently becoming available that it is not possible to discuss all known examples of these various types in detail here.

## Particular localities

### *Rural*

The most intensively studied rural site in which drastic changes have been observed is Epping Forest, Essex, to the north-east of London. Edward Forster (1765–1849) was the first lichenologist to examine the area and he made collections and notes mainly between 1784 and 1796 (Laundon, 1967, p. 306) which are preserved in the British Museum (Natural History) herbarium and library. Fifteen of the more interesting of his records were published by Turner and Dillwyn (1805, p. 289) and Crombie (1885, p. 55) lists a further forty species mentioned in his notebooks.

Crombie studied the Forest on two separate occasions, between 1865 and 1868, and later between 1881 and 1882. Crombie (1885) lists 171 species from all habitats of which 85 '. . . are to be expunged from the present lichen-flora of the Forest'. In the interval between the end of Forster's collecting and Crombie's first visit no fewer than 45 had disappeared, and between Crombie's first and later visits a further 40 also vanished. Crombie noted that it would be of interest for some lichenologist to study the Forest again in 50 or 100 years. Stimulated by Crombie's paper, Paulson and Thompson (1911, 1913, 1920) studied the area between 1909 and 1919. These authors discovered 129 species, including some not mentioned by Crombie, of which 49 were on trees. By this time the epiphytic flora was becoming very monotonous and Paulson and Thompson (1913, p. 93) speak of *Lecanora conizaeoides* as '. . . universally met with clothing the trunks and branches of trees . . .' and giving entire *Crataegus* bushes a '. . . dense tomentose fur . . .' In 1969–70 only 28 species occurred on trees and most of those only very rarely and in poor condition.

This wealth of information on Epping Forest enables the

decline of its epiphytic lichen flora to be correlated with the scale of Hawksworth and Rose (1970; ch 3, Table 1). This comparison is made in Table 1 in which the zone values in parenthesis refer

*Table 1 Changes in the epiphytic lichen flora of Epping Forest with reference to the zonal scale of Hawksworth and Rose (1970)*

| Collector(s) | Dates | Number of species | Zone(s) | Mean winter sulphur dioxide equivalents in µg/m³ (approx.) |
|---|---|---|---|---|
| Forster | 1784–96 | 55[1] | 9 or 10 | <30 |
| Crombie | 1865–68 | 120[1] | 7 | 40 |
| Crombie | 1881–82 | 86[1] | 5(6) | 50–60 |
| Paulson and Thompson | 1909–19 | 49[2] | 4(5) | 60–70 |
| Rose and Pentecost | 1969–70 | 28[2] | 3(4) | 70–125 |

[1] all habitats [2] epiphytes only

to sites towards the north-eastern end of the Forest (i.e. that furthest from the centre of London) as significant differences occur along the line north-east from Walthamstow. In 1969–70, for example, although 28 species were still present on trees, most occurred only in the extreme north-eastern parts of the Forest beyond Epping town and only six were discovered in the main Forest nearer London. The past and present lichen floras of this Forest are compared in Table 2 from which it can be seen that of the 118 epiphytic species reported at various times over the last 170 years 90 are now extinct.

Similar changes are also known to have taken place in other established woodland and parkland areas in regions which have also become subjected to increasing sulphur dioxide pollution of the air. A considerable amount of information is available on Gopsall Park, Leicestershire, which was studied by the Rev. A. Bloxam who was the vicar of Twycross between 1839 and 1871 (Rev. J. A. MacDonogh, *in litt.*). Bloxam's manuscript notes are housed in the British Museum (Natural History) and his specimens are preserved in that Museum and Leicester City Museum. The data on this Park have been analysed by Sowter and Hawks-

*Arthonia radiata* C
A. spadicea
*A. tumidula* C
*Arthopyrenia biformis* C
*A. gemmata* P
*A. punctiformis* F
*Bacidia rubella* C
*B. sphaeroides* F
*Biatorella moriformis* C
*Buellia alboatra* P
B. canescens
B. punctata
*Calicium abietinum* P
*C. quercinum* P
C. salicinum
*C. viride* C
*Caloplaca aurantiaca* C
*C. ferruginea* F
*C. luteoalba* C
*Candelaria concolor* C
*Candelariella vitellina* P
Catillaria griffithii
*C. lightfootii* F
*Chaenotheca chrysocephala* C
C. ferruginea
*Cladonia caespiticia* C
C. chlorophaea
C. coniocraea
*C. fimbriata* P
*C. furcata* P
C. macilenta
*C. ochrochlora* P
*C. polydactyla* C
*C. pyxidata* P
*C. squamosa* P
*Collema fragrans* C
*Coniocybe furfuracea* P
*Cyphelium inquinans* P
*C. tigillare* F
Enterographa crassa
*Evernia prunastri* P
*Graphis elegans* P
G. scripta
Hypogymnia physodes
*Lecanactis premnea* C
?*Lecanora allophana* P
*L. carpinea* F
L. chlarotera
L. conizaeoides
*L. dispersa* P
L. expallens
*L. pallida* C
?*L. parisiensis* F
*L. varia* P
Lecidea granulosa
L. quernea
*L. scalaris* P
L. uliginosa
*Lecidella elaeochroma* C
Lepraria incana
*Leptogium lichenoides* F
*L. tenuissimum* C
*Lobaria pulmonaria* F
*Micarea denigrata* C
*Ochrolechia parella* C
*O. turneri* C
Opegrapha atra
*O. herbarum* C
*O. lyncea* C
*O. niveoatra* F
*O. pulicaris* C
*O. rufescens* C
*O. varia* C
O. vulgata
*Parmelia acetabulum* F
*P. caperata* P
*P. glabratula* P
?*P. perlata* P
P. saxatilis
*P. subaurifera* C
*P. subrudecta* P
P. sulcata
*Peltigera canina* P
*P. polydactyla* C
*Pertusaria albescens* C
*P. amara* P
*P. flavida* C
P. hymenea
P. leioplaca
P. pertusa
*Phaeographis dendritica* C
*P. inusta* C
*Phlyctis agelaea* C
*P. argena* C
*Physcia caesia* P
?*P. clementii* F
*P. orbicularis* F
*P. tenella* P
*Physciopsis adglutinata* C
*Physconia grisea* C
*P. pulverulenta* F, ?P
*Platismatia glauca* P
Pyrenula nitidella
*Ramalina calicaris* C
*R. farinacea* C
*R. fastigiata* C
*R. fraxinea* C
*R. pollinaria* C
*Rinodina exigua* C
*R. roboris* C
Schismatomma decolorans
*Thelotrema lepadinum* P
*Toninia caradocensis* C
*Usnea ? hirta* C
*U. subfloridana* P
*Xanthoria aureola* P
*X. candelaria* P
*X. parietina* P

F: last seen by Forster, 1784–96; C: last seen by Crombie, 1865–82; P: last seen by Paulson and Thompson, 1909–19
italic type: not found in 1969–70 ?: identification possibly erroneous

worth (1970, p. 95) who found that of the 106 corticolous species recorded by Bloxam only 12 were present in 1968–9.

It is evident from the old records that declines of this type have also taken place in Sherwood Forest (Nottinghamshire), Chatsworth Park (Derbyshire), Bradgate Park (Leicestershire), Lyme Park (Cheshire), etc. Less drastic changes have occurred in similar sites affected by lower sulphur dioxide levels ($<c$ 70 $\mu g/m^3$). Only the more sensitive species have, for example, disappeared from Levens Park, near Kendal, Westmorland (Rose, Hawksworth and Coppins, 1970, p. 55).

Laundon (1958) discovered 48 corticolous and lignicolous species at Bookham Common, a rural site near Leatherhead, Surrey, immediately to the south-west of the London conurbation, between 1953 and 1956. In 1969 Mr P. A. Stott and one of us (F. Rose) refound only 15 species on trees and many of them appeared to have decreased in frequency since 1953–6. Mr J. R. Laundon revisited this site in February 1972 and confirmed this view. In this period smoke emissions from London decreased significantly while mean sulphur dioxide levels increased.

In contrast, open woodland and parkland sites in areas which now have mean winter sulphur dioxide levels of less than about 30 $\mu g/m^3$ retain floras almost identical to those they had last century. The New Forest, Hampshire, for example, has 250 extant corticolous species; Crombie found at least 133 between *c* 1890 and 1900 and although 21 discovered by Crombie have not been refound, many species not discovered by him occur. In Sussex, the Parks studied by William Borrer (1781–1862) still have rich floras; Ashburnham Park and Eridge Park, for example, now have 150 and 172 corticolous species, respectively. Lowther Park, Westmorland, studied by Martindale (1886–90), also appears to be almost unchanged (Rose, Hawksworth and Coppins, 1970, p. 53) and the northern Lake District is so similar that the comments of Winch (1833) on the distribution and frequency of many species are still largely correct some 140 years later.

Other parkland sites in areas which now have mean winter sulphur dioxide levels below about 35 $\mu g/m^3$ contain large numbers of species. Melbury Park (Dorset) has 171 corticolous species, Savernake Forest (Wiltshire) 108, Cranborne Chase

(Wiltshire) 133, Boconnoc Park (Cornwall) 181, and Brampton Bryan Park (Herefordshire) 101. The Slapton area (Devonshire), which lacks any very ancient trees, has, nevertheless, 167 corticolous species (Hawksworth, 1972).

From these data it is evident that an established ancient parkland with many ancient *Quercus* and *Ulmus* trees in England in an area affected by low mean levels of sulphur dioxide may be expected to have 80 to 130 or more corticolous species. Numbers of this order formerly occurred in sites such as Epping Forest (118) and Gopsall Park (106) which are now affected by much higher levels of this pollutant. It is therefore clear that the number of corticolous species present in an area of open woodland or parkland, including many ancient trees, provides some indication of the extent to which air pollution has affected it. The different areas of sites makes comparison difficult so in Fig. 1 we have estimated the number of corticolous species present per 1 km square for selected exposed (i.e. not ravine) parkland sites in England and Wales in 1969–71. From this Figure it is evident that the number of species in sites standardized in this way decreases as all major urban and industrial areas are approached.

*Urban*

Characteristics of the lichen flora in urban areas have already been discussed in chapter 6 and so are referred to only briefly here. More data are available on London (Laundon, 1967, 1970) than any other English city and this has been discussed in ch 6. The area immediately to the south of London is discussed further in chapter 4. Johnson (1632, 1638), however, found lichens which must have been conspicuous in the Hampstead and Tottenham areas; Sherard (*in* Ray, 1724) discovered some further taxa (e.g. in Greenwich); and Forster, whose work has already been referred to (p. 331), noted many species in the Walthamstow area. Of 165 species recorded for the London area 71 have been since 1950 but only 15 of these 71 are corticolous or lignicolous (Laundon, 1970; Coppins, unpublished). Some changes in the London area have occurred more recently. The *Hypogymnia physodes* found in 1957 by Laundon on *Ulmus* in Mill Hill (Barnet) has now disappeared; in 1969 it was discovered on *Betula* on Harrow Weald Common but by 1971 several of the plants seen in 1969 had been lost. Some of the corticolous species found by Bailey (1963) in the Ruislip area now also seem to have disappeared. *Parmelia caperata* was common south of Banstead in *c* 1930 (E. C. Wallace, *in litt.*) but has now gone from that area. In central London, sulphur dioxide levels have been falling in recent years and Laundon (1970, p. 28) reported that the frequency of *Lecanora conizaeoides* on trees in Holland Park (Kensington & Chelsea) increased between 1953 and 1967.

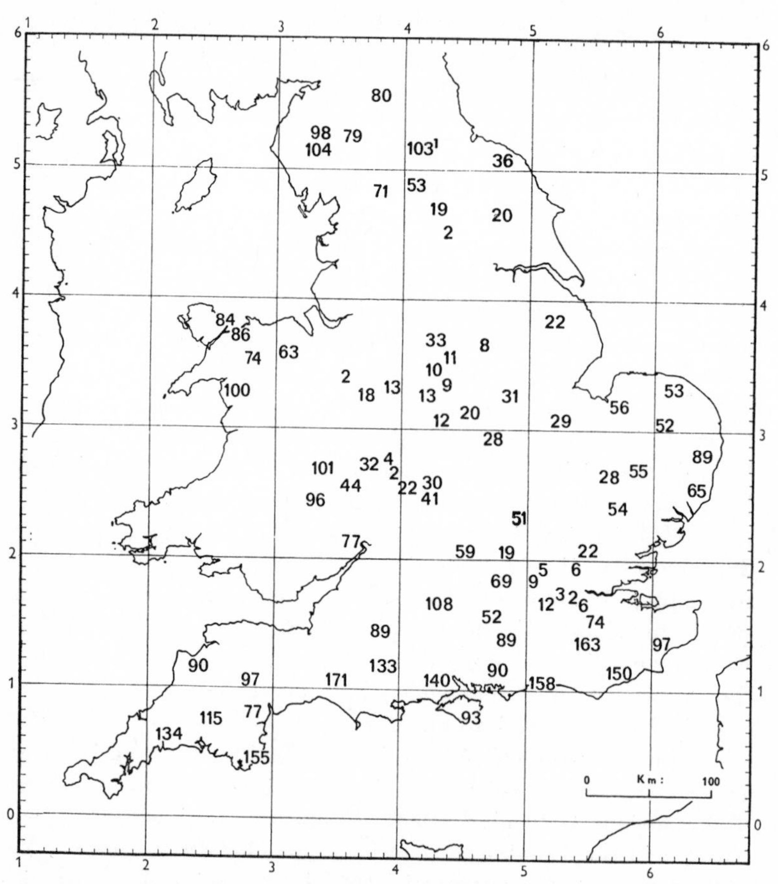


Fig. 1 Approximate number of corticolous species per km² in exposed parkland sites in England and Wales in 1969–71 (¹: includes some records from a ravine)

Edgbaston Park, Birmingham, was presumably a relatively rural site when visited by Dillenius in the early eighteenth century and then contained species such as *Pseudevernia furfuracea*. Specimens of *Anaptychia ciliaris*, *Bacidia rubella*, *Caloplaca cerina* and *Physconia pulverulenta* were present in this Park at least towards the middle of that century (Crombie, 1773–4). The area surrounding the Park is now built up and in 1967 only two crustaceous lichens occurred on trees in the Park. To the south-west of Birmingham at Hartlebury Common, near Kidderminster, Rhodes (1931) reported that *Physcia orbicularis* was '. . . in fine condition on *Aesculus* in 1927 but had disappeared by 1930'. In the south Lancashire and Manchester areas declines have been noted by Grindon (1859), Wheldon and Travis (1915), Savidge (1963) and Tallis (1964). Mr A. E. Wade found many species in the Braunstone area of Leicester between 1914 and 1920 (specimens in Leicester City Museum) which have since disappeared and Mr F. A. Sowter (*in litt.*) has observed a decline in the frequency of *Lecanora conizaeoides* in some parts of that city between 1950 and 1969.

Dr W. B. Johnson (1764?–1830) noted *Parmelia caperata*, *Physcia* cf *aipolia* and *Usnea* cf *subfloridana* '. . . betwixt Coxbench and Derby' (Pilkington, 1789, pp. 477–9) in an area which is now partly built up. In the Trent valley, particularly around Burton-upon-Trent, Edwin Brown (1818–76) informs us (*in* Mosley, 1863) that *Evernia prunastri*, *Ramalina calicaris* and *Usnea* were 'very common'. In 1966–8 no fruticose or foliose lichens occurred on trees within 8 km of the centre of Burton-upon-Trent.

Jonathan Salt (1759–1810) discovered many luxuriant specimens of foliose and fruticose lichens in the vicinity of Sheffield (Hawksworth, 1967) which have since disappeared. Air pollution control in Sheffield over the last ten years has, however, led to a slight improvement of the lichen vegetation on walls in some of the suburbs to the south-west of the centre of that city (Hawksworth, 1969, p. 110).

Laundon (1957) discovered 28 corticolous species in woods near Corby, Northamptonshire, but expansion of that town and the resultant increases in sulphur dioxide emissions from it have led to a reduction in the lichen flora.

Some changes in the luxuriance, fertility and distribution of species in the Newcastle upon Tyne area since 1807 are discussed by Gilbert (1968*c*, 1970*a*).

It is therefore clear that the lichen flora in and around urban areas in England has deteriorated drastically since the mid- and later decades of the nineteenth century but that where mean sulphur dioxide values have been reduced slightly in recent years minor improvements in the lichen vegetation have been noted.

Similar declines have been reported in other European cities in this same period (*cf* Barkman, 1958, 1961, 1964; Haugsjå, 1930; Schmid, 1956; Skye, 1968; Tobler, 1921). Andrews (1928) noted a decline of lichens in Indiana, USA, over a period of twenty years; Vareschi (*in litt.*) has observed a decline in Caracas, Venezuela, since 1953 (Vareschi, 1953); and Rydzak (1969) found a deterioration in the lichen vegetation of Lublin since 1948–52 (Rydzak, 1954; *see* also ch 7).

*Industrial*

Griffith (1966) studied a 6.4 km transect in rural areas to the west of the Consett iron and steel works in Co. Durham and found changes in the number and percentage cover of particular species on trees. In rural areas near the steel works to the north-east of Sheffield only one crustaceous lichen, *Lecanora conizaeoides*, occurs on trees and that rarely.

Gilbert (1971*a*) studied the effects of increasing sulphur dioxide emissions from a recently opened power station at Blyth on the Northumberland coast on wall-top colonies of *Parmelia saxatilis*. In permanent quadrats the percentage cover of this species decreased from about 40–50 per cent in 1964 to about 5 per cent in 1970 on walls 2.5 km north of the power station. Readings from volumetric gauges nearby showed a steady increase in mean annual sulphur dioxide levels from *c* 100 $\mu g/m^3$ in 1966 to *c* 150 $\mu g/m^3$ in 1970. Sulphur emissions from a rurally situated gas-making plant at Ambergate, Derbyshire, are causing this species to decline in a similar way there also. The effects of the Fawley oil refinery, Hampshire, are discussed in chapter 5.

Sulphur dioxide emissions from the tall stacks of power stations appear to be responsible for the paucity of lichen vegetation for many miles around them. That at Richborough, near Sandwich, Kent, for example, is certainly responsible for the absence of many species from an area of *c* 8.5 km around it. The chain of power stations along the Trent valley in the Midlands have comparable effects but extending over distances of at least 47 km (30 miles) to the east and north-east; an effect accentuated by the relatively high 'background' levels of this pollutant in the area.

Industrial sites may have more effect than moderately-sized towns. A park one mile east of Maidstone, Kent (a town with about 70 000 inhabitants), for example, has 45 corticolous species while trees in open situations three miles north-east of the nearby Aylesford paper works (which emit large amounts of sulphur dioxide) bear only one corticolous species. These paper works are situated four miles north-west of Maidstone.

Fluoride emissions from industrial plants have very severe but much more strictly localized effects as compared with sulphur dioxide emissions, and these are discussed in chapter 9.

While industrial sites producing gaseous pollutants have marked effects on lichens, rurally situated plants not emitting gases toxic to lichens have no significant effect. Lichen vegetation of zones 8 and 10 of Hawksworth and Rose (1970), for example, occur close to the Dungeness (Kent) and Dounreay (Caithness) nuclear power stations respectively.

The effect of industrial plants emitting gaseous pollutants on the adjacent lichen vegetation has also been noted in North America (LeBlanc and Rao, 1966; LeBlanc, Rao and Comeau, 1972; Nash, 1971*a*,*b*; Rao and LeBlanc, 1967), Sweden (Moberg, 1968; Skye, 1958), Poland (Kozik, 1970; Rydzak and Piórecki, 1971; Rydzak and Stasiak, 1971), France (Martin and Jacquard, 1968), Czechoslovakia (Pišút, 1962) and the USSR (Piterans, 1968).

**Particular species**

The past and present distribution of some 70 corticolous species have been mapped by us although most of these maps are as yet unpublished. Many species have been lost from areas which have been subjected to increasing sulphur dioxide levels in the air over the last century. Examples of species which are either very rare or now extinct in areas of England and Wales with mean winter sulphur dioxide values exceeding *c* 65 $\mu g/m^3$ are given in

Table 3. A few other species, however, now appear to be much more common than they were last century in affected areas. The different degrees of sensitivity of lichens to air pollution have been widely employed in studies concerned with the assessment of air pollution levels (*see* ch 3). It is not possible to discuss all the species listed in Table 3 in detail and only a few examples selected so as to be representative of differing degrees of sensitivity and tolerance to sulphur dioxide in the air will be treated more fully.

*Table 3 Examples of corticolous species which have become very rare or extinct in areas of England which now have mean winter $SO_2$ values of over* c *65 $\mu g/m^3$*

| | | |
|---|---|---|
| *Alectoria fuscescens* | *Graphis elegans* | *Pertusaria* spp. |
| *Anaptychia ciliaris* | *G. scripta* | *Phaeographis dendritica* |
| *Arthonia impolita* | *Gyalecta* spp. | *Physcia aipolia* |
| *A. radiata* | *Lecanactis premnea* | *Physciopsis adglutinata* |
| *A. spadicea* | *Lecania cyrtella* | *Physconia pulverulenta* |
| *A. tumidula* | *Lecanora chlarotera* | *Platismatia glauca* |
| *Arthopyrenia biformis* | *Lecidella elaeochroma* | *Porina* spp. |
| *A. gemmata* | *Lepraria candelaris* | *Pseudevernia furfuracea* |
| *A. punctiformis* | *Leptogium* spp. | *Pyrenula nitida* |
| *Bacidia endoleuca* | *Lobaria amplissima* | *Ramalina calicaris* |
| *B. naegelii* | *L. laetevirens* | *R. fastigiata* |
| *B. rubella* | *L. pulmonaria* | *R. fraxinea* |
| *Buellia alboatra* | *L. scrobiculata* | *R. obtusata* |
| *Calicium abietinum* | *Nephroma laevigatum* | *Rinodina exigua* |
| *C. viride* | *Ochrolechia yasudae* | *R. roboris* |
| *Caloplaca aurantiaca*[1] | *Opegrapha atra* | *Schismatomma decolorans* |
| *C. cerina* | *O. niveoatra* | *Sphaerophorus fragilis* |
| *C. holocarpa*[1] | *O. prosodea* | *S. globosus* |
| *C. luteoalba* | *O. vulgata* | *Sticta* spp. |
| *Candelaria concolor* | *Pachyphiale cornea* | *Teloschistes flavicans* |
| *Cetraria chlorophylla* | *Parmelia acetabulum* | *Thelotrema lepadinum* |
| *Collema* spp.[1] | *P. caperata* | *Toninia caradocensis* |
| *Coniocybe furfuracea* | *P. exasperata* | *Usnea articulata* |
| *Cyphelium inquinans* | *P. perlata* | *U. ceratina* |
| *Desmazieria evernioides* | *P. revoluta* | *U. florida* |
| *Dimerella diluta* | *P. subaurifera* | *U. rubiginea* |
| *Enterographa crassa* | *Parmeliopsis aleurites* | *U. subfloridana* |
| *Evernia prunastri* | *Peltigera horizontalis* | *Xanthoria polycarpa* |

[1] able to withstand higher mean winter sulphur dioxide levels when growing on calcareous rocks

The maps presented here of some of these species (Figs. 2–10) are based on a compilation of all field, herbarium and reliable literature reports known to us, and also include data from the British Lichen Society's Distribution Maps Scheme. Ireland and Scotland have been omitted in some cases because of a lack of detailed information and in the interpretation of the maps it is important to bear this in mind. Also, some areas of England and Wales have received less attention than most (i.e. W. Cornwall, N. Somerset, N.E. Cumberland, Isle of Man, Carmarthenshire, Cardiganshire and Montgomeryshire) and so the absence of records from these areas is of little significance. The lack of any records from well-worked regions such as the Midland counties, north-east England, East Anglia and the London area is, conversely, highly significant.

Further information on the distribution of some of the species treated here in south-east England is given in chapter 4, and around an isolated industrial plant in Hampshire in chapter 5.

*Usnea* spp.

The pendent corticolous fruticose yellow-green and greyish-green lichens of the genus *Usnea* are conspicuous and consequently well represented in herbaria and frequently referred to in the literature. Because of taxonomic problems it is convenient first of all to consider the genus as a whole.

Smith and Sowerby (1804, p. 1354) indicate that at least one species was 'extremely common' and this report is the essence of most nineteenth-century references to the frequency of the species of this genus. Bohler (*in* Howitt, 1839, p. 111) speaks of them as 'frequent' in Nottinghamshire, Abbot (1798, p. 270) as 'common' in Bedfordshire, Garner (1844, p. 432) as 'common on trees' in Staffordshire, and Brown's (*in* Mosley, 1863) report of them being 'common about Burton-upon-Trent' has already been referred to. From the works of Grindon (1859) and Crombie (1869, p. 406) it is evident that species of this genus were beginning to decline in Middlesex and south Lancashire by the mid-nineteenth century, but in other parts of the country they still seem to have been common into the first decade of the twentieth century. Amplett and Rea (1909, p. 491), for example, speak of them as 'general' in Worcestershire; Bloomfield (1905,

p. 124) reports them as 'common' in Norfolk and Suffolk; and Paulson (1919) lists several Hertfordshire localities.

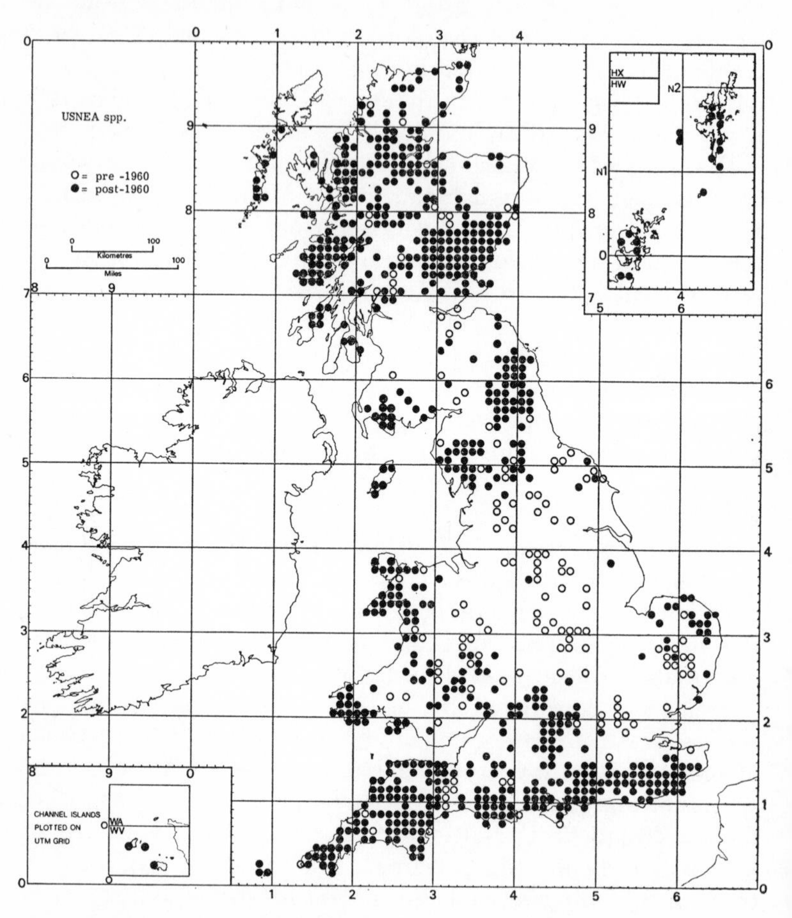


Fig. 2 Pre- and post-1960 distribution of *Usnea* spp. in the British Isles (excluding Ireland)

The past and present distributions of this genus are compared in Fig. 2 from which it is evident that *Usnea* species have almost completely disappeared from areas which now have mean winter sulphur dioxide values over *c* 50 $\mu g/m^3$.

The most sensitive British species of *Usnea* is *U. articulata.*

Large specimens of this species formerly occurred in sites now over 100 miles from its present nearest stations. A specimen collected by T. Willisell, probably in 1675–95 'In Lancastria prope *Burnley* pagum e Corylo', preserved in the Sherard herbarium in Oxford, measures 30 cm long. There are several late eighteenth- and early nineteenth-century records from near Halifax, west Yorkshire (Watling, 1967, p. 37), and a Mr Bradbury found it on 'old oaks . . . in plenty' at Lyme Park immediately to the south-south-east of Manchester (Turner and Dillwyn, 1805, p. 123). It also used to occur on oak in Whittlebury Forest, Northamptonshire (Morton, 1712; Turner and Dillwyn, 1805, p. 466), at Bagley in Berkshire (Bowen, 1968, p. 77), Gattely Park in Herefordshire (Dillenius, 1741, p. 61), and Wangford Warren in Suffolk (Bloomfield, 1905, p. 124). Specimens 20–25 cm long from Enfield Chase, Middlesex, only 16.5 km north of the centre of London, are preserved in the herbarium of the British Museum (Natural History), and a note on one of these reads 'common'. There are also several references to its occurrence at Stokenchurch Woods, Oxfordshire, some 57 km to the west of London and now about 9 km from the centre of High Wycombe where it was probably first noted by Dillenius (1741, p. 61). It formerly used to extend into east Sussex and was collected near Tunbridge Wells and West Hoathly by W. Borrer (specimens in herb. Borrer at Kew) but is now apparently extinct east of the New Forest, Hampshire, where it is now also extremely rare.

In contrast this species is still widely distributed in England in areas where it was also common last century (*cf* Turner and Dillwyn, 1805, p. 234), particularly Devon and Dorset where its frequency does not appear to have altered significantly in the last 170 years. In the Bodmin and Holsworthy areas of N.E. Cornwall and N.W. Devon it is still one of the commonest lichens on roadside hedges and trees and commonly has fronds 40–65 cm long. One specimen 94.5 cm long was discovered in Devon in 1971. It is interesting to note, however, that *U. articulata* has not been refound on Braunton Burrows in north Devon where it occurred last century; the centre of Braunton Burrows, whose calcicolous terricolous lichen flora has not altered appreciably at least over the last 60 years, is now about 3 km north-west of the

East Yelland Power Station. It is evident, therefore, that *U. articulata* was formerly widespread throughout England but has become restricted to areas which have mean winter sulphur dioxide values below about 30 $\mu g/m^3$.

*Usnea ceratina* has declined in a similar way to *U. articulata* but to a lesser extent and is still frequent in many parts of south-east England. It still extends into east Kent, where *U. articulata* is now extinct, and where mean winter sulphur dioxide levels are below *c* 40 $\mu g/m^3$.

The most tolerant species of *Usnea*, however, is *U. subfloridana* which accounts for almost all the recent records of this genus from Berkshire, Derbyshire, Gloucestershire, Lincolnshire, Norfolk, Northamptonshire, Suffolk, Warwickshire and Yorkshire. *U. subfloridana* was last seen in Leicestershire in 1941 (Sowter, 1950, p. 13), for example, while all other species of the genus had been lost from that county by about 1880. There were no recent records of this genus from Derbyshire in 1968 (Hawksworth, 1969, p. 169) but in March 1971 a few minute plants of *U. subfloridana* 5–8 mm tall were discovered in Lathkill Dale by M. S. Baddeley and O. L. Gilbert. There is no sulphur dioxide volumetric gauge near this site but two gauges in Buxton registered a significant drop in mean winter sulphur dioxide levels between 1967/8 and 1968/9; unfortunately no data are available for 1966/7 and 1969/70. Griffith (1966) only found rare stunted specimens of this species *c* 1 cm tall in cracks of *Quercus* bark 4.65 km west of the Consett iron and steel works in Co. Durham; and J. R. Laundon discovered a single specimen 1 cm tall at Wicken Fen, Cambridgeshire, in May 1972.

*Lobaria pulmonaria*

The past and present distributions of *Lobaria pulmonaria* are compared in Fig. 3 from which it is clear that this species has declined in a similar manner to *Usnea articulata*. Unfortunately many of the older records of this species are not accurately localized and it should be remembered that it has been reported from all English counties except Huntingdonshire, Middlesex, Norfolk and Northamptonshire (Hawksworth, Rose and Coppins, 1970, p. 54). In Cornwall, Cumberland, Devon, Dorset and south-west Hampshire it is probably as common as it was last century but it has disappeared from the areas affected by sulphur dioxide in the air.

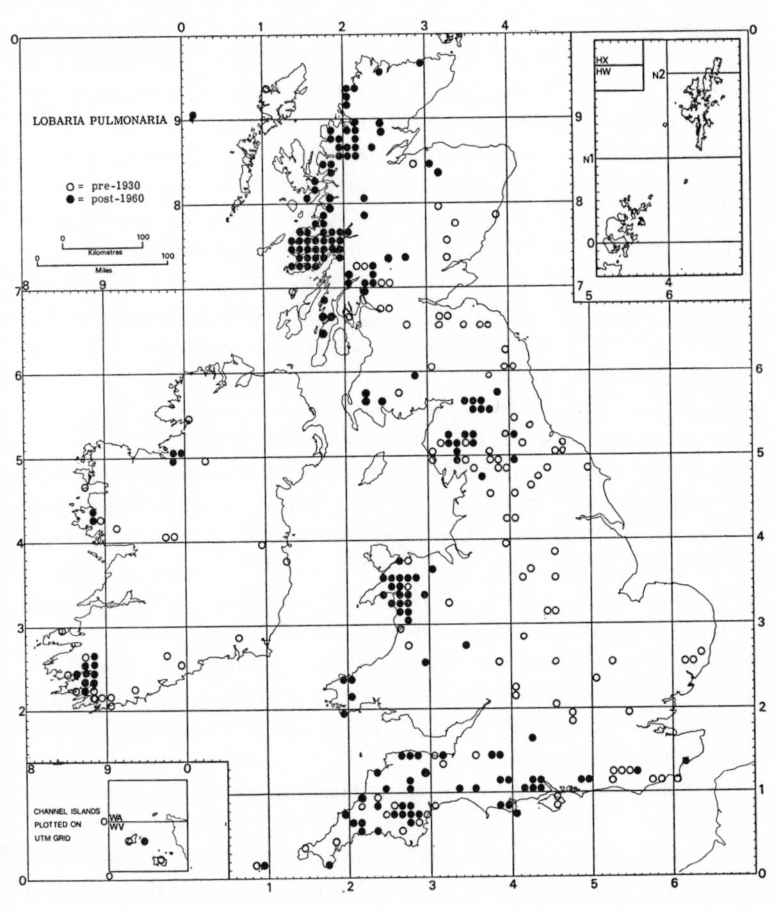


Fig. 3 Pre-1930 and post-1960 distribution of *Lobaria pulmonaria* in the British Isles

Brightman (1965, p. 5) considered that this species was 'oceanic' but many of the localities in which it occurred last century are not ones with high rainfall (e.g. Bedfordshire, Cambridgeshire, Lincolnshire, Nottinghamshire, Suffolk) and this species does not show the characteristic atlantic distribution patterns of, for example, *Parmelia laevigata* and *P. taylorensis*. Furthermore, *Lobaria pulmonaria* has a wide distribution in continental areas of Europe (*see* e.g. Grummann, 1963, p. 137), is circumboreal in the Northern Hemisphere (Yoshimura and Hawksworth, 1970, p. 38), and prefers markedly lower rainfall areas in Cumberland and Devon than those characterized by many 'atlantic' species. It is absent, for example, from the high-rainfall ancient oakwoods on Dartmoor but present in more lowland parkland sites of that county with lower rainfall.

The English distribution of this species is, however, also correlated with sites which have been continuously parkland or woodland for many centuries and it may be regarded as one of a group of lichens which appear to be 'old forest' indicator species. Consequently the modification of forests and the felling of ancient trees may have had some effect on the distribution of this species. Also, *Lobaria pulmonaria* was formerly collected and sold as a herbal cure for tuberculosis and bronchitis in, for example, the New Forest (Wise, 1894, p. 176), and this may also have been locally important, although in the New Forest this species is still luxuriant. Its disappearance from established woodland and parkland sites where it used to occur such as Epping Forest (Essex), Levens Park (Westmorland) and Sherwood Forest (Nottinghamshire) can only be explained with reference to increasing pollution of the air by sulphur dioxide. The sensitivity of this species to sulphur dioxide is indicated by the transplant experiments of Hawksworth (1971*b*). Material transplanted into a site where this species occurred last century in Derbyshire (now with zone 5 communities of Hawksworth and Rose, 1970) died over a period of 19 months showing symptoms characteristic of sulphur dioxide damage, whereas specimens transplanted into a relatively unaffected area of Hampshire (zone 8 of Hawksworth and Rose, 1970) still survive and have produced new growth.

The decline of this species in the Black Forest has been discussed by Wilmanns (1966) and Wirth (1968) who concluded that the felling of ancient trees and air pollution were responsible. Pišút (1971) prepared maps of the pre-1940 and post-1940 distribution of this species in Czechoslovakia which show a decline parallel to that in the British Isles. Pišút considered air pollution and forestry to be the main factors responsible for this decline.

*Anaptychia ciliaris*

From Fig. 4 it can be seen that *Anaptychia ciliaris* has an eastern distribution in the British Isles becoming very rare in western counties. Last century it was present on trees in the London area, Cambridgeshire, Essex, south Lancashire, the Midlands, and

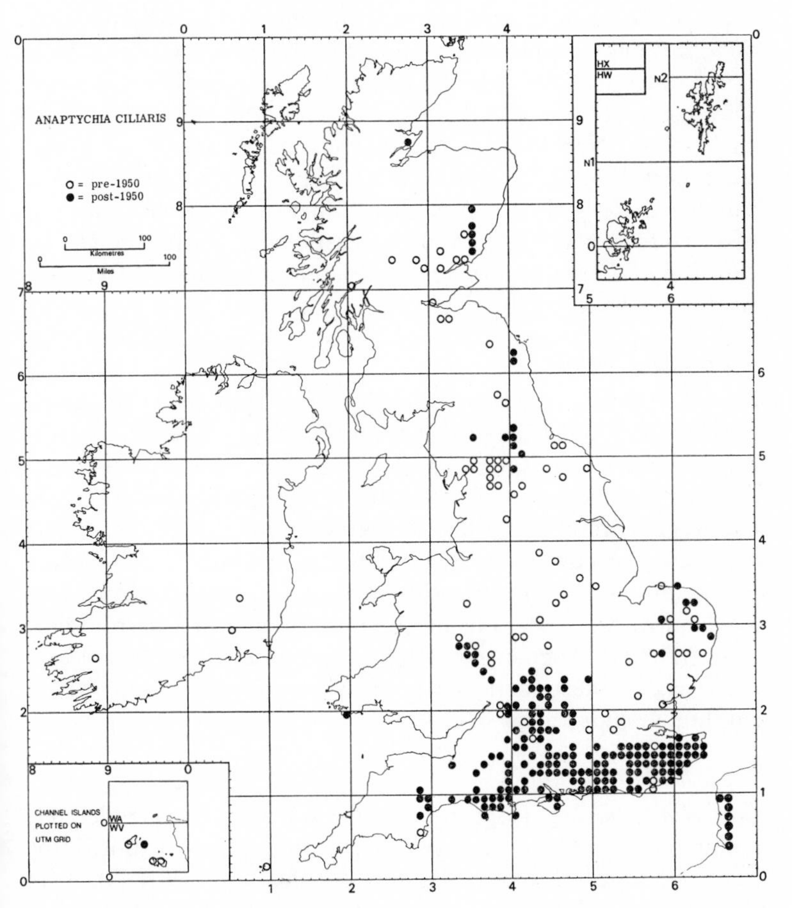


Fig. 4 Pre- and post-1950 distribution of *Anaptychia ciliaris* in the British Isles (excluding f. *saxicola*)

south and north-east Yorkshire, but is now absent from these areas. It should be noted that the grey-brown saxicolous form of this species (f. *saxicola*) which occurs on calcareous and maritime rocks is more tolerant and has been excluded from Fig. 4.

The grey-white corticolous form of this species (var. *ciliaris*) is characteristic of well-lit trees with eutrophiated barks by roadsides and in pastures and so its distribution cannot have been adversely affected by forest clearance. It is now absent from areas with mean winter sulphur dioxide levels of over about 50 $\mu g/m^3$ but is still local to common in those parts of its distributional range with levels below this figure (i.e. west Berkshire, east Devonshire, Dorset, Gloucestershire, Hampshire, Herefordshire, Kent, Norfolk, Oxfordshire, Sussex, Wiltshire and north-west Yorkshire). The map of the changes in the distribution of this species (Fig. 4) is very similar to that of the genus *Usnea* east of a line from south Devon to Newcastle upon Tyne. *Anaptychia ciliaris* and *Usnea subfloridana* both appear in zone 7 of Hawksworth and Rose (1970).

### *Parmelia perlata*

*Parmelia perlata* (Fig. 5) has declined in a similar way to *Anaptychia ciliaris* but has receded from the major conurbations to a much greater extent appearing only in areas with mean winter sulphur dioxide levels of below about 40 $\mu g/m^3$. The scarcity of old records from the Midlands may indicate that it was already very rare there by about 1870; i.e. that it had largely disappeared before the areas were investigated by lichenologists. In eastern England north of the Thames it survives only in a narrow zone near the East Anglian coast but is common in other areas in southern, western and northern England with mean winter sulphur dioxide values of less than about 35 $\mu g/m^3$.

### *Parmelia caperata*

*Parmelia caperata* (Fig. 6) extends further into moderately polluted areas of England (e.g. Cambridgeshire, Bedfordshire, Buckinghamshire, Essex, Huntingdonshire, E. Suffolk), with mean winter sulphur dioxide values below about 55 $\mu g/m^3$, than any of the species so far discussed. Like *Anaptychia ciliaris* it is a species of trees in well-lit situations but prefers non-eutrophiated bark. Last century it was often recorded in Leicestershire and in 1943 was still abundant in one wood in Rutland (Sowter,

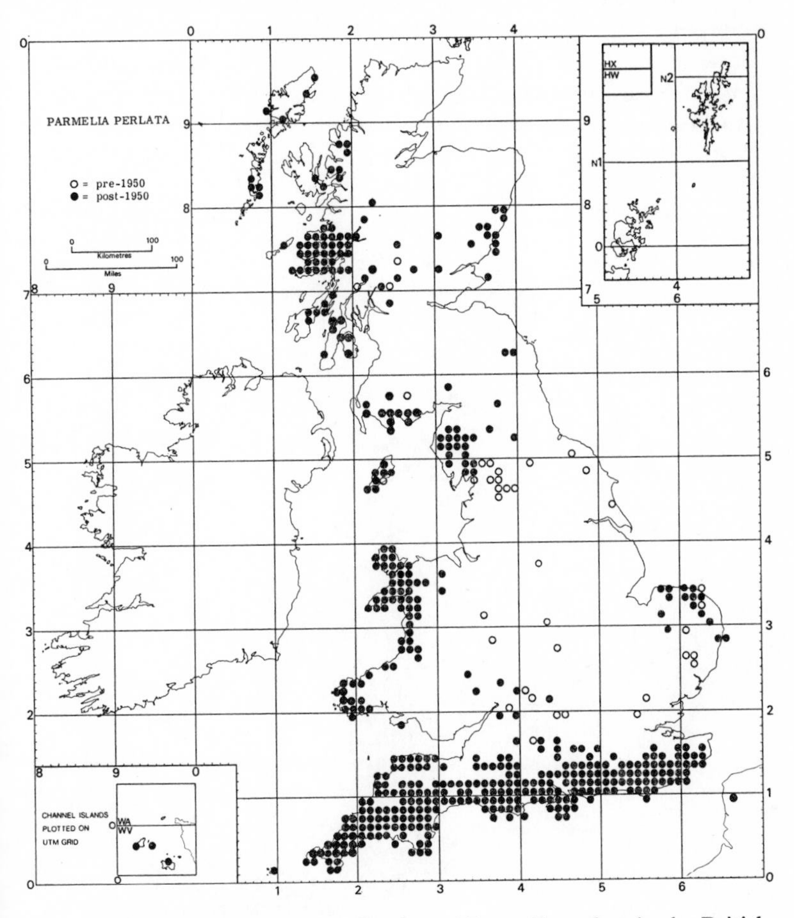


Fig. 5 Pre- and post-1950 distribution of *Parmelia perlata* in the British Isles (excluding Ireland)

1950, p. 14) but has now become extinct in these two counties (Sowter and Hawksworth, 1970, p. 96) as it has in Derbyshire (Hawksworth, 1969, p. 154). *P. caperata* was 'frequent on lower part of oak boles' at Bookham Common, Surrey, in 1953–6

(Laundon, 1958) but Laundon was unable to find any trace of it there in 1972. It should be noted that there are few old or recent records of this species from Durham, Northumberland, north Yorkshire, and central and eastern Scotland and its rarity in relatively unpolluted areas in these regions seems to be related to climatic factors causing the replacement of the *Parmelietum revolutae* var. *caperatosum* by the *Parmelietum furfuraceae* on well-lit trees with moderately acidic barks.

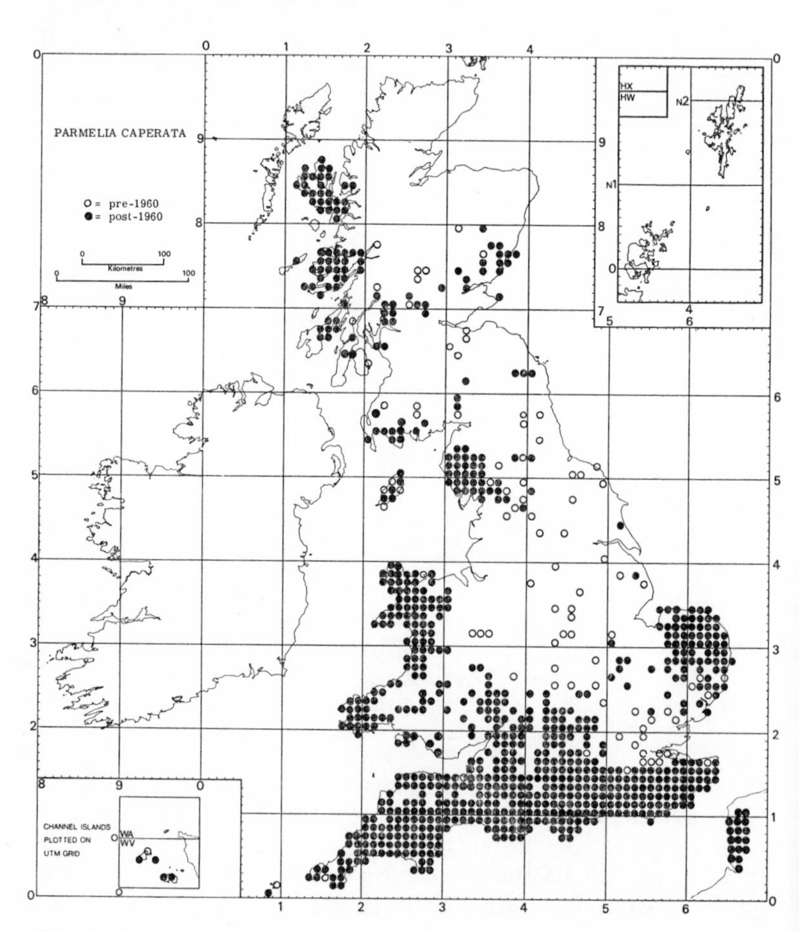


Fig. 6 Pre- and post-1960 distribution of *Parmelia caperata* in the British Isles (excluding Ireland)

*Ramalina* spp.

The genus *Ramalina* (Fig. 7) includes species with different degrees of tolerance to sulphur dioxide pollution in the air (*cf* Hawksworth and Rose, 1970). *R. farinacea* is the only one which

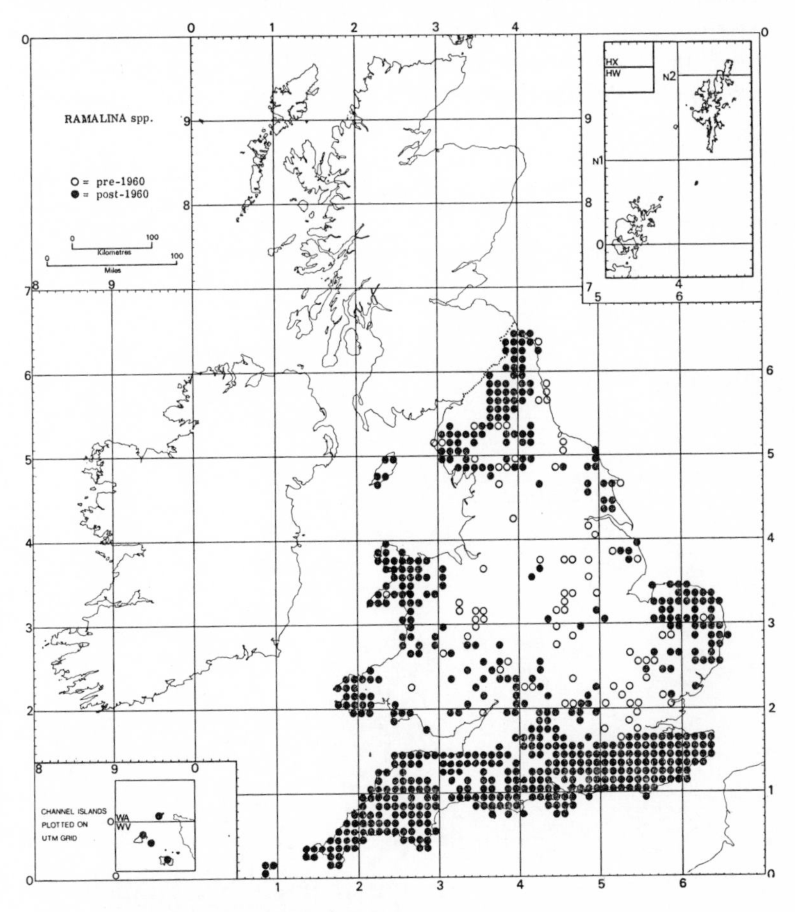


Fig. 7 Pre- and post-1960 distribution of *Ramalina* spp. in the British Isles (excluding Ireland and Scotland)

is still present in the Midland counties although other corticolous species of the genus were also once common there. Bloxam (MS) noted that 'all the varieties are common' in Leicestershire last century but now only *R. farinacea* remains. Similarly, in Northamptonshire, Laundon (1956, p. 92) observed that 'Species of *Ramalina*, common years ago in the County are now quite rare, . . . and only *Ramalina farinacea* has been recorded in recent years.' *R. farinacea* is also the only species to have been found in Derbyshire recently (Hawksworth, 1969, p. 163).

While *R. farinacea* is placed in zone 5 of Hawksworth and Rose (1970) the other corticolous species of this genus (i.e. *R. calicaris*,

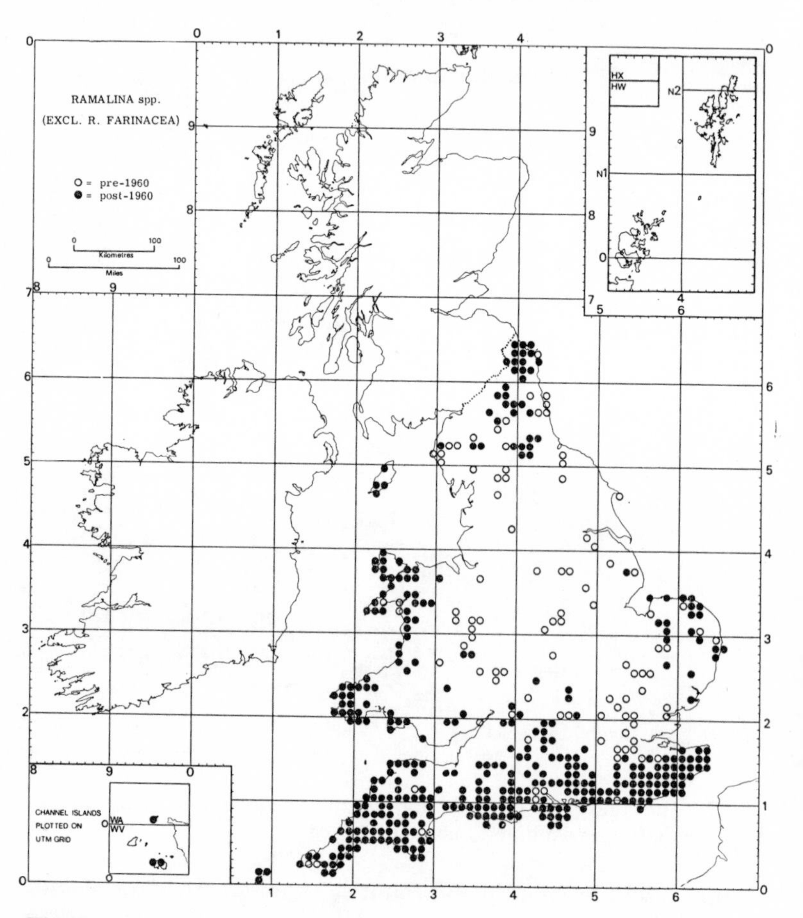


Fig. 8 Pre- and post-1960 distribution of *Ramalina* spp. (excluding *R. farinacea*) in the British Isles (excluding Ireland and Scotland)

*R. fastigiata*, *R. fraxinea*, *R. obtusata* and *R. subfarinacea*) occur only in zones 7–10. Consequently when *R. farinacea* is excluded from Fig. 7 a map is produced (Fig. 8) similar to that for the genus *Usnea* (Fig. 2). It should be noted that Fig. 7 and Fig. 8 also include saxicolous species of *Ramalina* and *Desmazieria evernioides*.

### *Evernia prunastri*

*Evernia prunastri* is an ubiquitous species of well-lit trees in England and Wales with mean winter sulphur dioxide values of less than about 50 $\mu g/m^3$ but also occurs more rarely in areas where this value is in the range 50–65 $\mu g/m^3$ (Fig. 9). In many Midland counties where it is now rare or local it was common and widely distributed last century. Bohler (*in* Howitt, 1839, p. 111) reported it as 'very common' in Nottinghamshire, Brown (*in* Mosley, 1863) as 'very common' in the Burton-upon-Trent area, Mott *et al.* (1886, p. 230) as 'common' in Leicestershire, and Bradbury (*in* Withering, 1818, p. 52) as 'common' at Stalybridge, Manchester.

Stansfield (1910, p. 359) found that although 'formerly common' it was then rare in the Todmorden area of south Lancashire and has since been lost altogether from that region (Tallis, 1964, p. 251).

Today *Evernia prunastri* approaches industrial and urban areas more closely than any of the species so far discussed and still occurs in the least polluted parts of the Midland counties. This species has a similar distribution to *Ramalina farinacea* but appears to be slightly more tolerant than that species although both occur in zones 5–10 of Hawksworth and Rose (1970). Some transplant experiments with this species were carried out by Hawksworth (1969, p. 142) who found that specimens transplanted into an area affected by sulphur dioxide died more rapidly than those transplanted into a slightly less affected one.

### *Parmeliopsis ambigua*

Not all species of lichens have decreased in frequency as a result of increasing sulphur dioxide levels in the air. One corticolous species which now appears to be much more common in the Midland and south-eastern counties with mean winter sulphur dioxide levels in the range *c* 55–65 μg/m³ is *Parmeliopsis ambigua* (Fig. 10). This species was only rarely found in Leicestershire last century (Sowter, 1950, p. 17) but has since been reported

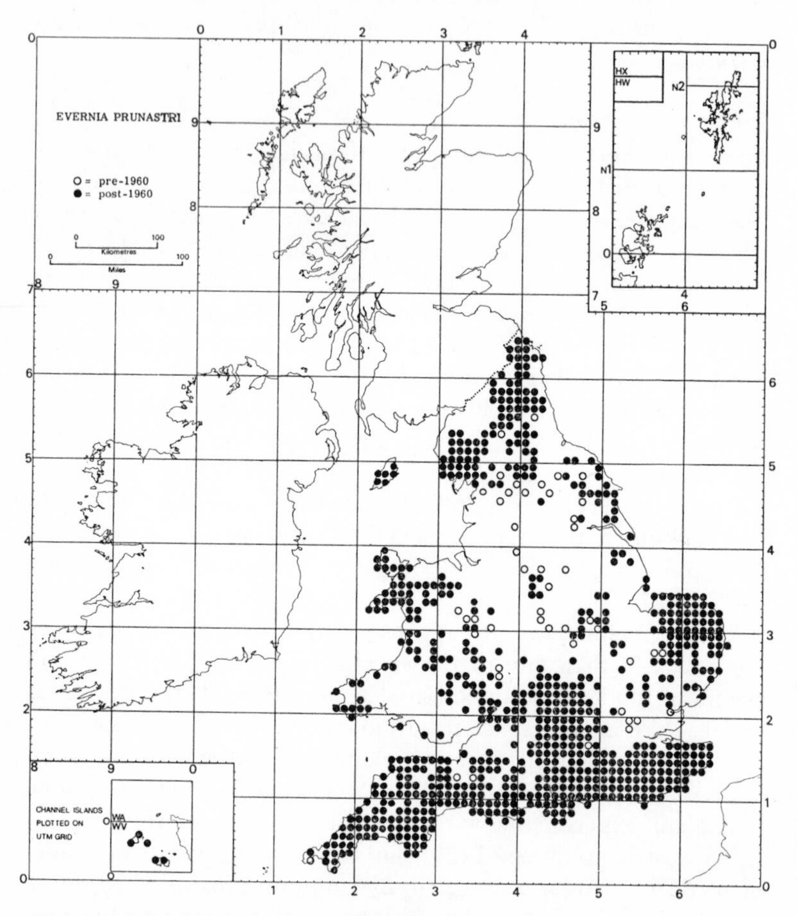


Fig. 9 Pre- and post-1960 distribution of *Evernia prunastri* in the British Isles (excluding Ireland and Scotland)

several times (Hawksworth and Sowter, 1969, p. 57; Sowter and Hawksworth, 1970, p. 98). There were no old records from Derbyshire at all but Hawksworth (1969, p. 156; unpublished) has now discovered it in 13 different 10 km squares in that county. In East Anglia it is not mentioned by Bloomfield (1905), there is only a single old record from Kent, and no early reports from Sussex. It is extremely rare in south-west England and

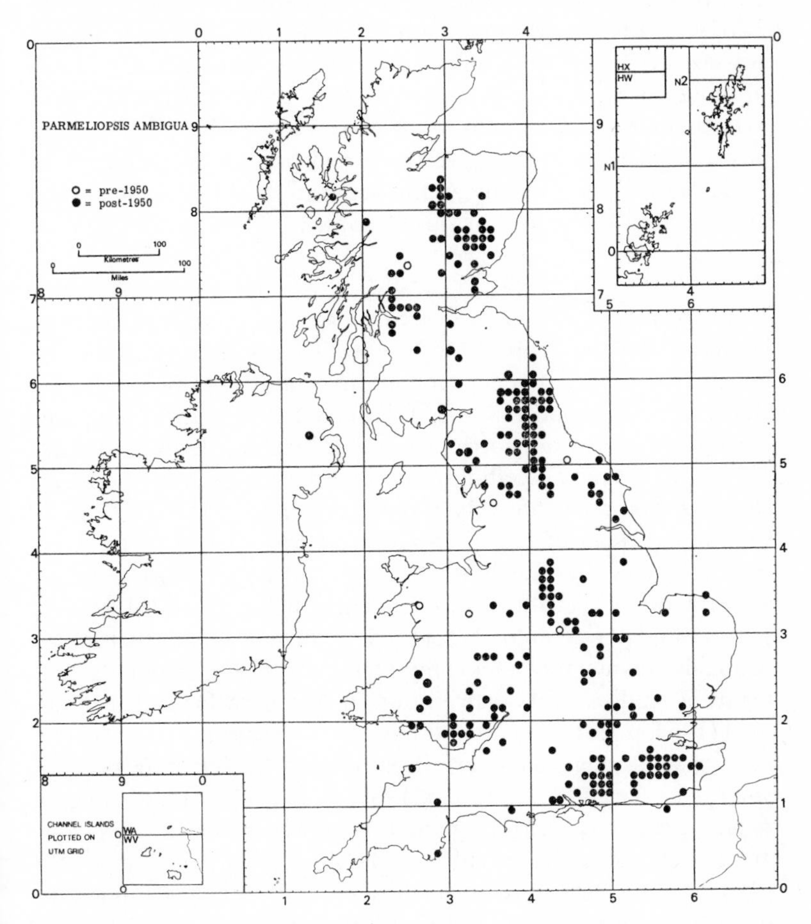


Fig. 10 Pre- and post-1950 distribution of *Parmeliopsis ambigua* in the British Isles

although known from three recent collections in Devonshire all these three are of small plants growing on lignum and not on bark; furthermore it now seems to have been lost from one of these three Devon sites (Hawksworth, 1972).

*Parmeliopsis ambigua* is a conspicuous yellow-green foliose species which is unlikely to have been overlooked in the past had it been present. Smith (1918, p. 135) indicates its habitat as '. . . trunks of old fir trees . . . and on old fir palings in upland districts'. In the Midland and south-eastern counties today, however, it occurs only on deciduous trees, lignum and (rarely) siliceous rocks. As coniferous trees tend to have barks of lower pH values than deciduous trees (Barkman, 1958, p. 108) it is probable that the lowering of the pH of bark of deciduous trees by sulphur dioxide in England in areas affected by this pollutant has favoured the spread of this species.

*Lecanora conizaeoides*

*Lecanora conizaeoides* was described as new to science by Nylander in 1885 and appears to be absent from all early European lichen collections. It was probably first discovered in Britain by Bloxam in the period 1839–71 in Leicestershire but was probably not uncommon to the north of London by about 1878 (Crombie, 1879) and is now exceedingly common in areas where the mean winter sulphur dioxide values are in the range 55–150 $\mu g/m^3$. A preliminary map of the distribution of this species in England was published by Kershaw (1963, p. 68) and a more detailed account of its distribution is currently being prepared by Mr J. R. Laundon (*see* ch 6). Ahti (1965, p. 92) considered that it was probably unknown from a completely natural environment. As a result of studies on its distribution in Northern Ireland, Brightman (1964, p. 261) suggested it might have a sulphur requirement and its subsequent discovery in a 'natural' habitat near sulphur springs in Iceland (Brightman, 1965, p. 7; Bailey, 1966) appears to support this view. In England it is, however, now known from areas with mean winter sulphur dioxide levels below about 30 $\mu g/m^3$ but is very rare in such sites and usually confined to palings, coniferous trees and small branches. Barkman (1969, p. 202) and Baddeley, Ferry and Finegan (1972) suggest that the relative non-wettability of this species may explain, at least in part, its resistance to sulphur dioxide in nature. It seems probable that the elimination of species with which *Lecanora conizaeoides* would have had to compete and its ability to tolerate sulphur dioxide levels in excess of those at which its competitors disappear accounts for its present abundance in England and Wales.

## Luxuriance and fertility

Reduction in luxuriance (i.e. cover and size of specimens) and fertility (i.e. frequency of production of ascocarps) are seen in sensitive species as sources of sulphur dioxide pollution are approached and before the species are eliminated altogether.

Luxuriance is most readily studied in the larger fruticose and foliose lichens and a superficial study of old herbarium material from areas which have since been subjected to this pollutant indicates how drastic such changes have been. In contrast, recent collections from relatively unaffected areas are often as luxuriant as those collected in the same areas last century. Specimens of *Usnea ceratina*, which are commonly 25–45 cm long in Devonshire and the New Forest, are much shorter in slightly polluted areas (<10 cm long), become contorted, and develop fewer lateral branches (i.e. 'var. *incurvescens*'). Similarly *U. subfloridana* is 4–8 cm long in unpolluted areas but may often be 1 cm or less in its closest stations to sulphur dioxide pollution sources (see p. 344). *Evernia* and species of *Ramalina* behave in a parallel manner becoming shorter and developing thinner lobes. Gilbert (1969, 1970*b*, 1970*c*) has demonstrated the changes in the sizes of specimens, percentage cover, and biomass of *Evernia prunastri* along an air pollution gradient from 13 to 30 km from the centre of Newcastle upon Tyne. Comparable differences have been described in these and other species in many other European countries (Barkman, 1958, 1961; Kovanen, 1961; Lundström, 1968; Skye, 1968).

The production of ascocarps is often related to the luxuriance of the specimens but this is not always the case. Hawksworth and Chapman (1971, p. 54) found that although 15 per cent of the British specimens of *Pseudevernia furfuracea* in the British Museum (Natural History) were fertile, all were collected prior to about 1890. The only recent collection of this species with ascocarps known to us is from West Ross (Braemore Forest, Dirrie More, north-west end of Loch Droma, 3 July 1965, *U. K. Duncan*, Herb. Duncan).

Many species which no longer produce ascocarps in polluted

areas, however, still do so in relatively unpolluted ones. *Evernia prunastri* formerly occurred in fruit near Virginia Water, Berkshire (Turner and Dillwyn, 1805, p. 30), near Oswestry, Shropshire (specimen in BM), about 5 miles from the centre of Newcastle upon Tyne (Winch, 1831, p. 91) and in Suffolk (Bloomfield, 1905, p. 124). Of 244 specimens of this species in the British Museum (Natural History) 24 have ascocarps but only three of these have been collected since 1960 (two of these are from Scotland and one from England; Dorset, Thorncombe, Sadborow, collected by Mr A. R. Vickery in 1970). Species which fail to produce ascocarps in areas of England affected by mean winter sulphur dioxide values over *c* 40 μg/m³ are listed in Table 4. A relationship between the production of apothecia and

*Table 4 Examples of corticolous species which fail to produce ascocarps in areas of England which now have mean winter* $SO_2$ *values of over* c *40 μg/m³*

| | | |
|---|---|---|
| *Alectoria fuscescens* | *P. crinita*[1] | *Ramalina farinacea* |
| *Anaptychia ciliaris* | *P. perlata*[1] | *R. fraxinea* |
| *Evernia prunastri* | *P. reticulata*[1] | *Sphaerophorus globosus* |
| *Hypogymnia physodes* | *P. saxatilis*[2] | *Sticta fuliginosa*[1] |
| *Lobaria amplissima*[1] | *P. sulcata* | *Usnea ceratina*[1] |
| *L. pulmonaria*[1] | *Peltigera canina* | *U. subfloridana* |
| *Ochrolechia androgyna* | *Physcia ascendens* | *Xanthoria candelaria* |
| *Parmelia caperata* | *Pseudevernia furfuracea* | |

[1] also at values of over *c* 30 μg/m³
[2] may fruit at higher values when saxicolous

the degree of air pollution was first noted by Haugsjå (1930) but has since been referred to by several different workers (*cf* Barkman, 1958, 1969; Hawksworth, 1971*a*). DeSloover and LeBlanc (1970) demonstrated a correlation between the percentage of specimens with apothecia and IAP values, and Kofler, Jacquard and Martin (1969) and Pyatt (1969, p. 124) discovered independently that the ability of ascospores to germinate was reduced in material from polluted areas.

In some instances the failure to produce ascocarps is related to an increased tendency to produce asexual reproductive structures, particularly soredia. *Lecanora conizaeoides* is usually abundantly fertile in England but has few or no ascocarps in the most polluted sites in which it occurs (with mean winter sulphur dioxide levels exceeding *c* 150 $\mu g/m^3$). This difference has been investigated by Pišút and Jelínková (1971) in Czechoslovakia although these workers appear to have confused fertile material of *L. conizaeoides* and *L. varia.* Laundon (1967) described a sorediate state of *Lecania erysibe* which is not uncommon on walls in polluted areas of England. Some species, in contrast, produce soralia more rarely in their innermost stations. Examples of this type are *Hypogymnia physodes*, *Parmelia caperata*, *P. perlata* and *Ramalina farinacea.* Margot (ch 15) has found that sulphur dioxide inhibits the germination of soredia in *Hypogymnia physodes.*

In moderately polluted areas (i.e. zones 4–6 of Hawksworth and Rose, 1970) larger numbers of species tend to be confined to the oldest trees (Hawksworth and Walpole, 1966, p. 54) and it seems probable that this is due to thalli established before the mean sulphur dioxide levels rose which are able to persist but are inhibited from colonizing younger trees at the prevailing sulphur dioxide levels. Laundon (1967, 1970) has demonstrated a similar situation for *Caloplaca heppiana* on calcareous tombstones erected before and after 1901 in the London area.

Accelerated senescence of the central parts of thalli of foliose species of *Parmelia* and *Xanthoria* appears to be related to increasing sulphur dioxide levels (Gilbert, 1970*a*, 1971*a*). Pyatt (1968) reported that the ability of *Peltigera canina*, usually a terricolous species, to inhibit the germination of grass seeds was reduced by sulphur dioxide.

## Discussion

From the preceding data it is clear that increases in mean levels of sulphur dioxide in the air have had an extremely deleterious effect on the lichen vegetation of England and Wales. Because changes which have occurred around particular sources of this pollutant parallel those observed over large areas of England and Wales in general, it is easy to speculate that sulphur dioxide is the major factor responsible for these changes. In considering rural sites, which have been the main concern of this chapter, local differences in meteorological factors which occur in urban areas can be ignored (*cf* ch 7), but any general climatic trends must be considered. A summary of the changes in the English climate has been prepared by Lamb (1970) who found that there had been no significant change in mean annual temperatures in the period 1790–1900 and only a very slight rise (0.5°C) between 1900 and 1950. The frequency of westerly winds has decreased since about 1950 but in 1965 they were at a similar level to those in 1885 despite an increase in their frequency between 1885 and 1955. As regards mean annual rainfall, Lamb (1965, p. 22) indicates that since 1800 this has risen slightly. Such meteorological changes as have occurred between 1800 and 1970 have, therefore, tended to produce improved conditions for lichen growth (i.e. slightly warmer and wetter) and not the reverse. Had any general climatic change occurred in Britain during this period it would, in any case, have affected species in areas subject to sulphur dioxide in the air and those free from it in the same way. The lichen vegetation in those areas of England which have mean winter sulphur dioxide levels below about 30 $\mu g/m^3$ has, however, remained almost unchanged.

Changes in woodlands, particularly the felling of deciduous trees and the planting of coniferous trees, are of profound local significance, but are not relevant to studies in relatively undisturbed ancient parkland and other woodland sites in England and Wales.

There is little information on air pollution levels in Britain before the end of World War II but it is certain that smoke and sulphur dioxide emissions increased markedly between about 1860 and 1940. Recent trends in the British Isles include a decline in smoke emissions and concentrations (Warren Spring Laboratory, 1967). Declines in sulphur dioxide have also been reported in some urban areas, but too few volumetric gauges are situated in rural areas (*cf* Clifton, 1969, p. 308) to substantiate this view for them. Since 1958 there has been a decline in emissions of sulphur dioxide from commercial, domestic and industrial sources but a correspondingly large increase in the emissions of this gas from power stations. Power stations emitted 1.5 million tonnes in 1958 and 2.5 million tonnes in 1969. The net effect of these changes is that the total sulphur dioxide emissions in the British Isles are currently continuing to rise (5.6 million tonnes in 1958, 6.1 in 1969, with a peak of almost 6.4 in 1963). As emissions from power stations are largely from very tall chimneys they are dispersed over very large tracts of country and it is consequently reasonable to assume that in many rural sites sulphur dioxide levels are currently increasing (*see* ch 2).

Relatively little data are available on the concentrations of other gaseous pollutants in England and Wales. While the role of ozone might merit further investigation (*see* Atkins *et al.*, 1972), fluorides have only very localized effects (*cf* ch 9) and cannot be responsible for the general trends discussed in this chapter. Smoke is not considered to be significant, as attempts to demonstrate correlations between lichen distributions and mean smoke levels have met with little success (Gilbert, 1965; ch 8).

It is therefore evident that, on the basis of data currently available on meteorological and air pollution trends in England and Wales, sulphur dioxide must be singled out as the agent responsible for the observed changes. This view is entirely in agreement with all the experimental work which has so far been carried out (*cf* ch 13, 14, 15). If the area of England and Wales currently experiencing mean winter sulphur dioxide levels over 50 $\mu g/m^3$ (*cf* ch 2, Fig. 3) is allowed to extend, as it seems still to be doing at the present time, severe reductions in the lichen flora and vegetation of further areas of these countries will certainly occur in the future.

**Acknowledgements**

We are very grateful to numerous colleagues who have kindly sent us records for inclusion in our maps and to the curators of herbaria in which we have worked. Dr M. R. D. Seaward kindly abstracted records from the British Lichen Society Distribution Maps Scheme for us, and Miss D. W. Scott of the Biological Records Centre (The Nature Conservancy) is thanked for her help in preparing Figs. 2–10. We are particularly indebted to Mr P. W. James and Mr J. R. Laundon who read a first draft of this chapter and made a number of helpful suggestions which have been incorporated into it.

## References

Abbot, C. (1798). *Flora Bedfordiensis*. Bedford: W. Smith.
Ahti, T. (1965). Notes on the distribution of *Lecanora conizaeoides*. *Lichenologist* **3,** 91–2.
Amplett, J. and Rea, C. (1909). *The Botany of Worcestershire*. Birmingham: Cornish Brothers.
Andrews, F. M. (1928). A study of lichens. *Proc. Indiana Acad. Sci.* **37,** 329–30.
Atkins, D. H. F., Cox, R. A. and Eggleton, A. E. J. (1972). Photochemical ozone and sulphuric acid aerosol formation in the atmosphere over southern England. *Nature, Lond.* **235,** 372–6.
Baddeley, M. S., Ferry, B. W. and Finegan, E. J. (1972). The effects of sulphur dioxide on lichen respiration. *Lichenologist* **5,** 283–91.
Bailey, R. H. (1963). The lichens of the Ruislip local Nature Reserve. *J. Ruislip nat. Hist. Soc.* **12,** 18–21.
Bailey, R. H. (1968). *Lecanora conizaeoides* in Iceland. *Lichenologist* **4,** 73.
Barkman, J. J. (1958). *Phytosociology and ecology of cryptogamic epiphytes*. Assen, Netherlands: Van Gorcum.
Barkman, J. J. (1961). De verarming van de cryptogamen-flora in ons land gedurende de laaste honderd jaar. *Natura, Amst.* **58,** 141–51.
Barkman, J. J. (1964). Over de biologie en oecologie der korstmossen. *Velewe* **8,** 1–18.
Barkman, J. J. (1969). The influence of air pollution on bryophytes and lichens. In: *Air pollution, Proceedings of the first European Congress on the influence of air pollution on plants and animals, Wageningen 1968*, 197–209. Wageningen: Centre for Agricultural Publishing and Documentation.
Bloomfield, E. N. (1905). Fauna and flora of Norfolk. Lichens of Norfolk and Suffolk. *Trans. Norfolk Norwich Nat. Soc.* **8,** 117–37.
Bloxam, A. (18—). *Leicestershire cellular cryptogamia*. Manuscript in the British Museum (Natural History), London.
Bowen, H. J. M. (1968). *The flora of Berkshire*. Oxford: the author.
Brightman, F. H. (1964). The distribution of the lichen *Lecanora conizaeoides* Cromb. in North Ireland. *Ir. Nat. J.* **14,** 258–62.
Brightman, F. H. (1965). Some patterns of distribution of lichens in southern England. *SEast Nat.* **69,** 10–17.
Clifton, M. (1969). The National Survey of air pollution in the United Kingdom. In: *Air Pollution, Proceedings of the first European Congress on the influence of air pollution on plants and animals, Wageningen 1968*, 303–13. Wageningen: Centre for Agricultural Publishing and Documentation.
Crombie, J. M. (1869). IV. Lichenes. In: Trimen, H. and Dyer, W. T., *Flora of Middlesex:* 405–7. London: R. Hardwicke.
Crombie, J. M. (1879). Note on *Lecidea farinaria*. Borr. *Grevillea* **7,** 142.
Crombie, J. M. (1883–4). On the lichens in Dr. Withering's herbarium. *Grevillea* **12,** 56–62, 70–6.

Crombie, J. M. (1885). On the lichen-flora of Epping Forest, and the causes affecting its recent diminution. *Trans. Essex Fld Club* **4,** 54–75.

DeSloover, J. and LeBlanc, F. (1970). Pollutions atmosphériques et fertilité chez les mousses et chez les lichens épiphytiques. *Bull. Acad. Soc. lorr. Sci.* **9,** 82–90.

Dillenius, J. J. (1741). *Historia muscorum.* Oxford: Sheldonian Theatre.

Garner, R. (1844). *The natural history of the county of Stafford.* London.

Gilbert, O. L. (1965). Lichens as indicators of air pollution in the Tyne Valley. In: Goodman, G. T., Edwards, R. W. and Lambert, J. M. (ed.) *Ecology and the industrial society,* 35–47. Oxford: British Ecological Society (Blackwell).

Gilbert, O. L. (1968). *Biological indicators of air pollution.* Ph.D. thesis, University of Newcastle upon Tyne.

Gilbert, O. L. (1969). The effect of $SO_2$ on lichens and bryophytes around Newcastle upon Tyne. In: *Air pollution, Proceedings of the first European Congress on the influence of air pollution on plants and animals, Wageningen 1968,* 223–35. Wageningen: Centre for Agricultural Publishing and Documentation.

Gilbert, O. L. (1970*a*). Further studies on the effect of sulphur dioxide on lichens and bryophytes. *New Phytol.* **69,** 605–27.

Gilbert, O. L. (1970*b*). A biological scale for the estimation of sulphur dioxide pollution. *New Phytol.* **69,** 629–34.

Gilbert, O. L. (1970*c*). New tasks for lowly plants. *New Scientist* **46,** 288–9.

Gilbert, O. L. (1971). Studies along the edge of a lichen desert. *Lichenologist* **5,** 11–17.

Griffith, J. L. (1966). *Some aspects of the effect of atmospheric pollution on the lichen flora to the west of Consett, Co. Durham.* M.Sc. thesis, University of Durham.

Grindon, L. H. (1859). *The Manchester flora.* London: W. White.

Grummann, V. (1963). *Catalogus lichenum Germaniae.* Stuttgart: G. Fischer.

Haugsjå, P. K. (1930). Über den Einfluß der Stadt Oslo auf die Flechtenvegetation der Bäume. *Nyt Mag. Naturvid.* **68,** 1–116.

Hawksworth, D. L. (1967). The lichens collected by Jonathan Salt between 1795 and 1807 now in the herbarium of Sheffield Museum. *Naturalist, Hull* **1967,** 47–50.

Hawksworth, D. L. (1969). The lichen flora of Derbyshire. *Lichenologist* **4,** 105–93.

Hawksworth, D. L. (1971*a*). Lichens as litmus for air pollution: A historical review. *Int. J. Environ. Studies* **1,** 281–96.

Hawksworth, D. L. (1971*b*). *Lobaria pulmonaria* (L.) Hoffm. transplanted into Dovedale, Derbyshire. *Naturalist, Hull* **1971,** 127–8.

Hawksworth, D. L. (1972). The natural history of Slapton Ley Nature Reserve. IV. Lichens. *Field Studies* **3,** 535–78.

Hawksworth, D. L. and Chapman, D. S. (1971). *Pseudevernia furfuracea*

(L.) Zopf and its chemical races in the British Isles. *Lichenologist* **5,** 51–8.

Hawksworth, D. L. and Rose, F. (1970). Qualitative scale for estimating sulphur dioxide air pollution in England and Wales using epiphytic lichens. *Nature, Lond.* **227,** 145–8.

Hawksworth, D. L. and Sowter, F. A. (1969). Leicestershire and Rutland lichens, 1950–69. *Trans. Leicester Lit. Phil. Soc.* **63,** 50–61.

Hawksworth, D. L. and Walpole, P. R. (1966). The lichens of Bradgate Park, Leicestershire. *Trans. Leicester Lit. Phil. Soc.* **60,** 48–56.

Howitt, G. (1839). *Flora of Nottinghamshire.* London: A. Hamilton.

Johnson, T. (1632). *Enumeratio plantarum in Ericeto Hampsteadiano locisque vicinis crescentium.* Manuscript in the Royal Botanic Gardens, Kew.

Johnson, T. (1638). *Catalogus plantarum iuxte Tottenham lectorum anno dom. 1638.* Manuscript in the Royal Botanic Gardens, Kew.

Kershaw, K. A. (1963). Lichens. *Endeavour* **22,** 65–9.

Kofler, L., Jacquard, F. and Martin, J.-F. (1969). Influence de fumées d'usines sur la germination des spores de certains lichens. *Bull. Soc. bot. Fr., Mém.* **1968,** 219–30.

Kovanen, M. (1961). Turun kaupungin jäkäläkasvillisuudesta. *Turun Ylioppilas* **8,** 135–52.

Kozik, R. (1970). Porosty miasta Tarnowa i okolicy. *Fragm. flor. geobot.* **16,** 361–81.

Lamb, H. H. (1965). Britain's changing climate. In: Johnson, C. G. and Smith, L. P. (ed.) *The biological significance of climatic changes in Britain,* 3–31. London and New York: Academic Press.

Lamb, H. H. (1970). Our changing climate. In: Perring, F. H. (ed.) *The flora of a changing Britain,* 11–24. London: Botanical Society of the British Isles.

Laundon, J. R. (1956). The lichen ecology of Northamptonshire. In: *'The first fifty years'—A history of Kettering and District Naturalists Society and Field Club,* 89–96. Kettering: Kettering and District Naturalists Society and Field Club.

Laundon, J. R. (1957). Lichens. In: Hodson, N. L. *et al.* (ed.) *A survey of Thoroughsale and Hazel Woods, Corby, Northants.* Kettering: Kettering and District Natural History Society. [Duplicated.]

Laundon, J. R. (1958). The lichen vegetation of Bookham Common. *London Nat.* **37,** 66–79.

Laundon, J. R. (1967). A study of the lichen flora of London. *Lichenologist* **3,** 277–327.

Laundon, J. R. (1970). London's lichens. *London Nat.* **49,** 20–69.

LeBlanc, F. and Rao, D. N. (1966). Réaction de quelques lichens et mousses épiphytiques à l'anhydride sulfureaux dans la région de Sudbury, Ontario. *Bryologist* **69,** 338–46.

LeBlanc, F., Rao, D. N. and Comeau, G. (1972). The epiphytic vegetation of *Populus balsamifera* and its significance as an air pollution indicator in Sudbury, Ontario. *Can. J. Bot.* **50,** 519–28.

Lundström, H. (1968). Luftföroreningars inverkan på epifytfloran hos barrträd i Stockholmsområdet. *Stud. Forest. suecica* **56,** 1–55.
Martin, J.-P. and Jacquard, F. (1968). Influence des fumées d'usines sur la distribution des lichens dans la vallée de la Romanche (Isère). *Pollution atmospherique* **10,** 95–9.
Martindale, J. A. (1886–90). The lichens of Westmorland. *Naturalist, Hull* **1886,** 317–24; **1887,** 47–54; **1888,** 25–32; **1890,** 157–64.
Moberg, R. (1968). Luftföroreningars inverkan på epifytiska lavar i Köpmanholmen. *Svensk Bot. Tidskr.* **62,** 169–96.
Morton, J. (1712). *The natural history of Northamptonshire.* London: Knaplock and Wilkin.
Mosley, O. (1863). *The natural history of Tutbury.* London.
Mott, F. T., Carter, T., Cooper, E. F., Finch, J. E. M. and Cooper, C. W. (1886). *The flora of Leicestershire, including the cryptogams.* Leicester: Leicester Literary and Philosophical Society.
Nash, T. H. (1971*a*). Lichen sensitivity to hydrogen fluoride. *Bull. Torrey bot. Club* **98,** 103–6.
Nash, T. H. (1971*b*). *Effects of effluents from a zinc factory on lichens.* PhD. thesis, Rutgers University. [Not seen.]
Paulson, R. (1919). The lichen flora of Hertfordshire. *Trans. nat. Hist. Soc. Herts.* **17,** 83–96.
Paulson, R. and Thompson, P. G. (1911). Report on the lichens of Epping Forest (first paper). *Essex Nat.* **16,** 136–45.
Paulson, R. and Thompson, P. G. (1913). Report on the lichens of Epping Forest (second paper). *Essex Nat.* **17,** 90–105.
Paulson, R. and Thompson, P. G. (1920). Supplemental report on the lichens of Epping Forest. *Essex Nat.* **19,** 27–30.
Pilkington, J. (1789). *View of the present state of Derbyshire,* 2 vols. Derby.
Pišút, I. (1962). Bemerkungen zur Wirkung der Exhalationsprodukte auf die flechtenvegetation in der Umgebung von Rudňany (Nordostslowakei). *Biológia, Bratisl.* **17,** 481–94.
Pišút, I. (1971). Verbreitung der Arten der flechtengattung *Lobaria* (Schreb.) Hue in der Slowakei. *Acta rer. nat. Mus. nat. Slov., Bratisl.* **17,** 105–30.
Pišút, I. and Jelínková, E. (1971). Über die Artberechtigung der Flechte *Lecanora conizaeoides* Nyl. ex Cromb. *Preslia* **43,** 254–7.
Piterans, A. V. (1968). Vliyaniya superfosfatnogo zavoda na razvitie lishaĭnikov. In: Nakhutsrishviti, I. G. (ed.) *Materialȳ III Zakavkazskoĭ Konferentsii po sporovȳm rasteniyam,* 251–3. Tbilisi.
Pyatt, F. B. (1969). *Atmospheric pollution in South Wales in relation to the growth and distribution of lichens.* Ph.D. thesis, University of Wales.
Rao, D. N. and LeBlanc, F. (1967). Influence of an iron-sintering plant on corticolous epiphytes in Wawa, Ontario. *Bryologist* **70,** 141–57.
Ray, J. (1724). *Synopsis methodica stirpium Britannicarum,* **1.** Ed. 3. London.
Rhodes, P. G. M. (1931). The lichen-flora of Hartlebury Common. *Proc. Birmingham nat. Hist. Soc.* **16,** 39–43.

Rimington, F. C. (1953). Lichens. In: Walsh, G. B. and Rimington, F. C. (ed.) *The natural history of the Scarborough district*, **1**, 167–83. Scarborough: Scarborough Field Naturalists' Society.

Rose, F., Hawksworth, D. L. and Coppins, B. J. (1970). A lichenological excursion through the north of England. *Naturalist, Hull* **1970**, 49–55.

Rydzak, J. (1954). Rozmieszczenie i ekologia porostów miasta Lublina. *Annls Univ. Mariae Curie-Skłodowska*, C, **8**, 233–356.

Rydzak, J. (1969). Lichens as indicators of the ecological conditions of the habitat. *Annls Univ. Mariae Curie-Skłodowska*, C, **23**, 131–64.

Rydzak, J. and Piórecki, J. (1971). Stan flory porostów w okolicach Tarnobrzeskiego Zagłębia Siarkowega. *Annls Univ. Mariae Curie-Skłodowska*, C, **26**, 343–52.

Rydzak, J. and Stasiak, H. (1971). Badnania nad stanem flory porostów w rejonie przemysłu azotowego w Puławach. *Annls Univ. Mariae Curie-Skłodowska*, C, **26**, 329–42.

Savidge, J. P. (1963). Climate. In: Savidge, J. P. (ed.) *Travis's flora of South Lancashire*, 29–59. Liverpool: Liverpool Botanical Society.

Schmid, A. B. (1956). *Die epixyle Flechtenvegetation von München*. Thesis, University of Munich.

Skye, E. (1958). Luftföroreningars inverkan på busk- och bladlavfloran kring skifferoljeverket i Närkes Kvarntorp. *Svensk Bot. Tidskr.* **52**, 133–90.

Skye, E. (1968). Lichens and air pollution. *Acta phytogeogr. suec.* **52**, 1–123.

Smith, A. L. (1918). *A monograph of the British lichens*, **1**. Ed. 2. London: British Museum (Natural History).

Smith, J. E. and Sowerby, J. (1804). *English botany*, **19**. London: the authors.

Sowter, F. A. (1950). *The cryptogamic flora of Leicestershire and Rutland —Lichenes*. Leicester: Leicester Literary and Philosophical Society.

Sowter, F. A. and Hawksworth, D. L. (1970). Leicestershire and Rutland cryptogamic notes, I. *Trans. Leicester Lit. Phil. Soc.* **64**, 89–100.

Stansfield, A. (1910). Flora of Todmorden. *Lancs. Nat.* **2**, 355–60.

Tallis, J. H. (1964). Lichens and atmospheric pollution. *Advmt Sci., Lond.* **21**, 250–2.

Tobler, F. (1921). Die Wolbecker Flechten-Standorte. *Hedwigia* **63**, 7–10.

Turner, D. and Dillwyn, L. W. (1805). *The botanist's guide through England and Wales*, 2 vols. London.

Vareschi, V. (1953). La influencia de los bosques y parques sobre el aire de la ciudad de Caracas. *Acta cient. venez.* **4**, 89–95.

Warren Spring Laboratory (1967). *The investigation of atmospheric pollution 1958–1966*. London: HMSO.

Watling, R. (1967). *The fungus and lichen flora of the Halifax parish 1775–1965*. Halifax: Halifax Scientific Society.

Wheldon, J. A. and Travis, W. G. (1915). The lichens of south Lancashire. *J. Linn. Soc., Bot.* **43**, 87–136.

Wilmanns, O. (1966). Anthropogener Wandel der kryptogamen-vegetation in Südwestdeutschland. *Ber. geobot. ForschInst. Rübel* **37,** 74–87.

Winch, N. J. (1831). Flora of Northumberland and Durham. *Trans. nat. Hist. Soc. Northumb.* **1831,** 1–150.

Winch, N. J. (1833). *Remarks on the flora of Cumberland.* Newcastle upon Tyne: Mercury Press.

Wirth, V. (1968). Soziologie, Standortsökologie und Areal des *Lobarion pulmonariae* im Südschwarzwald. *Bot. Jb.* **88,** 317–65.

Wise, J. R. (1894). *The New Forest, its history and its scenery.* Ed. 5. London.

Withering, W. (1818). *A systematic arrangement of British plants,* **4,** Ed. 4. London: Cadell & Davies, *etc.*

Yoshimura, I. and Hawksworth, D. L. (1970). The typification and chemical races of *Lobaria pulmonaria* (L.) Hoffm. *J. Jap. Bot.* **45,** 33–41.

# 17: Summary: Scope and Direction of Future Work

M. S. BADDELEY and B. W. FERRY

It is now well established that air pollution is a significant environmental factor in determining lichen distribution, particularly in industrial countries. Most of the data have been collected from field rather than laboratory experiments, and there is considerable need to confirm these findings by controlled experiments. The importance of specific air pollutants is not well understood, and there is a danger in using terms such as 'air pollution', and 'sulphur dioxide air pollution' interchangeably for this reason until further experimental evidence is available. The term air pollution is conveniently non-committal. A wide variety of air pollutants other than sulphur dioxide have been identified, and a few are of widespread occurrence. Surprisingly little attention has been paid to the effects of most of them on lichens, only fluoride and heavy metals apart from sulphur dioxide have been considered so far. These two pollutants are rather localized in their occurrence, but they have a marked effect on the lichen flora where they are found (ch 8, 9). Few reports are known on the effects of ozone, nitrogen oxides, organic effluents and agricultural chemicals on lichens although all these substances are major air pollutants in certain areas. The possibility that unidentified pollutants and derivatives of known pollutants occur should not be discounted.

There are numerous situations where two or more pollutants occur together in the air. An example is referred to in chapter 8, namely the zinc smelter in Pennsylvania where Nash mentions that sulphur dioxide, zinc and cadmium are important airborne pollutants. In these circumstances the effects of the pollutants may be additive or synergistic. There has only been one investigation of this type of situation so far (Gilbert, 1968). Other workers are aware of the likelihood of such interactions. Positive interactions are to be expected, but the possibility of negative effects should not be discounted. For example, a low concentration of heavy metal ions may increase the rate of oxidation of sulphur dioxide to the less toxic sulphate ion by catalysis, or the presence of a relatively alkaline pollutant might raise the pH of the environment thus reducing the effect of any sulphur dioxide present. There is much scope for further work both in the field, and in laboratory experiments in connection with the general problems of interaction.

Few would disagree that sulphur dioxide is an important, if not the most important, air pollutant on a global basis. It is worth noting, however, that virtually all the studies so far originate in Europe or North America. A considerable amount of data has been collected in field studies around sulphur dioxide sources, and several implications of general importance emerge. In particular lichens and mosses are found to be very sensitive to sulphur dioxide when compared with higher plants and animals, and species vary greatly in their sensitivity. As a result, lichens and mosses have considerable potential as biological indicators of sulphur dioxide levels, and it is in relation to this characteristic that most work has been done (*see* ch 3). The value of living organisms rather than man-made instruments for assessing sulphur dioxide levels is that they are cheap and give an 'instant' result. However, it needs to be realized that the living lichen is a much more complex and sensitive indicator than even sophisticated gauges, and will react to a host of environmental factors. The need to standardize sites with respect to these other factors is now well appreciated, as is evident from the good correlations obtained of sulphur dioxide levels assessed by lichen distribution and by gauges (*see* ch 3). The effect of a variety of environmental factors, such as water relations, the chemical and physical nature of the substrate, temperature and shelter, whether on a small microtopographical scale or on a large geographical scale, in modifying pollutant effects is not well understood (*see* ch 12). In some studies these environmental factors have been considered further than the simple standardizing of sites, for example by Gilbert (1970). Rydzak placed considerable emphasis on the importance of water relations in the urban environment, although many would regard this as unjustified (*see* ch 7). The paucity of data, and variation in opinion as to the importance of certain environmental factors to lichen survival in and around urban areas, suggest that these problems are worthy of a great deal more attention.

It is feasible to utilize lichens as indicators of pollution in a number of different situations. This method might well be applied in forestry to assess where conifers should be planted. Many conifers have been shown to be affected by sulphur dioxide at the same concentrations which cause a decline in lichen cover. Many other crop plants may also give a reduced yield at similar concentrations of sulphur dioxide, and this too merits further investigation (*see* ch 10). The use of lichens as pollution indicators might also be applied in urban planning, and in the siting and distribution of industrial sites (*see* ch 6). The value of such techniques in limiting the levels of pollution to which man is exposed cannot be fully assessed. However, there is no doubt that present levels of pollutants in some areas are a nuisance and potentially dangerous to health (Bach, 1972). So far there seems to have been little application of lichen mapping to these problems, perhaps this is due to ignorance of the method, or scarcity of those qualified to do it.

There are a number of difficulties in the application of lichen mapping techniques on a large scale. Identification, even by experts, is not always simple, and the standardizing of sites with respect to other environmental factors can pose a number of problems. Whether mapping, and its use to establish sulphur dioxide levels, is within the scope of the non-expert is doubtful. Nevertheless, much mapping has already been done in some countries, and a great deal can be achieved by a few people with expert knowledge.

The standardization of basic data and experimental techniques is very important in field-work. In particular the terminology used in mapping work can be misleading. The terms 'lichen desert', 'struggle zone' and 'normal zone' have been widely used without clear definition. Lichen vegetation described as 'normal' in a limited geographical region may be less normal in a wider context. It may be affected by local ecological factors, or more confusing in the present context, it may be subject to low levels of atmospheric pollution. Hence these classical terms may not be clear, and alternative forms of zonation as described in this volume may be more acceptable (*see* ch 3 and 5).

The accepted method of expressing sulphur dioxide concentrations in air in this country is in μg/m³. Much published material has been expressed in terms of ppm and pphm sulphur dioxide in air, but the term μg/m³ is less ambiguous as long as figures are given for standard temperature and pressure. In Fig. 1, the

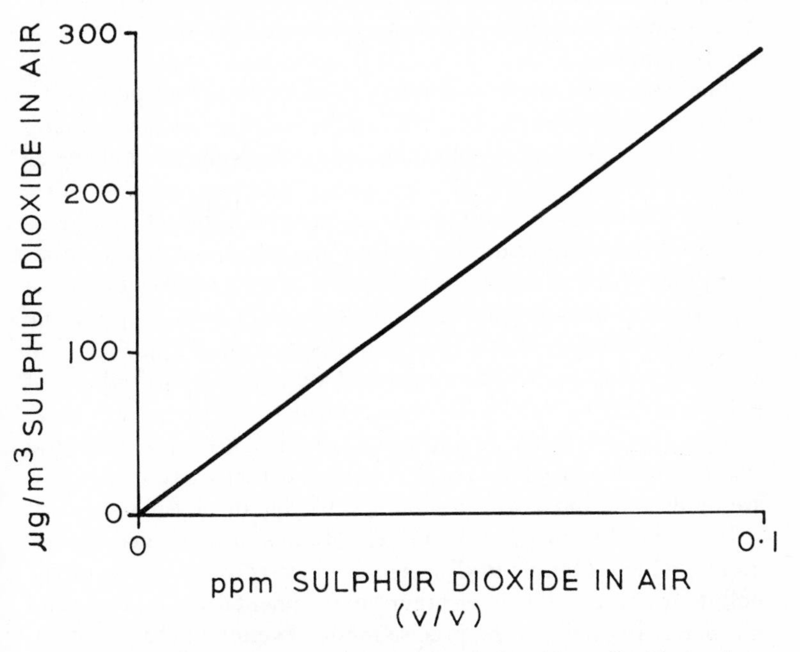


Fig. 1 Relationship between ppm and μg/m³ sulphur dioxide in air at N.T.P. 1 ppm = 2860 μg/m³ sulphur dioxide

relationship between the two forms of unit is given, and also the conversion factor for use at N.T.P. At temperatures above 0°C, the conversion factor is lower, being about 7 per cent lower at 20°C. The use of μg/m³ sulphur dioxide in air at N.T.P. is to be recommended.

The considerable number of papers on sulphur dioxide, and the few on fluoride and heavy metals which have appeared, indicate a logical and uniform pattern of approach to such investigations. The pollutant is first identified, and its source found. A gradient of decreasing levels of the pollutant as one moves from the source is then established, using suitable analytical techniques to analyse the air or to measure the level of pollutant present in the (lichen) substrate. This gradient is then correlated with the deterioration of the lichen thallus, changes in the species present, and presence of the pollutant in the thallus. It has proved difficult to fulfil certain of these requirements in studies on sulphur dioxide because of the lack of a single reliable analytical method.

The increasing levels of sulphur dioxide, and other pollutants, in the air, particularly in rural and remote areas, and arising mainly from high-level emissions, show the value of lichens as indicators of the extent of this spread. Lichens respond fairly quickly to increased sulphur dioxide levels, although the gross effects observed in mapping studies are not immediately apparent. This fact together with the length of time it takes to collect and correlate mapping data, makes the method most applicable to long-term experiments over months or years. The increased attention being paid to more immediate physiological effects of pollutants has led to the development of transplant and laboratory methods (*see* ch 3, 13, 14, 15) which give a more rapid evaluation of such changes. It is essential that these techniques are applied by those with a good knowledge of physiology.

It is logical to progress from field studies to controlled experiments, which attempt to differentiate between the effects of the pollutant and the effects of other environmental parameters, and ultimately to establish the precise mode of action of the pollutant. The combination of transplant experiments and laboratory experiments which simulate, as far as possible, natural conditions, would seem to be the best approach.

There is considerable difficulty in adequately simulating field conditions in the laboratory, and it is, therefore, advantageous to use material in a relatively undisturbed state in the field. The transplant techniques, referred to in chapter 3, have been widely used to demonstrate gross morphological effects of pollutants on lichens, but only to a limited extent in connection with the physiological deterioration of the thallus in a polluted environment. The transplant technique has great potential in that respect, and also in investigating the comparative sensitivities of different species to pollutants. The ability of lichens to recover from sub-lethal doses of pollutants, the comparative susceptibility in the field of major metabolic processes, and the modifying effects of other environmental factors on the response of lichens to pollutants, might all be further elucidated by use of transplants. A variety of other problems are also susceptible to this technique, including comparative studies with geographical races or ecotypes, and the assessment of the rate of accumulation of pollutants in thalli. Some experiments of this type have been carried out, but much of this work remains to be done. The possibility of transplanting healthy lichens into areas suspected of being polluted, and monitoring physiological parameters such as respiration and photosynthesis, to give a rapid indication of pollution levels is obvious. However, the need for carefully designed experiments with proper controls needs to be emphasized (*see* ch 12).

Experimental work in the laboratory is of value to corroborate observations made in the field, to establish more precisely the concentrations of pollutant which individual species can withstand, to study the interaction of certain factors, and to study the precise mode of action of pollutants on metabolic processes in lichens. One of the major problems confronting anyone setting up laboratory experiments is the imprecise nature of the field data on which any experiments must be based. To date, field sensitivities of lichens have been related to mean annual or mean winter sulphur dioxide concentrations, so that the actual concentrations to which the lichen has been exposed are not known. More precise information on this from laboratory experiments will be of great value. It is likely that sulphur dioxide enters the lichen thallus from solution, yet the precise equivalence between sulphur dioxide concentrations in the air and in solution is very uncertain. A few recent papers are relevant to this problem (Liss, 1971; Terraglio and Manganelli, 1967), although they are largely theoretical in value. The field situation is complicated by a variety of factors and processes likely to affect both the form of sulphur dioxide and its rate of entry into solution. These include the pH of natural water sources and variation in, or even lack of, concentration gradients in both liquid and gas (air) phases due to turbulence. In both field situations and in laboratory experiments the complex chemistry of sulphur dioxide in solution needs particular consideration.

Further examination of the state of sulphur dioxide in the environment is needed (*see* ch 2), and more precise data from laboratory experiments may be of particular value in this context.

The physiological state of the lichen, both before and at the time of exposure to a pollutant, must affect the response. Evidence suggests that lichens are more resistant to sulphur dioxide when they are dry, and therefore in a state of very low metabolic activity. This is presumed to be because the pollutant does not enter the thallus. Oddly enough, survival of lichens at the limit of their range into polluted areas is sometimes enhanced in damp ecological niches! Possibly the critical factor is the provision of shelter rather than moisture. In general, the variation in the physiological state of the lichen caused by seasonal changes, and short-term less regular fluctuations, is not well understood. It is essential to give careful consideration to this factor in laboratory experiments. In experiments designed to check field data it would seem advisable to expose lichens to pollutants under a variety of conditions and pretreatments, related, as far as possible, to the natural circumstances of exposure.

Response to any pollutant may be affected by material already accumulated in the thallus, and it may be important to analyse samples used in laboratory experiments, particularly if they come from a habitat which may be polluted.

Further work on the mechanisms of accumulation of pollutants in the lichen thallus, and the intracellular sites at which these substances are deposited might yield valuable information.

The source of material for laboratory experiments is very important. Freshly collected material from the field, which is collected in a standard way, and suitably pretreated in the laboratory is adequate in most cases. The use of laboratory-maintained material, kept in a growth chamber of the type used by Kershaw and Millbank (1969), may prove to be valuable for some experiments as it is genetically and physiologically more constant. The demand for a continuous supply of a species which may not be easily available may necessitate laboratory growth and maintenance. The value of cultured lichens, or the separate symbionts in studies on pollution is doubtful. Material of this type is unnatural and its value is likely to be confined to physiological and biochemical investigation of the symbiotic relationship.

The importance of using standard material cannot be overemphasized, and this relates not only to the source of the material, but also to the selection of samples for an experiment. It is important to differentiate between thallus lobes and older thallus tissue, and between fruiting and non-fruiting tissue. The constancy of inclusion or exclusion of thallus bearing isidia or soredia will also affect results. It is also essential to recognize the sensitivity of diaspores in this context, as the establishment of lichens is generally considered to be the most sensitive phase of growth to sulphur dioxide. Other workers have pointed out the value of ancient substrates to survival, which indicates that this is not a simple problem (ch 4, 6, 16). Possibly algal cells in soredia and young colonies are more accessible, and therefore more vulnerable to sulphur dioxide.

A number of physiological techniques are available for monitoring the effects of pollutants on the lichen, and some of these have been described and critically analysed in this volume (*see* ch 12, 13, 14, 15). It is, perhaps, surprising that so few experiments of this type have been carried out so far.

As stated earlier the initial aim of laboratory experiments must be to confirm field observations of lichen sensitivity to pollutants. The use of controlled experiments allows a clear identification of the pollutant, and the variation of one parameter at a time. Extrapolation of observations made under these conditions may throw light on many field observations.

Our knowledge to date is that realistic concentrations of sulphur dioxide applied in such experiments do affect physiological processes, both respiration and photosynthesis being inhibited. Photosynthesis would appear to be the more sensitive of the two processes (*see* ch 11, 14, 15). Several groups have correlated inhibition of physiological processes in the laboratory with field sensitivity, but where large numbers of species have been examined some anomalies have been observed. It would seem reasonable to conclude that sensitivity is primarily a function of the inhibition of metabolism, but this is moderated by characteristics of the morphology and physiology of individual species. The texture and hollowness of the thallus, surface area : volume ratios, wettability of the thallus and rates at which pollutants are adsorbed and inactivated by each of the symbionts, together with the buffering capacity of the species, will all affect sensitivity. Certain of these factors may be overcome under laboratory conditions, thus giving anomalies between field and laboratory results. Several workers have produced data demonstrating that substrates with a buffering capacity at high pH reduce the toxicity of sulphur dioxide. This is attributed to the conversion of sulphur dioxide to less toxic ionic forms at high pH.

There is obvious scope for laboratory experiments designed to differentiate between these possibilities. Aspects of metabolism other than photosynthesis and respiration merit attention, particularly uptake mechanisms. The possibility that different species may possess enzyme systems which differ in sensitivity to sulphur dioxide should not be ignored.

Present knowledge of the metabolism of sulphur by lichens is very meagre when compared with our knowledge concerning phosphorus metabolism, and this field of investigation requires urgent attention (*see* ch 12). A general knowledge of the biochemistry of known pollutants, and their effects on the metabolism of higher plants and animals, for instance the fluoride block of respiratory metabolism, is vital to detailed analysis of mechanisms of toxicity. Surprisingly little is known about the effects of sulphur dioxide on higher plants and animals including man. More precise information about the mode of action in lichens might therefore be of general interest, although any extrapolation of such results to other species should be considered carefully because of the symbiotic nature of the lichen.

Damage to the chlorophyll pigment system of the lichen on exposure to sulphur dioxide has been observed by a number of people, and recent work on the possible mechanism (*see* ch 13) may be highly significant. The chemistry of sulphur dioxide in solution has received little attention in the past, and it is likely that the oxidation-reduction properties are important in the mechanism of sulphur dioxide toxicity. It is reasonable to postulate that respiration and photosynthesis are affected in a similar way, and that it is the natural oxidation-reduction reactions which are sensitive to sulphur dioxide. Purely academic interest in the mode of action of pollutants on lichens should be sufficient motive for further investigation.

There is little doubt that sulphur dioxide and other pollutants have a deleterious effect on living organisms, particularly plants, and the correlation between the presence of pollutants and certain diseases in man is clear. It is likely that research directed towards the mechanisms of action of these pollutants will be of great value ultimately, in controlling the degradation of the environment. The value of lichens as research tools in this context is becoming evident and their use in the ancillary activity of tracing pollutant spread will continue to be of importance.

## References

Bach, W. (1972). *Atmospheric Pollution*. New York: McGraw-Hill.

Gilbert, O. L. (1968). *Biological indicators of air pollution*. Ph.D. thesis, University of Newcastle upon Tyne.

Gilbert, O. L. (1970). Further studies on the effect of sulphur dioxide on lichens and bryophytes. *New Phytol.* **69,** 605–27.

Kershaw, K. A. and Millbank, J. W. (1969). A controlled environment lichen growth chamber. *Lichenologist* **4,** 83–7.

Liss, P. S. (1971). Exchange of $SO_2$ between the atmosphere and natural waters. *Nature, Lond.* **233,** 327–9.

Terraglio, F. P. and Manganelli, R. M. (1967). The absorption of atmospheric sulphur dioxide by water solutions. *J. of Air Pollution Control Association* **17,** 403–7.

# Additional References

This section lists some papers containing information relevant to this book which have either appeared or come to the authors' or editors' attention while this book was in press.

Breur, H. (1971). Beitrag zur xerothermen Moos- und Flechtenvegetation und Flora im Urfttal zwischen Sötenich und Nettersheim (Eifel). *Decheniana* **123,** 121–34.

Brimblecombe, P. and Spedding, D. J. (1972). Rate of solution of gaseous sulphur dioxide at atmospheric concentrations. *Nature, Lond.* **236,** 225.

Brodo, I. M. (1972). Lichens and cities. In Westley, B. (ed.) *International symposium on identification and measurement of environmental pollutants,* 325–8. Ottawa: National Research Council.

DeSloover, J. R. (1971). Groupes ecologiques combination d'especes indicatrices et tolerance a l'egard des pollutions chez les lichens epiphytiques. In Sbornik z Mezinarodni Konference VTEI 5, *Bioindikatory deteriorizace krajiny,* 18–25. Prague: Ustav krajinne ekologie CSAV.

Gorham, E. (1959). A comparison of lower and higher plants as accumulators of radioactive fallout. *Can. J. Bot.* **37,** 327–9.

Grodzińska, K. (1971). Acidification of tree bark as a measure of air pollution in southern Poland. *Bull. Acad. Polon. Sci., ser. sci. biol.* II, **19,** 189–95.

Hanson, W. C. (1967*b*). Radiological concentration processes characterising arctic ecosystems. In Åberg, B. and Hungate, P. F. (ed.) *Radioecological concentration processes,* 183–91. Oxford: Pergamon Press.

Hanson, W. C. (1971). Fallout radionuclide distribution in lichen communities near Thule. *Arctic* **24,** 269–76.

Hanson, W. C. (1972). Plutonium in lichen communities of the Thule, Greenland region during the summer of 1968. *Health Phys.* **22,** 39–42.

Hawksworth, D. L. (1972). Regional studies in *Alectoria* (Lichenes). II. The British species. *Lichenologist* **5,** 181–261.

Kunze, M. (1972). Emittentenbezogene Flechtenkartierung auf Grund von Frequenzuntersuchungen. *Oecologia* **9,** 123–33.

Miettinen, J. K. (1967). Concentration of $^{137}Cs$ and $^{55}Fe$ through food chains in arctic and subarctic regions. In Åberg, B. and Hungate, P. F. (ed.) *Radiological concentration processes,* 267–74. Oxford: Pergamon Press.

Rose, F. and James, P. W. (1973). Regional studies on the lichen flora of Britain. I: The corticolous and lignicolous lichen flora of the New Forest. *Lichenologist* **5,** in press.

Schönbeck, H. and van Haut, H. (1972). Exposure of lichens for the recognition and the evaluation of air pollutants. In Westley, B. (ed.) *International symposium on identification and measurement of environmental pollutants*, 329–34. Ottawa: National Research Council.

Seaward, M. R. D. (1971). *Aspects of urban lichen ecology*. Ph.D. thesis, University of Bradford.

Showman, R. E. (1971). *Effects of sulfur dioxide on net photosynthesis and chlorophyll content in lichen thalli and cultured lichen symbionts*. M.Sc. thesis, Ohio State University.

Unsworth, M. H., Biscoe, P. V. and Pinckney, H. R. (1972). Stomatal responses to sulphur dioxide. *Nature, Lond.* **239,** 458–9.

Yeaple, D. S. (1972). Mercury in bryophytes (moss). *Nature, Lond.* **235,** 229–30.

# Index